PRINCIPLES OF ELECTRICITY

By ARTHUR MORLEY, O.B.E., D.Sc., Hon.M.I.Mech.E.
and EDWARD HUGHES, D.Sc.(Eng.), Ph.D., M.I.E.E.

First Year Course
ELEMENTARY ENGINEERING SCIENCE

Second Year Course

MECHANICAL	ELECTRICAL
ENGINEERING	ENGINEERING
SCIENCE	SCIENCE

First and Second Year Courses
PRINCIPLES OF ELECTRICITY

Third Year Course
APPLIED MECHANICS
By ARTHUR MORLEY, O.B.E., D.Sc., Hon.M.I.Mech.E.

APPLIED ELECTRICITY
By EDWARD HUGHES, D.Sc.(Eng.), Ph.D., M.I.E.E.

FUNDAMENTALS OF ELECTRICAL
ENGINEERING
By EDWARD HUGHES, D.Sc.(Eng.), Ph.D., M.I.E.E.

PRINCIPLES OF ELECTRICITY

Based on the Rationalized M.K.S. System of Units

By

ARTHUR MORLEY

O.B.E., D.SC., HON.M.I.MECH.E.

*Formerly Professor of Mechanical Engineering in University College,
Nottingham, and later H.M. Staff Inspector of Technical Schools*

AND

EDWARD HUGHES

D.SC.(ENG.), PH.D., M.I.E.E.

*Formerly Vice-Principal and Head of the Engineering Department,
Brighton Technical College*

WITH DIAGRAMS

LONGMANS, GREEN AND CO
LONDON ◆ NEW YORK ◆ TORONTO

LONGMANS, GREEN AND CO LTD
6 & 7 CLIFFORD STREET LONDON W I
BOSTON HOUSE STRAND STREET CAPE TOWN
531 LITTLE COLLINS STREET MELBOURNE

LONGMANS, GREEN AND CO INC
55 FIFTH AVENUE NEW YORK 3

LONGMANS, GREEN AND CO
20 CRANFIELD ROAD TORONTO 16

ORIENT LONGMANS LTD
CALCUTTA BOMBAY MADRAS
DELHI VIJAYAWADA DACCA

First published 1953
Second Impression 1954
Third Impression 1954
Fourth Impression 1955
Fifth Impression 1955
Sixth Impression 1956

Made and printed in Great Britain by
William Clowes and Sons, Limited, London and Beccles

PREFACE

Electrical theory has been burdened with several systems of units. In 1901, it was suggested by Prof. Giorgi, an Italian scientist, that the confusion caused by these different systems could be eliminated by the adoption of the metre, the kilogram and the second as the units of length, mass and time respectively and the adoption of one of the practical units, such as the ampere, as a fourth fundamental unit. This metre-kilogram-second (M.K.S.) system in its rationalized form was adopted unanimously by the International Electrotechnical Commission in 1950; and in April, 1952, the Council of the Institution of Electrical Engineers recommended that this system "should be employed by authors in papers submitted to the Institution and that all students of electrical engineering should become conversant with its use". The rationalized M.K.S. system has, therefore, been adopted in this volume and, apart from the conversion table given on p. 348, no reference has been made to the C.G.S. electromagnetic and electrostatic systems.

The symbols and nomenclature are in accordance with the recommendations of the British Standards Institution and the Institution of Electrical Engineers; and for the convenience of students, the symbols and abbreviations used in this book have been tabulated on pp. xi–xiii.

The text contains 73 worked examples and 376 problems. Most of the latter have been taken from examination papers; and for permission to publish these questions, we are grateful to the Institution of Electrical Engineers, the Institution of Mechanical Engineers, the City and Guilds of London Institute, the East Midland Educational Union, the Northern Counties Technical Examinations Council, the Union of Educational Institutions and the Union of Lancashire and Cheshire Institutes. The greatest care has been taken to eliminate errors in the text and in the answers, but should any mistakes be found, we shall be very grateful to have them brought to our notice.

We wish to express our thanks to Dr. F. T. Chapman, C.B.E., M.I.E.E. and Mr. E. F. Piper, A.M.I.E.E., for reading through the manuscript and making a number of valuable suggestions.

E. H.

A. M.

CONTENTS

SYMBOLS AND ABBREVIATIONS

Based upon British Standard Specification No. 560 (1934) and Amendment No. 1 (1945), and "List of Symbols and Abbreviations" published by The Institution of Electrical Engineers.

NOTES ON THE USE OF ABBREVIATIONS

1. Abbreviations should be used only when the meaning will be clear.

2. An abbreviation is the same for the singular and the plural: for example, 10 lb, 5 V.

3. Full-point should be omitted after abbreviation of a single word or when two abbreviations of single words are separated by a solidus (/) or a hyphen (-): for example, 5 mA, 10 Mc/s, 20 ft-lb.

4. Full-points should be used in a multi-word abbreviation: for example, e.m.f., h.p.

5. The solidus (/) should be used for "per" except in such well-established abbreviations as r.p.m. and m.p.h.: for example, c/s.

6. The use of capital letters is discouraged, but capitals should be used where it is customary: for example, M.K.S., C.G.S., B.Th.U.; p.d., m.m.f., r.m.s.

7. The abbreviated forms a.c. and d.c. should be used only as adjectives: for example, d.c. motor, a.c. circuit.

8. A hyphen is inserted between the numerical value and the unit when the combination is used as an adjective: for example, a 230-volt (or 230-V) motor, a 3-phase 50-c/s supply, a 2-ohm (or 2-Ω) resistor.

PRIMARY UNITS

Term	Unit	Abbreviation	Term	Unit	Abbreviation
Length	inch foot millimetre centimetre metre	in ft mm cm m	Volume	cubic inch „ centimetre „ metre	in³ cm³ m³
			Mass	pound gram kilogram	lb g kg
Area	square inch „ foot „ millimetre „ centimetre „ metre	in² ft² mm² cm² m²	Time	second minute hour	sec* min* h

* s and m may be used when combined with other abbreviations as in c/s, r.p.m.

xi

ELECTRICAL QUANTITIES (M.K.S. SYSTEM

Term	Symbol	Unit	Abbreviation of unit after numerical values
Angular velocity .	ω	radian per second .	radian/sec
Capacitance . .	C	farad . . .	F
		microfarad . .	μF
Charge or Quantity of electricity	Q	coulomb . .	C
Conductance . .	G	mho	
Current:			
Steady or r.m.s. value	I	ampere . . .	A
		milliampere . .	mA
		microampere . .	μA
Instantaneous value	i		
Maximum value .	Im		
Difference of potential:			
Steady or r.m.s. value	V	volt . . .	V
		millivolt . .	mV
		kilovolt . .	kV
Instantaneous value	v		
Maximum value .	Vm		
Electric force (Electric field strength)	$\mathscr{E}$	volt per metre .	V/m
Electric flux . .	Ψ	coulomb . .	C
Electric flux density .	D	coulomb per square metre	C/m²
Electromotive force:			
Steady or r.m.s. value	E	volt . . .	V
Instantaneous value	e		
Maximum value .	Em		
Energy . . .	W	joule . . .	J
		watt-hour . .	Wh
		kilowatt-hour .	kWh
Force . . .	F	newton	
Frequency . .	f	cycle per second .	c/s
		kilocycle per second .	kc/s
		megacycle per second	Mc/s
Impedance . .	Z	ohm . . .	Ω
Inductance, self .	L	henry (plural, henrys)	H
Inductance, mutual .	M	henry (plural, henrys)	H
Magnetising force (Magnetic field strength)	H	ampere-turn per metre	AT/m
Magnetic flux . .	Φ	weber . . .	Wb
		milliweber . .	mWb
		microweber . .	μWb
Magnetic flux density .	B	weber per square metre	Wb/m²
Magnetomotive force .	F	ampere-turn . .	AT
Permeability of free space (Magnetic space constant) .	μ_0		
Permeability, relative	μr		
Permittivity of free space (Electric space constant)	ϵ_0		
Permittivity, relative (Dielectric constant)	ϵr		

Term	Symbol	Unit	Abbreviation of unit after numerical values
Power . . .	P	watt . . . kilowatt . . megawatt . .	W kW MW
Reactance . .	X	ohm . . .	Ω
Reluctance . .	S	ampere-turn per weber	AT/Wb
Resistance . .	R	ohm . . . microhm . . megohm . .	Ω $\mu\Omega$ MΩ
Resistivity . .	ρ	ohm-metre . . microhm-metre .	Ω-m $\mu\Omega$-m
Volt-ampere . .	—	volt-ampere . . kilovolt-ampere .	VA kVA
Reactive volt-ampere .	—	volt-ampere (reactive)	VAr

ABBREVIATIONS FOR MULTIPLES AND SUB-MULTIPLES

M	mega or meg	10^6
k	kilo	10^3
c	centi	10^{-2}
m	milli	10^{-3}
μ	micro	10^{-6}
$\mu\mu$ or p	micromicro or pico	10^{-12}

ELECTRICAL MACHINES

Term	Symbol
Number of armature conductors . .	Z
„ commutator segments or bars	C
„ pair of poles . . .	p
„ phases . . .	m
„ turns	T or N

GREEK LETTERS USED AS SYMBOLS IN THIS BOOK

Letter	Capital	Small
Alpha	—	α (angles)
Epsilon	—	ϵ (permittivity)
Theta	—	θ (angles)
Mu	—	μ (micro and permeability)
Pi	—	π (circumference/diameter)
Rho	—	ρ (resistivity)
Phi	Φ (magnetic flux)	ϕ (phase difference)
Psi	Ψ (electric flux)	—
Omega	Ω (ohm)	ω (angular velocity)

CHAPTER I

FUNDAMENTAL AND MECHANICAL UNITS

1. Fundamental Units. All systems of measurement depend upon the adoption of certain absolute or fundamental units. In the *metre-kilogram-second* (M.K.S.) system, the unit of *length* is the *metre* as defined by the platinum-iridium standard kept at the International Bureau of Weights and Measures at Sèvres, France. The unit of *mass* is the *kilogram*, as defined by the platinum–iridium standard at Sèvres; and the unit of *time* is the *second*, namely 1/86,400 of the mean solar day.

2. Unit of Force. In the M.K.S. system, the unit of force is the *newton* (in commemoration of the great English scientist, Sir Isaac Newton, 1642–1727) and is defined as the force which gives a mass of 1 kilogram an acceleration of 1 metre per second per second. Hence the force, F newtons, required to give a mass of m kilograms an acceleration of f metres/sec² is:

$$F \text{ (newtons)} = m \text{ (kg)} \times f \text{ (m/sec}^2) \quad . \quad \textbf{(1)}$$

For a body having a weight of W kilograms at a place where the acceleration due to gravity is g metres/sec² (9·81 m/sec² in this country), the force F kilograms * required to give an acceleration of f metres/sec² is:

$$F \text{ (kg)} = \frac{W \text{ (kg)}}{g \text{ (m/sec}^2)} \times f \text{ (m/sec}^2).$$

It follows that a force of 1 kg = 9·81 newtons.

* A force of F kilograms is sometimes referred to as a force of F kilograms weight; similarly, a force of F pounds may be referred to as a force of F pounds weight. In actual practice, it is customary for engineers to use the term "pound" for both the unit of mass and the unit of force.

1   1

Example 1. *Calculate the numerical relationships between* (a) *the pound* (*force*) *and the newton and* (b) *the dyne and the newton.*

(a)   Since 1 lb = 0·4536 kg

and a force of 1 kg = 9·81 newtons,

∴   a force of 1 lb = 0·4536 × 9·81 = 4·45 newtons

or   1 newton = 0·225 lb (force).

The relative magnitudes of the newton, the kilogram (force) and the pound (force) are indicated by the lengths of the lines in Fig. 1.

FIG. 1.—The relative magnitudes of the newton, the kilogram (force) and the pound (force).

(b) The *dyne* is the C.G.S. unit of force, namely the force which gives a mass of 1 gram an acceleration of 1 cm/sec². Hence the force in dynes to give a mass of 1 kg (1000 g) an acceleration of 1 m/sec² (100 cm/sec²) is 1000 × 100, namely 100,000 dynes.

∴   1 newton = 100,000 dynes.

It will be seen that the dyne is a force of about 1/1,000,000 kg or 1 milligram and is so small that it is practically impossible to appreciate its magnitude. The newton, on the other hand, is equal to a force of nearly ¼ lb or about 1/10 kg and is therefore a quantity whose value can be easily appreciated.

Example 2. *A force of 50 newtons is applied to a mass of 200 kg. Calculate* (a) *the force in lb and* (b) *the acceleration in m/sec², assuming the frictional resistance to be negligible.*

(a) For g of 9·81 m/sec², 1 newton = 0·225 lb (force),

∴   accelerating force = 50 × 0·225

          = 11·25 lb.

(b) From expression (1),   50 = 200f

∴   f = 0·25 m/sec².

3. Unit of Turning Moment or Torque. If a force of F newtons is acting at right angles to a radius of d metres from a point,

$$\left.\begin{array}{l}\text{turning moment or torque}\\\text{about that point}\end{array}\right\} = Fd \text{ newton-metres} \quad (2)$$

$$= \frac{Fd}{9\cdot81} \text{ kilogram-metres.}$$

4. Unit of Work or Energy. In the M.K.S. system, the unit of energy is the *joule* (after an English physicist, James P. Joule, 1818–89), namely the work done when a force of 1 newton acts for a distance of 1 metre in the direction of the force. Hence if a force of F newtons acts for a distance of d metres in its own direction,

$$\text{work done in joules} = F \text{ (newtons)} \times d \text{ (metres)} \quad . \quad (3)$$

$$= Fd \text{ (metre-newtons)}$$

If a body of mass m kilograms, initially at rest, is given a uniform acceleration of f metres/sec² by a force of F newtons over a period of t seconds,

$$\text{final speed} = v = ft \text{ metres/sec.}$$

Distance travelled = average speed in m/sec × time in sec

$$= \tfrac{1}{2}vt \text{ metres,}$$

$$\therefore \quad \left.\begin{array}{l}\text{kinetic energy}\\\text{acquired by mass}\end{array}\right\} = F \times d = m \times f \times d$$

$$= m \times \frac{v}{t} \times \frac{vt}{2} = \tfrac{1}{2}mv^2 \text{ joules} \quad . \quad (4)$$

By experiment, it has been found that 1 kilogram-calorie = 4187 joules.

The numerical relationships between the various units of energy used in engineering are given on p. 349.

Example 3. *Calculate the numerical relationships between* (a) *the foot-pound and the joule and* (b) *the erg and the joule.*

(a)   Since 1 ft = 0·3048 m

and a force of 1 lb = 4·45 newtons,

$\therefore$ 1 ft-lb = 0·3048 × 4·45 = 1·356 joules.

(b) The *erg* is the C.G.S. unit of energy, namely the work done when a force of 1 dyne acts for a distance of 1 cm in the direction of the force,

$$\therefore \quad 1 \text{ joule} = 1 \text{ metre-newton}$$

$$= 100 \text{ (cm)} \times 100,000 \text{ (dynes)} = 10^7 \text{ ergs.}$$

5. Unit of Power. Since power is the rate of doing work, it follows that in the M.K.S. system, the unit of power is the *joule/second* or *watt* (after the famous Scottish engineer, James Watt, 1736–1819). In practice, the watt is often found to be inconveniently small and so the *kilowatt* is frequently used, the kilowatt being 1000 watts. Similarly, when we are dealing with a large amount of energy, it is more convenient to express the latter in *kilowatt-hours* rather than in joules.

$$\left.\begin{array}{r} 1 \text{ kilowatt-hour} \\ \text{(or kWh)} \end{array}\right\} = 1000 \text{ watt-hours}$$

$$= 1000 \times 3600$$

$$= 3,600,000 \text{ watt-seconds or joules.}$$

If T be the torque or turning moment, in *newton-metres*, due to a force acting about an axis of rotation and if N be the speed in r.p.m.,

$$\text{power} = \frac{2\pi TN}{60} = \omega T \text{ watts} \quad . \quad . \quad (5)$$

where ω = angular velocity in radians/second.

Example 4. *Calculate the numerical relationship between the horsepower and the watt.*

In Example 3, it was shown that 1 ft-lb = 1·356 joules,

$$\therefore \quad 1 \text{ h.p.} = 550 \text{ ft-lb/sec}$$

$$= 550 \times 1\cdot356 = 746 \text{ joules/sec or watts.}$$

Example 5. *A block of stone, weighing 120 lb, is hauled along a horizontal floor for a distance of 100 yards in 2 minutes. The coefficient of friction is 0·3. Calculate (a) the horizontal force required in newtons, (b) the work done in joules and (c) the power in watts.*

(a) Weight of stone $=120 \times 0.4536 = 54.43$ kg,

$\therefore$ force required $=0.3 \times 54.43$ kg

$$=0.3 \times 54.43 \times 9.81$$

$$=160.2 \text{ newtons.}$$

(b) Since 1 yard $=0.9144$ metre,

$\therefore$ distance moved $=100 \times 0.9144 = 91.44$ metres,

and work done $=160.2$ (newtons) $\times 91.44$ (m)

$$=14,650 \text{ joules.}$$

(c) $\qquad$ Power $=\dfrac{14,650}{2 \times 60}=122$ watts.

Example 6. *An electric motor is developing 10 h.p. at a speed of 800 r.p.m. Calculate the torque (a) in lb-ft, (b) in newton-metres and (c) in kilogram-metres.*

(a) $\qquad$ Since h.p. $=\dfrac{2\pi \text{ torque in lb-ft} \times \text{speed in r.p.m.}}{33,000}$

$\therefore \qquad 10 = \dfrac{2\pi T (\text{lb-ft}) \times 800}{33,000}$

$\therefore \qquad T = 65.7$ lb-ft.

(b) Since power developed

$$=10 \times 746 = 7460 \text{ watts,}$$

from (5), $\qquad 7460 = \dfrac{2\pi T \text{ (newton-metres)} \times 800}{60}$

$\therefore \qquad T = 89$ newton-metres.

(c) Since a force of 1 kg $=9.81$ newtons,

$\therefore \qquad T = \dfrac{89}{9.81} = 9.08$ kg-m.

Example 7. *An electric heater is required to heat 3 gallons of water from 15° C to the boiling point in 40 minutes. Assuming the efficiency of the heater to be 80 per cent, calculate (a) the electrical energy consumed in kWh and (b) the cost of the energy if the charge is 2d per kWh. 1 gallon of water weighs 10 lb and assume 1 kg-calorie = 4200 joules.*

(a)   Weight of water $=3 \times 10$ lb

$$=30 \times 0\cdot4536 = 13\cdot608 \text{ kg}$$

$\therefore$ useful heat required $=13\cdot608 \times (100-15)$

$$=1157 \text{ kg-calories}$$

$$=1157 \times 4200 = 4,859,000 \text{ joules.}$$

Total energy supplied $= \dfrac{4,859,000}{0\cdot8} = 6,074,000$ joules

$$= \dfrac{6,074,000}{3,600,000} = 1\cdot69 \text{ kWh.}$$

(c)   Cost of energy $=1\cdot69 \times 2 = 3\cdot38d.$

Summary of Important Formulae and Relationships

$$F \text{ (newtons)} = m \text{ (kg)} \times f \text{ (m/sec}^2) \quad . \quad (1)$$

$$\text{Work done (joules)} = F \text{ (newtons)} \times d \text{ (metres)} \quad (3)$$

$$= Fd \text{ (metre-newtons)}$$

$$\text{Kinetic energy (joules)} = \tfrac{1}{2}m \text{ (kg)} \times v^2 \text{ (m/sec)}^2 \quad (4)$$

$$\text{Power (watts)} = \dfrac{2\pi T \text{(newton-metres)} \times N \text{ (r.p.m.)}}{60} \quad . \quad (5)$$

(Force)   1 lb $=4\cdot45$ newtons

or 1 newton $=0\cdot225$ lb

(Force)   1 kg $=9\cdot81$ newtons

(Energy)   1 ft-lb $=1\cdot356$ joules

(Energy)   1 kWh $=3,600,000$ joules

(Power)   1 h.p. $=746$ watts

1 kilogram-calorie $=4187$ joules

1 British Thermal Unit $=0\cdot252$ kg-calorie $=1055$ joules.

EXAMPLES I

1. A force of 120 newtons is applied to a mass of 350 **kg**. Calculate (a) the force in lb and (b) the acceleration in m/sec², assuming the frictional resistance to be negligible.

2. Calculate the force in newtons necessary to give a mass of 200 lb an acceleration of 5 ft/sec², assuming the frictional resistance to be negligible.

3. A force of 8 newtons applied to a stone block on a horizontal surface of ice is found to give an acceleration of 0·1 m/sec². Assuming the friction to be negligible, calculate the mass of the stone in kg.

4. A metal cylinder weighing 150 g is given an acceleration of 20 cm/sec². Assuming the frictional resistance to be negligible, calculate the accelerating force (a) in newtons and (b) in grams. Also, calculate the kinetic energy in joules when the speed is 600 cm/sec.

5. A weight of 60 lb is raised vertically through a distance of 110 feet in 30 seconds. Calculate the work done in joules and the power in watts.

6. A load of 2000 kg is lifted vertically at a speed of 80 m/minute. Calculate the power in kW taken by the driving motor if the combined efficiency of the motor and gearing is 70 per cent. Also, calculate the kinetic energy of the load in joules.

7. A motor is developing 50 h.p. at a speed of 600 r.p.m. Calculate the torque in (a) lb-ft, (b) newton-metres and (c) kg-metres.

8. A motor is required to lift a weight of 200 kg by means of a rope wound on a drum having a diameter of 1·5 metres. If the speed of the drum is 80 r.p.m., calculate the power required (a) in watts and (b) in h.p. Also, calculate the work done in joules and in kWh when the weight is lifted 30 metres.

9. In a wheel-and-axle lifting machine, the wheel has a diameter of 18 inches and the axle 2 inches. For a load of 30 kg, calculate (a) the effort required in newtons, assuming the efficiency to be 90 per cent, (b) the work done, in joules, by the effort when the load is lifted 2 metres and (c) the corresponding power, in watts, if the time taken is 6 seconds.

10. A screw-jack is used to raise a load of 3000 kg. The lead of the screw is ½ inch. Find the force, in newtons, required at the end of a 15-inch arm, assuming the efficiency to be 30 per cent. Also, calculate the input energy, in joules, and the corresponding power, in watts, if the load is lifted 5 cm in 3 minutes.

11. A block of metal weighing 150 kg is dragged along a horizontal floor over a distance of 20 metres in 8 seconds. The coefficient of friction is 0·27. Calculate (a) the horizontal force required in newtons, (b) the work done in joules and (c) the power in watts.

12. A train weighing 150 tons is hauled at a constant speed of 40 m.p.h. along a horizontal track. The track resistance is 12 lb per ton. Calculate the tractive effort in newtons, (b) the energy in joules and in kWh expended in 20 minutes, (c) the power in kW and (d) the kinetic energy of the train in kWh (neglecting rotational inertia).

13. An electrically-driven pump lifts 15,000 gallons of water a minute through a height of 23 feet. Allowing an overall efficiency of 68 per cent for the motor and pump, calculate the input power in kW to the motor. If the pump is in operation for an average of 2 hours a day for a year, calculate the energy consumed in kWh and the cost of the energy at 0·75d per kWh.

14. A certain factory has the following electrical load: electric motors totalling 28 b.h.p. with an efficiency of 82 per cent; electric heaters taking 4·7 kW; electric lamps taking 3·8 kW. If the motors and heaters are on for 8 hours a day and the lamps are on for 2 hours a day, calculate the cost of energy consumed in 26 days if the tariff be 5d per kWh for lighting and 0·9d per kWh for motors and heaters.

15. A boiler is required to raise the temperature of 40 gallons of water per hour by 75° F. Calculate the cost per hour: (a) for a gas-fired boiler having an efficiency of 80 per cent, with gas costing 1s 8d per therm; (b) for an electrically-heated boiler having an efficiency of 95 per cent with electrical energy at 1·6d per kWh. 1 therm = 100,000 B.Th.U.

16. An electric furnace is being used to melt 20 pounds of aluminium. The melting point is 660° C and its specific heat may be taken as 0·24 and its latent heat of fusion as 92·4 calories per gram. The temperature of the surrounding air is 20° C. Calculate the power required to perform the work in 20 minutes. Assume the efficiency of the furnace to be 60 per cent. Also, find the cost of energy consumed at 1d per kWh.

17. The heater of an electric furnace has a rating of 2 kW. The mass of metal to be heated is equivalent to 3 lb of iron having a specific heat of 0·16. Calculate the time required for the metal to be heated from 15° C to 600° C, assuming the efficiency to be 90 per cent and 1 gram-calorie = 4·2 joules. Also, calculate the cost of the energy consumed if the charge is 0·8d per kWh.

18. An engine of 100 b.h.p. drives a dynamo of 90 per cent efficiency. The output of the dynamo is used for power and lighting. The power load consists of five 10 b.h.p. motors of 85 per cent efficiency and six 2-kW electric fires. What is the maximum number of 100-W lamps that must be used to give full load on the dynamo? (U.L.C.I., S1)

19. An electric furnace is to smelt 85 kg of tin per hour from an initial temperature of 15° C. Find the power required and the cost of operating the furnace for 40 hours, given:

Specific heat of tin 0·055; melting point of tin 235° C; latent heat of fusion of tin 13·31 k.cal/kg; efficiency of furnace 80 per cent.; cost of electrical energy ¾d per unit.   (U.E.I., S2)

CHAPTER II

ELECTRIC CURRENT

6. Effects of an Electric Current. All the phenomena that an electric current can produce may be grouped under one or other of the following headings:

(a) Magnetic effects.
(b) Heating effects.
(c) Chemical effects.

Let us assume that we have available at the terminals of a double-pole switch S (Fig. 2) a direct-current supply, namely, a supply that causes the electric current to flow

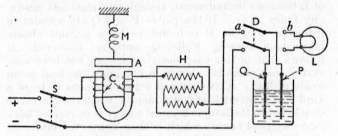

FIG. 2.—Magnetic, heating and chemical effects of an electric current.

in one direction only. This direct-current supply may be obtained either from a direct-current generator or from accumulators, the principle of action of which is referred to later in this article. To the output side of S, let us connect the following items in series, so that the same current passes through each of them:

(1) Coil C wound on an iron core bent into an U shape.
(2) Electric fire element H, of suitable size.
(3) Double-pole change-over switch D, to which are also connected a flash-lamp bulb L and a pair of lead

1*　　　　9

plates, P and Q, dipping into a dilute solution of sulphuric acid in water.

When S is closed and D is put over to side *a*, an electric current passes through C and H, from which it proceeds to P, through the liquid to Q, and then returns to the generator or accumulators.

If an iron plate or armature A be suspended by a spring M a little above the ends of the iron core, it will be attracted downwards immediately S is closed.   In other words, the iron core becomes magnetised and mechanical work is done in extending M.

The element H indicates the presence of an electric current by the fact that it begins to give out heat, and its temperature may rise sufficiently for it to emit an appreciable amount of light.   Hence electrical energy is being converted into heat and light energy.

After the current has been passing for a few minutes, let us open S and switch D over to side *b*.   The filament of L becomes incandescent, though its brightness gradually fades away.   If the plates P and Q are withdrawn from the solution, P is found to have a faint choco-late-colour coating while Q appears unaltered.   It follows that in this case electrical energy has been con-verted into chemical energy in changing the lead to an oxide of lead.   This chemical action happens to be of a kind that is reversible; consequently, when the plates are connected to the lamp, chemical energy is converted back into electrical energy which is then converted into heat and light energy.   This reversible chemical action is the basis upon which accumulators operate (see Chap. XVIII).

7. Measurement of an Electric Current.   It is very important that we should have some idea of the magni-tude of the current in a circuit, and we shall now consider how each of the three effects mentioned in Art. 6 can be utilised for indicating the value of the current.

In Fig. 3, E and F represent the cross-section of two co-axial coils,* E being suspended from a spring balance

---

* If the coils have a mean diameter of about 8 inches and if each coil is wound with 50 turns, then when they are spaced an inch apart and each coil is carrying a current of 10 A, the force of attraction is of the order of 100 grams.

G about an inch above F which rests on a table or bench. The coils are connected so that they carry current in the same direction, the current being led into and out of coil E by flexible wires. A coil B, also shown in section in Fig. 3, is wound on a hollow cylindrical former and an iron core C is suspended from a spring balance S.

A relatively long thin wire W, of high resistance material such as eureka, is fixed at the two ends DD. Another thin wire J passes round a pulley P and has its upper end attached to the middle of W, while its lower end is fastened to a spring Q.

A glass vessel M contains a solution of copper sulphate

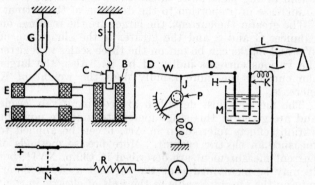

Fig. 3.—Measurement of an electric current.

in water; and H and K are two copper plates, K being suspended from one arm of a sensitive balance L. Electrical connection is made to K by a thin, loosely-coiled copper wire.

The four pieces of apparatus just described are connected in series, as shown in Fig. 3. A variable resistance R for controlling the value of the current and an ammeter A (i.e. an instrument calibrated to indicate the magnitude of the current directly in amperes) are also inserted in the circuit.

When the double-pole switch N is closed, an electric current flows round the circuit. The magnetic effect produced by the currents in coils E and F causes the latter to attract each other (the reason for this behaviour is given in Art. 43). Also core C is attracted towards B, while wire W is heated and its elongation causes it to sag. Wire J thereby tends to become slack and allows spring Q to contract. The result is that pulley P, to which the pointer is attached, is rotated slightly.

If the current be maintained at a suitable value—8 to 10 amperes usually suffice—it is found that the balance arm L soon begins to tilt counterclockwise, and the weight required on the right-hand side to maintain a balance increases steadily. This shows that the chemical action taking place at K causes the weight of the latter to increase in proportion to the duration of the current.

The greater the current, the larger are the readings on balances G and S and the greater is the elongation of W; and marks can be put on the three scales to register the various currents indicated by A. Also, the larger the current, the more rapidly does the weight of K increase.

The methods just described are comparatively crude and are given at this stage merely to indicate how the various effects referred to in Art. 6 can be applied to measure an electric current. More precise methods of current measurement are described in Chap. XVII, but it may be mentioned that the method used for determining the absolute value of the unit of electric current is based upon the principle involved in the mutual attraction of the two coils, E and F, in Fig. 3.

8. Effect of Reversing the Current. Let us change over the connections at switch N in Fig. 3, so that the supply wire marked " — " will now go to coil F and that marked " + " to resistance R. It is found that the effect of the reversed current is still to attract coil E and core C downwards and cause W to elongate. In fact, a given current, as indicated by ammeter A, gives exactly the same deflections as before on the three scales. The balance, on the other hand, shows K to be getting lighter, so that the chemical action at K must now be taking place in the reverse direction. Further, the decrease in the weight of K due to a given current for a given time is the same as the increase that took place before the connections were reversed.

Let us go a step further and connect the circuit of Fig. 3 across an alternating-current supply. The electric current now reverses its direction many times every second. Coil E and core C are still found to be attracted downwards and wire W elongates, but no change takes place in the weight of plate K. The chemical (or electrolytic) method is therefore useless for measuring an alternating current, whereas it is possible to construct instruments of the magnetic and thermal types that read direct and alternating currents equally accurately.

9. Direction of an Electric Current. The experiments described above suggest that an electric current may be regarded as a flow of electricity, but the direction which has been accepted for this flow is a purely arbitrary one and was based originally upon a theory of Benjamin Franklin, long since discarded. This matter is referred to more fully in Art. 68. At this stage it will suffice to state that if a circuit such as the filament of a lamp be connected across a direct-current supply, the electric current is regarded as flowing from the positive terminal (usually painted red) through the circuit to the negative terminal (painted black). If this convention be applied to Fig. 3, it will be seen that plate K becomes heavier when current flows from H through the liquid (or electrolyte) to K, and that it becomes lighter when current passes from K to the electrolyte.

It is therefore possible to utilise the chemical effect of a current for determining its direction in accordance with the convention universally accepted.

10. Quantity of Electricity. Let us carry out a further series of experiments with the copper plates and electrolyte referred to in Fig. 3 (an *electrolyte* being any liquid that can be decomposed electrically). The suspension of one of the plates from a balance arm was mainly for the convenience of a class demonstration; but far greater accuracy may be obtained by washing, drying and weighing plate K before it is placed in the copper sulphate solution, and then repeating the process at the conclusion of the experiment. In this way we can determine accurately the amount of copper deposited on K by a given current in, say, 10, 20 and 30 minutes, and also the amount deposited by different currents in, say, 10 minutes. It is found that the weight of copper deposited is directly proportional to the current and to the time; in other words, it is proportional to the quantity of electricity. Owing to the accuracy and the ease with which the increase in the weight of a plate can be determined, this chemical effect of an electric current may be employed for measuring the quantity of electricity with a high degree of precision.

11. Units of Electric Current and of Quantity. By an electric current is meant the rate at which electricity flows past a given point of an electric circuit, and the *unit of current* is termed the *ampere*, to commemorate a famous French scientist, André-Marie Ampère (1775–1836). It follows that the *unit quantity* of electricity, called the *coulomb* after another great French scientist, flows past a given point of a circuit when a current of 1 ampere is maintained for 1 second. Consequently, if a current of I amperes is maintained constant for t seconds, the corresponding quantity of electricity is represented by Q coulombs, where

$$Q \text{ (coulombs)} = I \text{ (amperes)} \times t \text{ (seconds)} \quad (6)$$

The abbreviations for "ampere" and "coulomb" are "A" and "C" respectively.

The value of the ampere, adopted internationally in 1948, is defined as that current which, when flowing in each of two infinitely long parallel conductors in a vacuum, separated 1 metre between centres, causes each conductor to have a force acting upon it of 2×10^{-7} newton per metre length of conductor (Art. 41). The apparatus required to measure a current accurately in terms of this definition is very elaborate and expensive and is seldom available outside the principal national laboratories, such as the National Physical Laboratory in Great Britain. By means of very carefully-conducted experiments, however, it has been found that when a current of 1 ampere is passed between two copper plates immersed in a copper sulphate solution, copper is deposited on the negative plate (i.e. plate K in Fig. 3) at the rate of 0·0003294 g/sec. When the experiment is performed with a silver *voltameter*, namely two plates of silver immersed in a silver nitrate solution, it is found that a current of 1 ampere causes silver to be deposited on the negative plate at the rate of 0·0011182 g/sec.

Since 1 ampere is 1 coulomb per second, the unit quantity of electricity may also be termed an *ampere-second*. For many purposes, such as for stating the quantity of electricity an accumulator is capable of giving, the coulomb is inconveniently small, and a larger unit, called the *ampere-hour* (Ah), is preferable. Thus, if an accumulator gives 4 A for 10 hours, the quantity of electricity is 4 (amperes) ×10 (hours), namely, 40 Ah.

12. Electrochemical Equivalent. In Art. 10 it was found that the amount of copper deposited on the negative plate (or *cathode*) was proportional to the quantity of electricity flowing through the electrolyte. This relationship was discovered by Michael Faraday in 1832 when he enunciated two laws:

(1) the amount of chemical change produced by an electric current is proportional to the quantity of electricity, and

(2) the amounts of different substances liberated by a given quantity of electricity are proportional to their chemical equivalent weights, where chemical equivalent

$$\text{weight} = \frac{\text{atomic weight}}{\text{valency}}.$$

The atomic weights and valencies of some of the most common elements are given in Table I.

The mass of a substance liberated from an electrolyte by 1 coulomb is termed the *electrochemical equivalent* of that substance; thus, the electrochemical equivalents of copper and silver are respectively 0·0003294 and 0·0011182 gram/coulomb.

TABLE I

Element	Atomic weight	Valency	Electrochemical equivalent
Aluminium . .	27·0	3	
Chlorine . .	35·5	1	
Chromium . .	52·0	3 or 6	
Copper (cuprous) .	63·6	1	
,, (cupric) .	,,	2	0·0003294 g/C
Gold . . .	197·2	3	
Hydrogen . .	1·008	1	
Iron . . .	55·8	2 or 3	
Lead . . .	207·2	2	
Nickel . . .	58·7	2	0·000304 g/C
Oxygen . . .	16·0	2	
Potassium . .	39·1	1	
Silver . . .	107·9	1	0·0011182 g/C
Sodium . . .	23·0	1	
Tin . . .	118·7	2 or 4	
Zinc . . .	65·4	2	0·000338 g/C

If z = electrochemical equivalent of a substance in grams per coulomb,

and I = current in amperes for time t seconds,

mass of substance liberated = zIt grams . (7)

Example 8. *If a current of 15 A is maintained constant for 20 minutes, calculate the quantity of electricity in* (a) *coulombs,* (b) *ampere-hours.*

(a) Quantity of electricity (coulombs)

= current (amperes) × time (seconds)

= 15 × 20 × 60 = 18,000 coulombs

(b) Quantity of electricity (ampere-hours)

= current (amperes) × time (hours)

= $15 \times \frac{20}{60} = 5$ Ah.

Example 9. *A steady current of 6·3 A is passed for 45 minutes through a solution of copper sulphate. Calculate the mass of copper deposited.*

Quantity of electricity (coulombs)

$$= \text{current (amperes)} \times \text{time (seconds)}$$
$$= 6\cdot3 \times 45 \times 60$$
$$= 17{,}010 \text{ coulombs.}$$

But 1 coulomb deposits 0·0003294 gram of copper,

$\therefore$ mass of copper deposited $= 0\cdot0003294 \times 17{,}010$
$$= 5\cdot6 \text{ g.}$$

Example 10. *A current of 2 A is passed for 30 minutes between two platinum plates (or electrodes) immersed in a dilute solution of sulphuric acid in water. Calculate the weight of hydrogen and oxygen released.*

The effect of electrolysis in this case is to decompose water into its constituents, hydrogen and oxygen, the former being liberated at the negative plate (or cathode) and the latter at the positive plate (or anode).

Quantity of electricity $= 2 \times 30 \times 60 = 3600$ coulombs. From the data given in Table I,

$$\left. \begin{array}{c} \text{chemical equivalent weight} \\ \text{of hydrogen} \end{array} \right\} = 1\cdot008/1 = 1\cdot008$$

Hence, by Faraday's Second Law,
electrochemical equivalent of hydrogen

$$= 0\cdot0011182 \times \frac{1\cdot008}{107\cdot9}$$
$$= 0\cdot00001045 \text{ g/C}$$

$\therefore$ weight of hydrogen released

$$= 0\cdot00001045 \times 3600$$
$$= 0\cdot0376 \text{ g.}$$

Similarly, chemical equivalent weight of oxygen

$$= 16/2 = 8$$

$\therefore$ electrochemical equivalent of oxygen

$$= 0\cdot0011182 \times \frac{8}{107\cdot9}$$
$$= 0\cdot0000829 \text{ g/C}$$

and weight of oxygen released

$$= 0\cdot0000829 \times 3600$$
$$= 0\cdot298 \text{ g.}$$

Summary of Important Formulae

$$Q \text{ (coulombs)} = I \text{ (amperes)} \times t \text{ (seconds)} \quad . \quad (6)$$

$$\left. \begin{array}{l} \text{Mass of substance} \\ \text{liberated from} \\ \text{electrolyte} \end{array} \right\} = z \text{ (g/C)} \times I \text{ (amperes)} \times t \text{ (sec)} \quad (7)$$

$$= z \text{ (g/C)} \times Q \text{ (coulombs)}.$$

EXAMPLES II

1. An ammeter is calibrated by being connected in series with a copper voltameter through which a constant current is maintained for 15 minutes. The ammeter reading is 4 A. The initial and final weights of the cathode are 16·347 and 17·518 grams respectively. Find the error in the ammeter reading and state whether the ammeter is reading high or low.

2. A steady current was passed through a copper voltameter for half an hour. The weight of the cathode was found to increase by 1·65 grams. Calculate the value of the current.

3. A metal plate having a surface of 120 cm² is to be copper-plated. If a current of 2 A be passed for one hour, what thickness of copper will be deposited? Should the plate be made the positive or the negative electrode? Density of copper is 8·9 g/cm³.

4. A solid metal cylinder, 3 cm diameter and 20 cm long, is to have copper deposited to a thickness of 0·1 mm over its *curved* surface. Find the time taken by a current of 40 A. Assume the electrochemical equivalent of copper to be 0·00033 gram per coulomb and the density of copper to be 8·9 g/cm³.

5. A steady current of 3 A is passed for 16 minutes through a silver voltameter. If 1 ampere deposits 0·001118 gram of silver per second, find the increase in the weight of the cathode. Also find the quantity of electricity: (a) in coulombs, (b) in ampere-hours.

6. It is required to deposit a layer of nickel 0·2 mm thick on a surface area of 150 cm². Find the minimum time required if the maximum permissible current be 8 A. Assume the electrochemical equivalent of nickel to be 0·000304 g/C, and 1 cm³ of nickel to weigh 8·8 grams. Also, find the quantity of electricity required: (a) in coulombs, (b) in ampere-hours.

7. (a) Describe how you would proceed to determine the electro-chemical equivalent of copper in a laboratory.

(b) A steady current of 4 A is passed for 12 minutes through a silver voltameter consisting of two silver plates immersed in a solution of silver nitrate. If 1 A deposits 0·001118 g of silver per second, calculate the increase in weight of the cathode.   (E.M.E.U., S1)

8. Define the *ampere*.

A layer of nickel, 0·3 mm thick, is deposited in 4 hours on a surface having an area of 60 cm². If the electrochemical equivalent of nickel is 0·000306 g per coulomb and the specific gravity of nickel is 8·8, what is the value of the current?

State whether the surface to be nickel-plated is the positive or the negative electrode and give the reason.

(I. Mech. E., Prin. of Elect.)

9. Define the electrochemical equivalent of an element. A metal plate having a surface of 200 cm² is to be silver-plated. If a current of 0·5 A is used for a period of 1 hour, what thickness of silver will be deposited on the plate, given that the E.C.E. of silver is 0·001118 and its density is 10·6 g/cm³. (U.E.I., S1)

10. In an experiment to determine the electrochemical equivalent of copper, the following results were obtained:

Initial weight of plate, 29·82 g; final weight of plate, 30·48 g; current, 2 A; time, 16 min 40 sec.

Calculate the experimental value of the electrochemical equivalent of copper. What precautions should be taken in carrying out this experiment? (U.E.I., S1)

11. How would you utilise the chemical effects of a current (a) to measure the current; (b) to determine the polarity of the supply mains?

The electrochemical equivalent of copper is 0·000328 g/C. How long will it take a current of 2 A to copper-plate a surface, 10 cm × 12 cm, with a deposit of 0·01 mm thick? (The specific gravity of copper is 8·9.) (E.M.E.U., S1)

12. Define "electro-chemical equivalent." A copper voltameter and an ammeter are arranged in series with a resistance and a battery. The reading of the ammeter is 0·95 A and the weight of the copper deposited in 1 hour 40 minutes is 1·8 grams. What correction must be applied to the reading of the ammeter in order that the true value of the current may be obtained? Give a diagram of the circuit. (Electrochemical equivalent = 0·000328.) (E.M.E.U., S1)

13. A steady current flowing through acidulated water liberates 1248 cm³ of hydrogen, measured under normal temperature and pressure, per hour. Assuming the electrochemical equivalent of hydrogen to be 0·0000104 gram per coulomb and its density at normal temperature and pressure to be 90 grams per cubic metre, calculate the value of the current.

14. A metal plate, having a total surface of 200 cm², is to be chromium-plated. If a current of 5 A is used for a period of 1 hour, what thickness of chromium will be deposited on the plate. Assume the E.C.E. of chromium to be 0·0898 milligram per coulomb and the density 6·6 g/cm³.

15. From the data given in the table on p. 16, calculate the electro-chemical equivalents of aluminium, gold and chlorine.

16. State Faraday's Laws of Electrolysis and define the term "electro-chemical equivalent."

A thin rectangular metal plate, 20 cm by 12·5 cm, is to be completely nickel-plated, with a coating 0·08 mm thick, in an electrolytic tank. If a steady current of 2·0 A is passed through the tank, how long must the plate remain immersed? Take the density of nickel as 8·8 grams per cubic centimetre and its electro-chemical equivalent as 0·000304 gram/coulomb. (C. & G., Telecom. Prin. I)

CHAPTER III

ELECTRIC CIRCUIT

13. Conductors and Insulators. We have become so accustomed to the idea of an electric current being confined to a metallic circuit surrounded by a non-metallic substance, such as air or cotton, that we find it difficult to appreciate the significance of some remarkable experiments made in 1729 by an Englishman, Stephen Gray, when he discovered electrical conductors and insulators. He found that a brass wire allowed electricity to pass through it, whereas silk would not do so; and by means of a wire suspended by silk threads he transmitted electricity a distance of about 300 yards. Gray's discovery provided the key to the remarkable progress which electrical science made in the following one hundred years, to be crowned by Faraday's discovery of electromagnetic induction in 1831 (Art. 44).

Though it is usual to divide materials into two categories, conductors and insulators, it should be realised that these are only relative terms. No material is a perfect conductor and no material is a perfect insulator. In general, metals such as copper and silver are very good conductors, whereas non-metallic materials such as rubber and glass are good insulators.

The insulating property of oil and of fibrous materials, such as paper and cotton, is greatly affected by the amount of moisture they contain. The greater the moisture content, the poorer is the insulating property.

14. Heating Effect of an Electric Current. When a block of stone is dragged along a horizontal surface, it is found that the friction between the two surfaces tends to resist the movement of one surface relative to the other and that the work done in overcoming friction is converted into heat. In an electric circuit we also find that the material of which the circuit is made tends to resist the passage of electricity through it, and that the electrical energy which has to be supplied to overcome this resistance is converted into heat. It follows that good conductors have very low electrical resistance, whereas good insulators have very high electrical resistance.

The laws relating to the heating effect of an electric current were discovered by James Prescott Joule, a British scientist whose name is perpetuated by the unit of energy, the *joule* (Art. 4). The general principle of the apparatus used by Joule is shown in Fig. 4. A copper calorimeter B con-

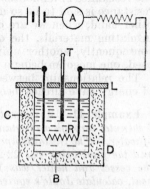

FIG. 4.—Verification of Joule's laws.

tains a known weight of water, and any loss of heat is minimised by a layer of cotton wool C between B and an outer container D. Stout copper wires pass through a wooden lid L and are attached at the lower ends to a spiral of known resistance R. The temperature of the water is measured by a thermometer T. A constant current is passed through R for a known time and the rise of tempera-ture of the water is noted. It is necessary to stir the water very thoroughly during the test to ensure uniform distribution of the heat.

From his researches, Joule deduced that the heat generated in a wire is proportional to :

(1) the square of the current, e.g. if the current is doubled, the rate of heat generation is increased fourfold,

(2) the resistance of the wire ; e.g. if the length of the wire is doubled, the rate of heat generation by a given current is also doubled,

(3) the time during which the current is flowing.

Consequently, if a current I amperes flows through a resistance R for t seconds,

$$\text{heat energy generated} \propto I^2 Rt.$$

The *unit of resistance* is that resistance in which a current of 1 ampere flowing for 1 second generates 1 joule of heat energy. This unit of resistance is termed the *ohm* in commemoration of Georg Simon Ohm (1787–1854), the German physicist who enunciated Ohm's Law (Art. 18). Hence if a current of I amperes flows through a resistance of R ohms for t seconds,

$$\text{heat energy generated} = I^2Rt \text{ joules} \qquad (8)$$

The ohm is represented by the abbreviation Ω (capital omega). Sometimes it is more convenient to express the resistance in millionths of an ohm, in which case the resistance is said to be so many *microhms* ($\mu\Omega$). On the other hand, when we are dealing with the resistance of insulating materials, the ohm is inconveniently small; consequently, another unit called the *megohm* ($M\Omega$) is used, one megohm being a million ohms.

The relationships between the joule and other units of energy have already been given in Art. 4.

Example 11. *A current of 5 A was maintained for 6 minutes through a resistance of 1·3 Ω immersed in 440 g of water. The initial temperature of the water was 16·3° C and the final value was 22·2° C. The water equivalent of the vessel and heater was 17·2 g. Assuming no loss of heat, calculate Joule's equivalent in joules per kg-calorie.*

Heat generated in the resistance $= I^2Rt$ joules

$$= 5^2 \times 1\!\cdot\!3 \times 6 \times 60$$
$$= 11{,}700 \text{ joules.}$$

Heat absorbed by water and vessel

$$= (440 + 17\!\cdot\!2) \text{ g} \times (22\!\cdot\!2 - 16\!\cdot\!3)° \text{ C}$$
$$= 457\!\cdot\!2 \text{ g} \times 5\!\cdot\!9° \text{ C}$$
$$= 2700 \text{ gram-calories}$$
$$= 2\!\cdot\!7 \text{ kg-calories}$$

$$\therefore \quad 1 \text{ kg-calorie} = \frac{11{,}700}{2\!\cdot\!7} = 4330 \text{ joules.}$$

The difference between this value and 4187 given in Art. 4 may be due to experimental error and to some loss of heat during the test.

15. Electrical Power. Since power is the rate of doing work, it follows that in the electrical circuit, power may be expressed in joules per second or *watts*; and since the electrical energy converted into heat energy when a current of I amperes flows through a resistance of R ohms for t seconds is I^2Rt joules,

$$\therefore \quad \text{electrical power} = \frac{I^2Rt}{t} \text{ joules per second}$$

$$= I^2R \text{ watts} \quad . \quad . \quad . \quad (9)$$

From Art. 5, 1 kilowatt $=1000$ watts.

Example 12. *The wire used in an electric heater has a resistance of 57 ohms. Calculate* (a) *the electrical power when the heater is taking a current of* $3\cdot8$ *A*, (b) *the energy absorbed in 4 hours* (i) *in kWh and* (ii) *in kg-calories,* (c) *the cost of the energy consumed if the charge is* $1\cdot5$ *d/kWh. Assume 1 kg-calorie* $=4200$ *joules.*

(a) Electrical power

$$= 3\cdot8^2 \times 57 = 823 \text{ W}$$

$$= 0\cdot823 \text{ kW.}$$

(b) (i) Energy absorbed

$$= 0\cdot823 \text{ (kW)} \times 4 \text{ (hours)}$$

$$= 3\cdot292 \text{ kWh.}$$

(ii) Energy absorbed

$$= 823 \text{ (W)} \times 4 \text{ (h)} \times 3600 \text{ (sec/h) joules}$$

$$= \frac{823 \times 14,400}{4200} = 2820 \text{ kg-calories.}$$

(c) Cost of energy

$$= 3\cdot292 \times 1\cdot5 = 4\cdot94d.$$

16. Fall of Potential along a Circuit. Suppose CD in Fig. 5 to represent a long thin wire of uniform diameter made of an alloy such as eureka (60 per cent copper and 40 per cent nickel) having a much higher resistance than the same length and diameter of copper. The wire is connected across the terminals of an accumulator. A milliammeter A in series with a resistance R of, say,

1000 ohms is connected between terminal D and a contact K that can be moved along CD. The function of R is to limit the current through A, thereby protecting the latter from an excessive current and preventing an appreciable fraction of the current being diverted from length KD of the wire.

It is found that as the distance between K and D is increased, the current through A also increases, as indicated by the height of the graph shown in Fig. 5, where PQ represents the ammeter reading with K at C. Since the direction of the current I in CD is assumed to be from C to D, C is said to be at a higher *potential* than

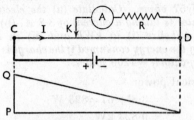

FIG. 5.—Fall of electrical potential.

D. In other words, when two points at different electrical potentials are connected together by a conductor, electricity is assumed to flow from the one at the higher potential to that at the lower potential. In Fig. 5, the difference of potential between K and D is directly proportional to the deflection on A and therefore to the distance between D and the movable contact, the latter being at a higher potential than D.

17. Hydraulic Analogy of Fall of Potential. A brass tube T (Fig. 6) has a number of glass tubes attached to it. The tube is connected to a large jar A filled with a solution, such as methylene blue, which stands out clearly against a white background. At the other end of T there is a tap C by which the flow of the liquid can be controlled. When C is shut, the level of the liquid in the glass tubes is the same as that in the jar; that is, the whole pressure head of the liquid is available at C and there is no pressure drop in the pipe. Such a condition corresponds to a cell on open circuit, namely when there is no conducting path between the terminals. The whole of the e.m.f. then appears as a difference of potential between the terminals and there is no voltage drop in any of the connecting wires.

As tap C is opened, the liquid flows out at an increasing rate, and it is found that the height of the liquid in the glass tubes varies from a minimum in E to a maximum in D; in fact, if a straight rod be placed opposite the heights of the liquid columns in D and E it will also coincide with the heights in the intermediate tubes, showing that the difference of pressure between any two

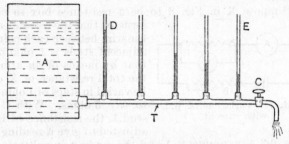

Fig. 6.—Hydraulic analogy.

points along the tube is proportional to the distance between them. Also, it is found that the more rapidly the liquid is allowed to run out at C, the greater is the difference of pressure between two adjacent tubes; in other words, the greater is the fall of pressure in a given length of pipe. These effects are somewhat similar to the electrical relationships discussed in the next article, where it is shown that the difference of potential across a resistor is proportional to the current and to the resistance.

18. Ohm's Law. As long ago as 1827 Dr. G. S. Ohm discovered that the current through a conductor, under constant conditions, was proportional to the difference of potential across the conductor. This fact can easily be verified by connecting, as shown in Fig. 7, a fixed resistance X, made of eureka or other material whose resistance is not affected by temperature, in series with a variable resistance B and an ammeter A across the terminals of an accumulator. A voltmeter * V is connected across X.

Different currents are obtained by varying B, and for each current the reading on V is noted. It is found that the ratio $\dfrac{\text{potential difference across X}}{\text{current through X}}$ remains constant within the limits of experimental error, i.e. the current through a circuit having a constant resistance is proportional to the difference of potential across that circuit.

Suppose X in Fig. 8 to be a resistance box so constructed that the resistance of the wire between each pair of adjacent studs is 1 ohm and that by means of an arm C, the total resistance of X can be varied in steps of 1 ohm up to, say, 5 ohms. With C on stud 1, the resistance of B is adjusted to give a reading of,

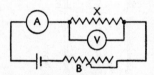

FIG. 7.—Variation of p.d. with current.

say, 0·3 A on ammeter A and the reading on voltmeter V is noted. Arm C is then moved to stud 2, B is readjusted to bring the current back to 0·3 A and the reading on V is again noted. The test is repeated with C on each of the other studs. It is found that the ratio $\dfrac{\text{potential difference across X}}{\text{resistance of X}}$ remains practically constant, i.e. for a given current, the difference of potential between two points is directly proportional to the resistance of the circuit between those points.

The *unit of potential difference* (or p.d.) is taken as the

---

* All voltmeters, except the electrostatic type (Art. 146), consist of a milliammeter connected in series with a high resistance, as shown in Fig. 5. At this stage, however, a voltmeter may be regarded merely as an instrument that indicates the difference of electric potential between the two points across which it is connected.

difference of potential across a resistance of 1 ohm carrying a current of 1 ampere and is termed the *volt* (V) after Count Alessandro Volta (1745–1827), an Italian physicist who was the first to discover how to make an electric battery. It follows from the above experiments that if the current through a resistance of 1 ohm is increased to, say, 3 A, the p.d. is 3 volts, and that if the resistance is increased to, say, 4 Ω with the current maintained at 3 A, the p.d. across the resistance becomes 3×4, namely 12 V. Hence if a circuit having a resistance of R ohms

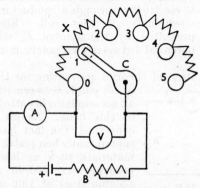

FIG. 8.—Variation of p.d. with resistance.

is carrying a current of I amperes, the p.d., V volts, across the circuit is given by:

$$V = IR, \quad \text{or} \quad I = V/R, \quad \text{or} \quad R = V/I \quad . \quad (10)$$

This relationship, known as *Ohm's Law*, is more complete and useful than that originally enunciated by Ohm. At this stage it is best to memorise Ohm's Law in one form only; and for this purpose the form $I = V/R$ is probably the most convenient.

From (9), electrical power

$$= I^2 R \text{ watts}$$
$$= I \times IR = IV \text{ watts} \quad . \quad . \quad (11)$$
or
$$= \left(\frac{V}{R}\right)^2 \times R = \frac{V^2}{R} \text{ watts} \quad . \quad (12)$$

19. Electromotive Force. It was shown in Art. 6 that when a current is passed for several minutes between two lead plates immersed in a dilute solution of sulphuric acid in water, a chocolate-colour coating is formed on the positive plate and that an electric current is obtained when the plates are then connected to a separate circuit; i.e. the combination of plates and acid became a voltaic cell * capable of converting chemical energy into electrical energy. Such an arrangement is a source † of an *electromotive force* (e.m.f.); in other words, an electromotive force represents something in the cell which impels electricity through a conductor connected across the terminals of that cell. Electromotive force is represented by the symbol E, whereas difference of potential between two points is represented by V.

Consideration of theories accounting for the presence

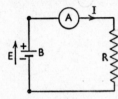

FIG. 9.—E.M.F. of a cell.

of an e.m.f. between the plates of an accumulator is outside the scope of this book. As far as we are concerned, the fact has to be accepted that when plates of different materials, such as lead and lead peroxide (as used in a lead-acid accumulator) or zinc and carbon (as used in the Leclanché primary cell), are placed in suitable solutions, an e.m.f. exists between the plates; and if a resistor is connected across them, an electric current flows through it.

Suppose E volts to be the e.m.f. of cell B in Fig. 9 and I amperes to be the current when a circuit having a resistance R ohms is connected across the terminals. If the *internal resistance of the cell is negligible*,‡ the

* A *voltaic cell*, named after Count Volta (Art. 18), is a source of electrical energy depending upon chemical action, e.g. a primary cell or an accumulator.

† There are sources of e.m.f. other than voltaic cells, e.g. magnetic flux cutting a conductor and junctions of dissimilar metals at different temperatures (Art. 44 and 144).

‡ The effect of the internal resistance of a cell is considered in Art. 25.

terminal voltage of the cell is the same as its e.m.f., namely E volts;

hence $\qquad E = IR \quad$ or $\quad I = E/R \quad . \quad . \quad . \quad$ (13)

The e.m.f. of a cell can be measured by connecting a voltmeter across the terminals of the cell when the latter is on open circuit, i.e. when there is no other circuit connected across the terminals of the cell.

20. The Standard Cell. By following a certain specification drawn up by the International Electrotechnical Commission—a committee of experts from different countries—it is possible to construct a cell, known as the Weston or cadmium cell, which has an e.m.f. of exactly 1·0186 * volts at 20° C. Consequently, the volt can be taken as 1/1·0186 of the e.m.f. of a cadmium cell. This cell has a high internal resistance and is intended only as a standard for comparison with other e.m.f.'s and not as a source of electrical energy.

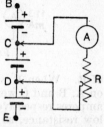

FIG. 10.—Cells in series.

21. Series Connection of Cells. Three accumulators were connected in series as in Fig. 10, i.e. the negative terminal of the first cell was connected to the positive terminal of the second, and the negative of the second to the positive of the third. A resistance R and a milliammeter A, having a total resistance of 1000 ohms, were connected in series across various pairs of terminals in turn and the following results obtained :

Terminals	Current, mA	E.M.F. $= IR$, volts
ED	2·16	2·16
DC	2·08	2·08
CB	2·1	2·1
EB	6·32	6·32

* This is the value of the e.m.f. in terms of the Absolute Electrical Units adopted internationally in 1948.

The sum of the e.m.f.'s across ED, DC and CB = 6·34 volts, which is the same—within experimental error—as the total e.m.f. across EB. It is therefore evident that the e.m.f. of a number of cells connected in series is the sum of their individual e.m.f.'s.

22. Parallel Connection of Cells. The positive ends of two similar accumulators were joined together to one end of a resistance R as shown in Fig. 11. The negative ends were connected through milliammeters to the other end

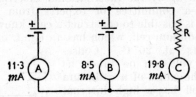

FIG. 11.—Cells in parallel.

of R. When R was adjusted to 100 ohms, the readings on A, B and C were found to be 11·3, 8·5 and 19·8 milliamperes respectively. The milliammeters had relatively low resistance, so that the e.m.f. of the parallel cells is approximately $\frac{19·8}{1000} \times 100 = 1·98$ V. These results indicate that when similar cells are in parallel, the e.m.f. is the same as that of one cell. On the other hand, the current is divided between the cells and the total current is the sum of the currents through the individual cells.

Summary of Important Formulae

Electrical energy $= I^2Rt$ joules . . . . . . (8)

$\qquad\qquad\quad = IVt$ joules

Electrical power $= I^2R$ watts . . . . . . (9)

$\qquad\qquad\quad = IV$ watts . . . . . (11)

$\qquad\qquad\quad = V^2/R$ watts . . . . . (12)

Ohm's Law: $\qquad I = V/R, \ \ V = IR$ or $R = V/I$. (10)

EXAMPLES III

1. The heating element of an electric kettle has a resistance of 80 ohms. Find the time required by a current of 3·1 amperes to raise 1 quart (2·5 pounds) of water from 14° C to the boiling-point, if the efficiency of the kettle is 78 per cent. Also find: (a) the electrical power, and (b) the cost of electricity consumed at 2d per kWh.

2. A current of 2·6 A was passed through a coil of wire immersed in 0·726 kg of water for 10 minutes. The initial temperature of the water was 13·2° C and the final temperature was 17·8° C. Assuming the water equivalent of the containing vessel and heater to be 24 g, and neglecting any loss of heat, find: (a) the resistance of the coil and (b) the electrical power.

3. An immersion heater having a resistance of 210 Ω is placed in a jar containing 1½ pints of water. If a current of 1·1 A passes through the heater for 5 minutes, find the increase in the temperature of the water, assuming an efficiency of 86 per cent.

4. An electric heater is required to heat 500 cm³ of water from 12° C to the boiling-point in 6 minutes. The efficiency of the heater is 75 per cent and the supply voltage is 230 volts. Find: (a) current taken; (b) resistance of heating element; (c) cost of energy consumed, at 2d per kWh.

5. An electric furnace is required to raise the temperature of 7 pounds of iron from 16° C to 750° C in 20 minutes. The furnace works off 230 volts. The efficiency may be assumed to be 76 per cent and the specific heat of iron 0·11. Find: (a) the current; (b) resistance of the heating element; (c) electrical power; (d) energy absorbed in kWh.

6. A battery of 60 cells in series is charged for 12 hours at 25 amperes, the average p.d. per cell being 2·25 volts. Find: (a) the number of ampere-hours, and (b) the number of kilowatt-hours supplied to the battery.

7. Find the current taken by a motor driving a pump which raises 500 gallons of water a minute against a head of 200 feet. The supply voltage is 400 V. Assume the overall efficiency of the motor and pump to be 70 per cent.

8. A dynamo is supplying 80 lamps, each taking 60 watts at 200 volts. Calculate: (a) total current supplied by dynamo; (b) number of kWh consumed in 4 hours; (c) b.h.p. of engine to drive the dynamo, if the efficiency of the latter is 85 per cent.

9. An electric motor connected across a 440-V supply is developing 57 h.p. with an efficiency of 90 per cent. Calculate (a) the current; (b) the input power in kilowatts and (c) the cost of running the motor at that load for 6 hours if the charge for electrical energy be 1·2d per kWh.

10. State briefly the principle of the conservation of energy.
An electric motor takes a current of 37·3 A at 200 V. Neglecting all losses, calculate the horsepower of the motor and the number of foot-pounds of work which can be obtained from the motor in 10 min. (746 watts are equivalent to 1 h.p.).   (N.C.T.E.C., S1)

11. What do you understand by the terms "ohm," "ampere" and "volt"? State the law which connects these three quantities. The power taken by an electric kettle when used on a 220-V d.c. supply is 300 W. Determine (a) the resistance of the heating element of the

kettle, (b) the electrical energy taken by the kettle in five minutes, (c) the quantity of water in pints which could be heated in the kettle from 15° C to boiling-point in the time stated, if the whole of the electrical energy were used to heat the water.   (E.M.E.U., S1)

12. Distinguish between a joule and a watt. A small factory has forty 100-W lamps, thirty-five 200-W lamps, six 500-W lamps; it has also electric motors taking 15 kW and electric heaters taking 25 kW. What will be the maximum current taken from a 240-V supply? What will be the cost of electrical energy, at 1½d per "unit," for a 44-hour week, if the motors and heaters run continuously, but the lamps are only in use for one-quarter of the time?   (E.M.E.U., S1)

13. A lagged water-tank with a thermostatically controlled immersion heater is rated at 230 V, 3 kW. It is designed to heat water from 15° C to 50° C. Water at 50° C is drawn off intermittently to the extent of 40 gallons per 24 hours. The heat losses cause the heater to switch itself on for a total of 30 minutes in each 24 hours. Calculate the daily consumption in kWh. What is the current rating of the heater? (1 gallon of water weighs 10 lb; 454 g = 1 lb; 4·18 joules = 1 calorie.)   (Joint Section A)

14. State the name of and define the electrical unit of power. Explain carefully the difference between power and energy.
The energy absorbed in 10 min by a piece of electrical apparatus, from a 240-V supply, is $1·32 \times 10^6$ joules. Calculate (a) the current taken by it, (b) the quantity of electricity in coulombs taken in 1 minute and (c) the energy in kWh absorbed in 96 hours.
        (E.M.E.U., S1)

15. A current of 5 A passes through a coil of 20-Ω resistance for 15 minutes. If the heat dissipated could be entirely used in heating water, what mass of water could have its temperature raised by 50° C? (1 joule = 0·24 calorie.)   (U.L.C.I., S1)

16. The field winding of an electric motor has a resistance of 157 ohms. Find the power in kilowatts in the winding when the current is 2·8 amperes.

17. Calculate the current taken by a 100-watt lamp connected across a 230-volt supply. Also, find the corresponding resistance of the filament.

18. An electric fire takes 0·9 kW when connected across a 220-V supply. Calculate the resistance of the heating element.
If the supply voltage is increased to 240 V, what is the percentage increase in the power? Assume the resistance to remain constant.

19. The heating element of an indirectly-heated wireless valve takes a current of 0·4 A when the terminal voltage is 3·8 V. Calculate (a) the resistance of the element and (b) the power.

20. Calculate the resistance of the metal filament of an electric lamp which takes 60 W when connected across a 110-V supply. What would be the current and the power if the voltage decreased to 100 V? Assume the resistance of the filament to remain unaltered.

21. Define the coulomb. How many coulombs will flow in 10 hours if a p.d. of 1 millivolt is applied across the ends of a resistance of 1 microhm?   (E.M.E.U., S1)

22. If a voltmeter has a resistance of 30 kΩ, calculate the current and the power absorbed when it is connected across a 460-V supply.

23. The insulation resistance between a certain conductor and earth is 18 megohms. If the p.d. between the conductor and earth is 115 V, calculate (a) the leakage current and (b) the power absorbed.

24. A resistance of 25 Ω is connected across the terminals of a battery having an e.m.f. of 6 V and a negligible internal resistance. Calculate (a) the current, (b) the power and (c) the energy, in joules, dissipated in the 25-Ω resistor, if the current remains constant for 20 minutes.

25. When a resistance of 850 Ω is connected across a battery having negligible internal resistance, the current is 4·8 mA. Calculate (a) the e.m.f. of the battery and (b) the power.

CHAPTER IV

ELECTRIC CIRCUIT (*continued*)

23. Resistances in Series. Two resistors (i.e. a wire or other form of material used simply because of its resistance) R_1 and R_2 were connected in series across a battery, as shown in Fig. 12, the current being indicated by an ammeter A. Also, voltmeters V_1, V_2 and V_3 were connected to measure the p.d.'s across R_1, R_2 and the whole circuit respectively. The following readings were obtained:

A	V_1	V_2	V_3
0·92 ampere	2·2 volts	3·6 volts	5·8 volts

By applying Ohm's Law we find that $R_1 = \dfrac{2·2}{0·92} = 2·39\ \Omega$,

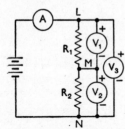

FIG. 12.—Resistances in series.

$R_2 = \dfrac{3·6}{0·92} = 3·92\ \Omega$ and the resistance of the whole circuit $= \dfrac{5·8}{0·92} = 6·31\ \Omega$. But the sum of R_1 and $R_2 = 2·39 + 3·92 = 6·31\ \Omega$. Hence, it is seen that the total resistance of a circuit is the sum of the resistances connected in series; in other words, if R_1, R_2 and R_3 be in series, the total resistance R is given by

$$R = R_1 + R_2 + R_3 \quad . \quad . \quad . \quad . \quad (14)$$

Also, if the voltmeters are of the moving-coil type (Art. 141), V_1 and V_2 indicate that L is at a higher potential than M and that M is at a higher potential than N; and V_3 indicates that L is at a higher potential than N by an amount equal to the sum of the p.d.'s across LM and MN.

24. Resistances in Parallel. Two resistors R_1 and R_2 were connected in parallel as in Fig. 13, the currents being measured by ammeters A_1 and A_2. The total current was read on A_3. A voltmeter V read the p.d. across the circuits. It was found that the instrument readings were:

Voltmeter	A_1	A_2	A_3
5·9 volts	1·5 amperes	0·9 ampere	2·4 amperes

It will be seen that the total current is equal to the sum of the currents in the parallel circuits. Also, from Ohm's Law, it follows that $R_1 = \dfrac{5·9}{1·5} = 3·93$ Ω and $R_2 = \dfrac{5·9}{0·9} = 6·55$ Ω.

The two resistances R_1 and R_2 in Fig. 13 can be replaced by a single resistance R, as in Fig. 14, the only

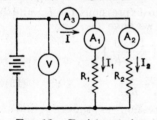

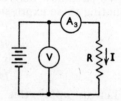

Fig. 13.—Resistances in parallel.

Fig. 14.—Equivalent circuit of Fig. 13.

condition being that the value of R must be such that the total current remains unaltered; that is, in the above case:

$$2·4 \ (A) = \frac{5·9 \ (V)}{\text{resistance of R in ohms}}$$

$\therefore$ resistance of $R = \dfrac{5·9}{2·4} = 2·46$ Ω.

Hence, 2·46 Ω may be said to be *equivalent* to 3·93 Ω and 6·55 Ω in parallel. It is evident that the equivalent resistance is less than either of the parallel resistances, but there does not seem to be any obvious connection between the values. For this problem it is more satisfactory to derive the relationship by considering the general case than by taking particular values.

Suppose I_1 and I_2 amperes to be the currents in parallel resistances R_1 and R_2 respectively when the p.d. is V volts (Fig. 13). Then, by Ohm's Law, $I_1 = \dfrac{V}{R_1}$ and $I_2 = \dfrac{V}{R_2}$. If I is the total current indicated by A_3,

$$I = I_1 + I_2$$
$$= \frac{V}{R_1} + \frac{V}{R_2} = V\left(\frac{1}{R_1} + \frac{1}{R_2}\right).$$

If R in Fig. 14 represents the value of a single or equivalent resistance through which a p.d. of V volts produces the same current I amperes, then $I = \dfrac{V}{R}$.

We have now derived two expressions for I; and by equating these expressions, we have

$$\frac{V}{R} = V\left(\frac{1}{R_1} + \frac{1}{R_2}\right)$$

$\therefore \qquad \dfrac{1}{R} = \dfrac{1}{R_1} + \dfrac{1}{R_2}$ . . . . . (15)

Let us apply this expression to the experimental results considered above:

$$\frac{1}{R_1} = \frac{1}{3\cdot93} = 0\cdot254 \quad \text{and} \quad \frac{1}{R_2} = \frac{1}{6\cdot55} = 0\cdot1527$$

$\therefore \qquad \dfrac{1}{R} = \dfrac{1}{R_1} + \dfrac{1}{R_2} = 0\cdot254 + 0\cdot1527 = 0\cdot4067$

and $\qquad R = \dfrac{1}{0\cdot4067} = 2\cdot46\ \Omega,$

which is the same as the value previously derived.

The reciprocal of the resistance, that is, $\dfrac{1}{\text{resistance}}$, is termed the *conductance*, the unit of conductance being 1 *mho* ("ohm" spelt backwards). From the expression derived above it follows that for resistors connected in parallel, the conductance of the equivalent resistor is the sum of the conductances of the parallel resistors.

The current in each of the parallel resistances R_1 and R_2 in Fig. 13 can be expressed in terms of the total current thus:

$$V = I_1 R_1 = I_2 R_2 = IR$$

$$\therefore \qquad I_1 = \frac{IR}{R_1}$$

But

$$\frac{1}{R} = \frac{1}{R_1} + \frac{1}{R_2} = \frac{R_1 + R_2}{R_1 R_2}$$

Hence,

$$I_1 = \frac{I}{R_1} \times \frac{R_1 R_2}{R_1 + R_2} = I \cdot \frac{R_2}{R_1 + R_2} \qquad . \quad (16)$$

Similarly,

$$I_2 = I \cdot \frac{R_1}{R_1 + R_2}$$

Example 13. *Three coils A, B and C have resistances 8, 12 and 15 ohms respectively. Find the equivalent resistance when they are connected* (a) *in series,* (b) *in parallel.*

(a) With the resistances in series,

$$\text{Total resistance} = 8 + 12 + 15 = 35 \ \Omega.$$

(b) If R be the equivalent resistance of the three parallel resistances, then

$$\frac{1}{R} = \tfrac{1}{8} + \tfrac{1}{12} + \tfrac{1}{15} = 0 \cdot 125 + 0 \cdot 0833 + 0 \cdot 0667$$

$$= 0 \cdot 275 \ \text{mho}$$

$$\therefore \qquad R = 3 \cdot 64 \ \Omega.$$

Example 14. *If B and C of Example 13 are connected in parallel and A connected in series, as in Fig. 15, across a 20-volt supply, find* (a) *the resistance of the combined circuit,* (b) *the current in each coil.*

(a) Let R be the equivalent resistance of B and C, then

$$\frac{1}{R} = \tfrac{1}{12} + \tfrac{1}{15} = 0 \cdot 0833 + 0 \cdot 0667 = 0 \cdot 15 \ \text{mho}$$

$$\therefore \qquad R = 6 \cdot 67 \ \Omega,$$

and total resistance $= 8 + 6 \cdot 67 = 14 \cdot 67 \ \Omega.$

(b) Total current $=\dfrac{20 \ V}{14\cdot67 \ \Omega}=1\cdot364$ A, which is the current in A.

The p.d. across B and C in Fig. 15 is the same as the p.d. across the equivalent resistance 6·67 ohms,

$$\therefore \qquad \text{total current} = \dfrac{\text{p.d. across B and C}}{\text{equivalent resistance of B and C}}$$

i.e. $\qquad 1\cdot364 = \dfrac{\text{p.d. across B and C}}{6\cdot67}$

$\therefore$ p.d. across B and C $= 1\cdot364 \times 6\cdot67 = 9\cdot09$ V.

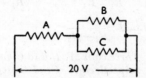

Fig. 15.—Circuit of Example 14.

Hence, current in B $= \dfrac{\text{p.d. across B}}{\text{resistance of B}}$

$$= \dfrac{9\cdot09}{12} = 0\cdot758 \text{ A}$$

and current in C $= 1\cdot364 - 0\cdot758 = 0\cdot606$ A.

Alternatively, using expression (16), we have:

$$\text{current in B} = 1\cdot364 \times \dfrac{15}{12+15}$$

$$= 0\cdot758 \text{ A}.$$

Example 15. *The resistance of the heating element of an electric iron is* 180 Ω. *It is connected to a* 220-*V supply by two conductors, each having a resistance of* 1·25 Ω. *Find :* (a) *voltage across the heating element,* (b) *voltage drop in the cable,* (c) *power of the electric iron and* (d) *power wasted in cable.*

(a) The circuit is shown in Fig. 16.

Total resistance of circuit $= 1 \cdot 25 + 180 + 1 \cdot 25$

$$= 182 \cdot 5 \ \Omega.$$

$$\therefore \quad \text{current} = \frac{\text{p.d. (volts) between A and D}}{\text{resistance (ohms) between A and D}}$$

$$= \frac{220}{182 \cdot 5} = 1 \cdot 205 \ \text{A}.$$

But $\quad$ current also $= \dfrac{\text{p.d. between B and C}}{\text{resistance between B and C}}$

$$\therefore \quad 1 \cdot 205 = \frac{\text{p.d. between B and C}}{180}$$

$\therefore$ p.d. between B and C

$$= 1 \cdot 205 \times 180 = 217 \ \text{V}.$$

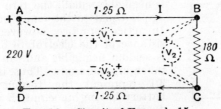

FIG. 16.—Circuit of Example 15.

(b) $\quad$ Current also $= \dfrac{\text{p.d. between A and B}}{\text{resistance between A and B}}$

$$\therefore \quad 1 \cdot 205 = \frac{\text{p.d. between A and B}}{1 \cdot 25}$$

$\therefore$ p.d. between A and B

$$= 1 \cdot 205 \times 1 \cdot 25 = 1 \cdot 5 \ \text{V}.$$

Similarly, p.d. between C and D $= 1 \cdot 205 \times 1 \cdot 25 = 1 \cdot 5$ V.

Hence, total voltage drop in cable $= 1 \cdot 5 + 1 \cdot 5 = 3$ V.

The existence of these potential differences can be demonstrated by connecting moving-coil voltmeters V_1, V_2 and V_3, as shown dotted in Fig. 16. The readings on the instruments indicate that the potential of A is

1·5 volts above that of B, the potential of B is 217 volts above that of C and the potential of C is 1·5 volts above that of D. Further, it is seen that the sum of the readings on V_1, V_2 and V_3 is equal to the total voltage between A and D.

(c) Since power (watts) = current (amps) × p.d. (volts)

∴   power of electric iron = 1·205 × 217

$$= 261·5 \text{ W}.$$

(d) Similarly, power wasted in cable

$$= \text{current} \times \text{voltage drop in cable}$$
$$= 1·205 \times 3 = 3·615 \text{ W}.$$

25. Effect of the Internal Resistance of a Cell.   In Art. 19 it was pointed out that when a cell is supplying

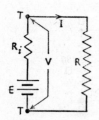

FIG. 17.—Internal and external resistances.

a current and the internal resistance is negligibly small, the terminal voltage is equal to the e.m.f. of the cell. In actual practice, however, the resistance of the electrolyte of the cell is seldom negligible and can easily be taken into account. Thus, in Fig. 17, TT represent the terminals of a battery having an e.m.f. E volts and R_i represents the internal resistance of the battery. If a resistance R be connected externally across TT, then, from expression (14), the total resistance of the circuit is $R + R_i$, and the current I is given by:

$$I = \frac{E}{R + R_i}$$

and the terminal voltage $= V = IR$

$$= E - IR_i.$$

Example 16.   *Two resistors, A and B, having resistances 10 and 15 Ω respectively, are connected in parallel across a battery of four cells in series, as in Fig. 18. Each cell has an e.m.f. of 2 V and an internal resistance of 0·2 Ω. Calculate: (a) the p.d. between battery terminals PQ, (b)* *the current through each resistor and* (c) *the total power in the resistors.*

(a) Total e.m.f. of battery $=2\times4=8$ V

and total internal resistance of battery
$$=0\cdot2\times4=0\cdot8\ \Omega.$$

If R is the equivalent resistance of A and B:
$$\frac{1}{R}=\frac{1}{10}+\frac{1}{15}=0\cdot1+0\cdot0667=0\cdot1667\ \text{mho}$$

$\therefore\qquad R=6\ \Omega$

Hence, total resistance of circuit $=6+0\cdot8=6\cdot8\ \Omega$

and $\qquad$ current $=\dfrac{\text{total e.m.f.}}{\text{total resistance}}$

$$=\frac{8}{6\cdot8}=1\cdot177\ \text{A}.$$

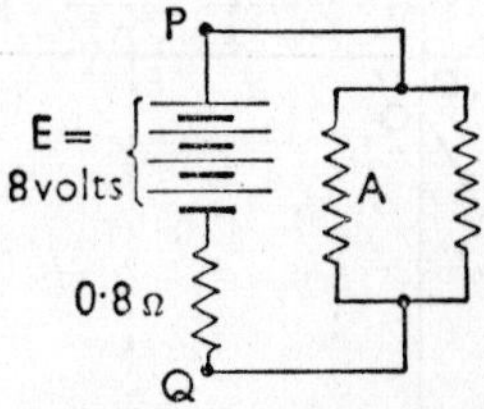

Fig. 18.—Circuit diagram for Example 16.

P.d. across A and B $=$ total current $\times$ equivalent resistance of A and B

$$=1\cdot177\times6=7\cdot06\ \text{V}$$

$$=\text{terminal voltage of battery}$$

Alternatively, p.d. across the $0\cdot8\ \Omega$ in Fig. 18 $\Big\}=1\cdot177\times0\cdot8$

$$=0\cdot94\ \text{V}$$

$\therefore$ terminal voltage of battery $\Big\}=$ battery e.m.f. $-\begin{pmatrix}\text{voltage drop}\\\text{due to internal}\\\text{resistance}\end{pmatrix}$

$$=8-0\cdot94=7\cdot06\ \text{V}.$$

2*

(b)   Current in A $= \dfrac{\text{p.d. across A}}{\text{resistance of A}}$

$$= \dfrac{7 \cdot 06}{10} = 0 \cdot 706 \text{ A}$$

and   current in B $= \dfrac{7 \cdot 06}{15} = 0 \cdot 471$ A

or alternatively,

current in B $= 1 \cdot 177 - 0 \cdot 706 = 0 \cdot 471$ A.

(c) Loss in resistors $=$ total current $\times$ p.d. across resistors

$$= 1 \cdot 177 \times 7 \cdot 06 = 8 \cdot 3 \text{ W}.$$

26. Comparison of the Resistance of Different Materials.
In Fig. 19, CD represents, say, one yard of No. 26 S.W.G.

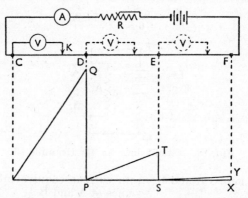

Fig. 19.—Fall of potential in wires of different materials.

eureka wire, and DE and EF represent the same length
and diameter of iron and copper wires respectively.
The current is adjusted to about $0 \cdot 5$ ampere by means of
R, and the differences of potential are measured by means
of voltmeter V.

One end of V is connected to terminal C and the other
end to a sliding contact K.   As the latter is moved from
C to D the p.d. increases uniformly from zero to PQ, as
shown by the graph.

The test is repeated with one end of V connected to terminal D, and K is moved from D to E. The p.d. again increases uniformly from zero to ST. A repetition of the test on wire EF gives a p.d. increasing from zero to XY.

Since both the currents and the dimensions are the same for the three wires it follows that different materials having the same dimensions offer different resistances to the passage of an electric current. Thus, in the above experiment, ST is found to be about 7·5 times XY, while PQ is about 30 times XY: in other words, an iron wire of given length and diameter has 7·5 times the resistance of a similar copper wire, while an eureka wire of the same dimensions has 30 times the resistance of the copper wire.

27. Relationship between the Resistance and the Dimensions of a Conductor. From the experiment described in the preceding article, it follows that for a uniform wire of a given material the value obtained by dividing the p.d. between any two points by the current, that is, the resistance between those two points, is directly proportional to the distance between them.

Also, in Art. 24 it is explained that if two resistances, each R ohms, are connected in parallel, the equivalent resistance R_e is given by:

$$\frac{1}{R_e} = \frac{1}{R} + \frac{1}{R} = \frac{2}{R}$$

$$\therefore \qquad R_e = \tfrac{1}{2}R.$$

Hence, if two wires of the same material and having the same length and diameter are connected in parallel, the resistance of the parallel wires is half that of one wire alone. But the effect of connecting two wires in parallel is exactly similar to doubling the area of the conductor. In just the same way the effect of connecting, say, five wires in parallel is the same as increasing the sectional area of a wire five times, and the result is to reduce the resistance to a fifth of that of the original wire. In general, we may therefore say that the resistance of a conductor is inversely proportional to its cross-sectional area.

Apart from the effect of temperature, referred to in Art. 28, the only other factor that influences the resistance is the nature of the material, as shown experimentally in the last article; hence we may now say that:

$$\left.\begin{array}{c}\text{Resistance}\\\text{of a wire}\end{array}\right\} = \frac{\text{length of wire}}{\text{cross-sectional area}} \times \left(\begin{array}{c}\text{a constant for a}\\\text{given material}\end{array}\right)$$

$$= \frac{l}{a} \times \rho \text{ ohms} \quad . \quad . \quad . \quad . \quad . \quad . \quad (17)$$

where l and a are the length and cross-sectional area respectively, and ρ (Greek letter, pronounced "rho") represents the constant.

If l be 1 inch and a be 1 inch² (for instance, if the resistance is being measured between the opposite faces of an inch cube of the material), the value $= \frac{1}{1} \times \rho$, namely, ρ ohm. Consequently the constant may be regarded as the resistance of a specimen of unit length and unit cross-sectional area, and is termed the *resistivity* (or sometimes the *specific resistance*) of the material. It may be expressed either in inch or metre units; thus the resistivity of annealed copper at 20° C is 0·000000679 ohm-inch or 0·00000001725 ohm-metre. It is generally more convenient to use microhms rather than ohms, so that the above values then become 0·679 $\mu\Omega$-inch and 0·01725 $\mu\Omega$-m (or 1·725 $\mu\Omega$-cm) respectively. The International Electrotechnical Commission, in 1913, specified the resistance of Standard Annealed Copper wire, 1 metre long and 1 mm² in cross-section, as $\frac{1}{58}$ ohm at 20° C.

Example 17. *The resistivity of aluminium is* 0·0283 $\mu\Omega$-m *at* 20° C. *Find the corresponding value in* $\mu\Omega$-inch.

Since 1 inch = 2·54 cm = 0·0254 m, then from expression (17), the resistance of a specimen of aluminium 1 inch long and 1 inch² in cross-section

$$= 0·0283 \ (\mu\Omega\text{-m}) \times \frac{0·0254 \ (\text{m})}{0·0254 \ (\text{m}) \times 0·0254 \ (\text{m})}$$

$$= \frac{2·83}{2·54} = 1·11 \ \mu\Omega.$$

Hence the resistivity of aluminium = 1·11 $\mu\Omega$-inch.

Example 18.   *Calculate the length of copper wire, 1·5 mm diameter, to have a resistance of 0·3 ohm, given that the resistivity of copper is 0·017 μΩ-m.*

Sectional area of wire $= \dfrac{\pi}{4} \times (0\cdot15)^2 = 0\cdot785 \times 0\cdot0225$

$$= 0\cdot01766 \text{ cm}^2$$

$$= 1\cdot766 \times 10^{-6} \text{ m}^2$$

∴ $0\cdot3 \ (\Omega) = 0\cdot017 \times 10^{-6} \ (\Omega\text{-m}) \times \dfrac{\text{length (m)}}{1\cdot766 \times 10^{-6} \ (\text{m}^2)}$

∴   length $= 31\cdot2$ metres.

28. Effect of Temperature on Resistance. Let us connect an incandescent lamp L in series with an ammeter A and a variable resistance R across a 230-volt supply, as in Fig. 20. A voltmeter V is connected across the lamp.   The resistance of the lamp is obtained

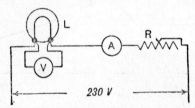

Fig. 20.—Measurement of filament resistance at different voltages.

by dividing the voltmeter reading by the corresponding ammeter reading.   By varying the value of R we can vary the current through the lamp and thus vary the filament temperature.   In this way, we can determine the resistance of the lamp over a wide range of filament temperature.

Curve A in Fig. 21 shows graphically the results obtained with a 100-watt 230-volt gas-filled lamp having a tungsten filament, while curve B was obtained on a 50-candlepower carbon-filament lamp.   It will be seen that as the filament gets hotter the resistance of the tungsten filament increases rapidly, and that the resistance at normal working temperature, that is, with a

terminal voltage of 230 volts, is about ten times that
of the lamp when cold. With carbon, on the other hand,
the resistance decreases with increase of temperature,
the resistance at working temperature being about a
half of that of the cold filament.

It is found that the resistance of all pure metals, such
as copper, iron, tungsten, etc., increases with increase of

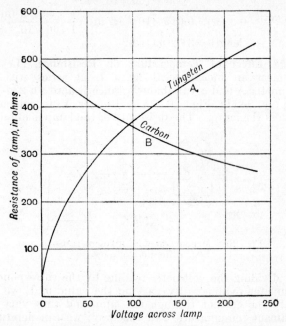

FIG. 21.—Variation of filament resistance with voltage.

temperature, whereas the resistance of carbon, electro-
lytes and insulating materials, such as rubber, paper, etc.,
decreases with increase of temperature. Certain alloys,
such as eureka (60 per cent copper, 40 per cent nickel),
show practically no change of resistance for a considerable variation of temperature, and are consequently
employed whenever the resistance has to remain as

constant as possible, for instance in the construction of resistance boxes.

29. Temperature Coefficient of Resistance. If the resistance of a coil of copper wire be measured at various temperatures up to, say, 200° C, it is found to vary as shown in Fig. 22, the resistance at 0° C being, for convenience, taken as 1 ohm. The resistance increases uniformly with increase of temperature until it reaches 1·426 ohms at 100° C; that is, the increase of resistance is 0·426 ohm for an increase of 100° C in the temperature, or 0·00426 ohm per 1° C rise of temperature.

The ratio of the increase of resistance per ° C rise of

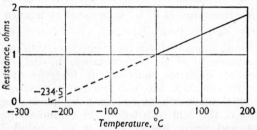

FIG. 22.—Variation of resistance of copper with temperature.

temperature to the resistance at 0° C is termed the *temperature coefficient of resistance*, and is usually represented by the Greek letter α (alpha). From the above figures it follows that the temperature coefficient of resistance of copper is $\dfrac{0 \cdot 00426 \text{ ohm per } ^\circ \text{C}}{1 \text{ ohm}} = 0 \cdot 00426$.

If the straight line of Fig. 22 is extended backwards, the point of intersection with the horizontal axis is found to be −234·5° C. This means that for the range of temperature over which copper conductors are usually operated, the resistance varies as if it would be zero at −234·5° C. (Actually, the resistance-temperature relationship is not a straight line below about −50° C.) Hence, over a range of 234·5° C, the variation of resistance in Fig. 22 is 1 ohm, so that the variation for 1° C is 1/234·5 ohm,

i.e. temperature coefficient of resistance for standard annealed copper

$$= \frac{\text{change of resistance for 1° C change of temperature}}{\text{resistance at 0° C}}$$

$$= \frac{1}{234 \cdot 5} = 0 \cdot 004264.$$

If a material has a resistance R_0 ohms at 0° C and a temperature coefficient of resistance α, the increase of resistance for 1° C rise of temperature is $R_0\alpha$ ohms. For a temperature rise of t° C, the increase of resistance is $R_0\alpha t$ ohms. Hence, if R ohms be the resistance at t° C,

$$R = \text{resistance at 0° C} + \text{increase of resistance}$$

$$= R_0 + R_0\alpha t = R_0(1 + \alpha t) \quad . \quad . \quad . \quad . \quad (18)$$

It is usually inconvenient and unnecessary to measure the resistance at 0° C; for instance, in the case of windings of electrical machines it is frequently the practice to calculate the temperature rise after, say, three hours' operation at full load by measuring the resistance of the field coils before the commencement of the test and again immediately it is concluded. If t_1° C be the initial temperature—usually taken as the temperature of the surrounding atmosphere—and t_2° C be the average temperature of the coils at the conclusion of the test, and if R_1 and R_2 be the corresponding resistances (Fig. 23), then

$$R_1 = R_0(1 + \alpha t_1)$$

and $$R_2 = R_0(1 + \alpha t_2)$$

$$\therefore \quad \frac{R_1}{R_2} = \frac{1 + \alpha t_1}{1 + \alpha t_2}$$

Since $\alpha = 1/234 \cdot 5$ for standard annealed copper, then for this material,

$$\frac{R_1}{R_2} = \frac{1 + t_1/234 \cdot 5}{1 + t_2/234 \cdot 5} = \frac{234 \cdot 5 + t_1}{234 \cdot 5 + t_2} \quad . \quad . \quad (19)$$

$$\therefore \quad t_2 = \frac{R_2}{R_1}(234 \cdot 5 + t_1) - 234 \cdot 5 \quad . \quad . \quad (20)$$

The relationship given in expression (19) can be easily deduced from the graph of Fig. 23. It is obvious that triangles ABC and ADE are similar,

$$\therefore \quad \frac{BC}{DE} = \frac{AC}{AE}$$

i.e.

$$\frac{R_1}{R_2} = \frac{t_1 + 234 \cdot 5}{t_2 + 234 \cdot 5}$$

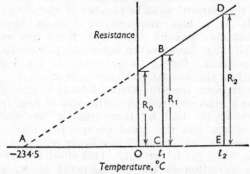

FIG. 23.—Variation of resistance of copper with temperature.

Example 19. *The resistance of a coil of copper wire at the beginning of a heat test is 173 ohms, the temperature being 16° C. At the end of the test the resistance has increased to 212 ohms. Calculate the temperature rise of the coil, assuming the temperature coefficient of copper to be 1/234·5.*

Since $R_1 = 173\ \Omega$, $R_2 = 212\ \Omega$ and $t_1 = 16°$ C, then

$$t_2 = \frac{212}{173}(234 \cdot 5 + 16) - 234 \cdot 5$$

$$= 72 \cdot 4°\ C,$$

and temperature rise of coil $= 72 \cdot 4 - 16 = 56 \cdot 4°$ C.

30. Applications of the Heating Effect of an Electric Current. We have already seen in Art. 6 that when an electric current passes through a resistance, heat is generated and the temperature of the resistor is raised. The following applications are a few examples of the many ways in which this effect is utilised:

(a) *Electric Fires, Cookers, etc.* The heating element is usually an alloy of nickel and chromium, since this material has a high resistivity and is capable of withstanding a high temperature without becoming oxidised when exposed to the air.

(b) *Incandescent Electric Lamps.* In the incandescent lamp, the filament must be capable of operating for long periods at a high temperature without appreciable deterioration, and for this work there are only two materials that have proved satisfactory, namely carbon and tungsten. Owing to its relatively low efficiency, the carbon filament lamp, however, is obsolete.

The modern tungsten-filament lamp is gas-filled. If the gas is removed from the bulb, loss of heat from the filament to the bulb by convection is prevented; but the vacuum has the disadvantage that the filament volatilises or "evaporates" at a lower temperature than it does when gas is present. This effect is very similar to the variation in the boiling-point of water with pressure.

The evaporation of the filament not only reduces the sectional area of the filament, thereby increasing its resistance and reducing the temperature and the candlepower of the lamp, but it also allows tungsten to condense on the internal surface of the bulb, blackening the latter and reducing the candlepower still further. Consequently, the highest temperature at which it is practicable to work the filament is limited to about 2000° C, with a vacuum corresponding to a pressure of about 0·0001 mm of mercury.

By introducing a chemically inert gas (namely a gas which has no chemical action on the filament), such as nitrogen or argon, the temperature of the latter can be raised to about 2500° C before blackening takes place at an excessive rate. But if no other change were made except merely to introduce a gas, it would be found that the amount of heat lost by convection between the filament and bulb would be so great that the power required to maintain the filament temperature at 2500° C would have increased more in proportion than the light given out by the lamp. Consequently, the efficiency would be lower than that of the vacuum lamp. This difficulty is overcome by winding the filament as a very close helix (Fig. 24), in fact so close that the gas is unable to pass between the spirals and can merely pass over the outside of the helix. In other words, the surface with which the gas can come into contact is practically the same as that of a rod of diameter d and length l (Fig. 24); and since this area is far less than the surface area of the filament itself, the loss of heat by convection is very considerably reduced.

In gas-filled lamps up to 100-watt size, the coiled

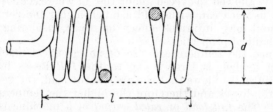

FIG. 24.—Spiralised filament.

filament is wound into a coarser helix, though even this second helix is actually very small. In this way the effective filament surface exposed to the gas is reduced still further. This "coiled-coil" lamp has an efficiency of about 10–15 per cent higher than that of the corresponding lamp with the filament wound as a single helix.

(c) *Fuses.* A fuse is a wire or strip of metal inserted in a circuit for the purpose of interrupting or opening that circuit when the current exceeds a certain pre-arranged value. The wire is usually made of a metal, such as copper, tin, lead or an alloy, which melts comparatively easily. The fusing current depends upon a large number of factors, such as the material, the diameter and length of the wire, the ventilation of the fuseholder and the duration of the current.

The fuse wire should be mounted on a fireproof holder,

such as porcelain. Large fuses are often covered with asbestos sleeves to prevent any metal vapour being deposited on the porcelain when the fuse "blows," since such a deposit may be sufficient to provide a conducting path between the fuse terminals.

(d) *Temperature Rise permissible in Electrical Machines.* When a dynamo is supplying electrical power or an electric motor is supplying mechanical power, the machine is said to be *loaded,* and the power lost in the machine is converted into heat, thereby raising the temperature of the windings. The maximum temperature that is permissible depends upon the nature of the insulating materials employed; thus, materials such as paper and cotton become brittle if their temperature is allowed to exceed about 100° C, whereas materials such as mica can withstand a much higher temperature without any injurious effect on their insulating and mechanical properties.

Since the temperature rise of an electrical machine, when loaded, is largely due to the I^2R losses in the windings, it follows that the greater the load, the greater are the losses and therefore the higher the temperature rise. The *full load* or *rated output* of a machine is the maximum output power obtainable from the machine under certain specified conditions, e.g. for a specified temperature rise after the machine has supplied that load continuously for several hours.

31. Kirchhoff's Laws. A German physicist, Gustav Kirchhoff (1824–87), enunciated two laws which can be very useful when problems on the electric circuit have to be solved.

First Law. *If several conductors meet at a point, the total current flowing towards that point is equal to the total current flowing away from it, i.e. the algebraic sum of the currents is zero.*

Thus, if five wires were joined together at J (Fig. 25) and if the arrow-heads represent the directions of the respective currents, then total current flowing towards $J = I_1 + I_4$, while total current flowing away from

$J = I_2 + I_3 + I_5$. Since there is no accumulation of electric charge at J, it follows that:

$$I_1 + I_4 = I_2 + I_3 + I_5 \quad \text{or} \quad I_1 - I_2 - I_3 + I_4 - I_5 = 0$$

Second Law. *In any closed circuit, the algebraic sum of the products of the current and the resistance of each part of the circuit is equal to the resultant e.m.f. in the circuit.*

Let us consider the simple case of a circuit consisting of a battery B_1 (Fig. 26) having an e.m.f. E_1 volts and another battery B_2 having an e.m.f. E_2 volts connected in opposition and two resistances R_1 and R_2 in series as

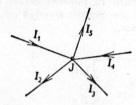

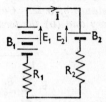

FIG. 25.—Circuit to illustrate Kirchhoff's First Law.

FIG. 26.—Circuit to illustrate Kirchhoff's Second Law.

shown. If E_1 is greater than E_2, the resultant e.m.f. is $(E_1 - E_2)$ volts acting in a clockwise direction round the circuit and circulating a current I amperes. The sum of the products of the current and the resistances is $I(R_1 + R_2)$.

In such a case, the above law merely states that

$$I(R_1 + R_2) = E_1 - E_2$$

which is Ohm's Law.

Let us now consider the effect of adding a resistance R as shown in Fig. 27. Suppose the current through B_1 to be I_1 and that through B_2 to be I_2, each current being assumed to be in the same direction as the corresponding e.m.f. Since both I_1 and I_2 are assumed to flow towards junction A, it follows from Kirchhoff's First Law that the current flowing from A towards R must be $I_1 + I_2$.

By applying Kirchhoff's Second Law to the circuit formed by B_1, R_1 and R, we have:

$$E_1 = I_1 R_1 + (I_1 + I_2) R.$$

Similarly for circuit B_2, R_2 and R, we have:

$$E_2 = I_2 R_2 + (I_1 + I_2) R.$$

Also, for circuit B_1, R_1, B_2 and R_2,

$$E_1 - E_2 = I_1 R_1 - I_2 R_2$$

Example 20. *Two batteries, B_1 and B_2, having e.m.f.'s of 6 V and 2 V respectively and internal resistances of 2 Ω and 3 Ω respectively, are connected in parallel across a resistance of 5 Ω. Calculate (a) the current through each battery and (b) the terminal voltage.*

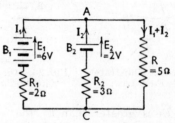

FIG. 27.—Circuit to illustrate Kirchhoff's Laws.

The batteries and resistances are as shown in Fig. 27 For the circuit formed by B_1, R_1 and R,

$$6 = 2I_1 + 5(I_1 + I_2) = 7I_1 + 5I_2 \quad . \quad . \quad (21)$$

and for circuit B_2, R_2 and R,

$$2 = 3I_2 + 5(I_1 + I_2) = 5I_1 + 8I_2 \quad . \quad . \quad (22)$$

Multiplying equation (21) by 5 and equation (22) by 7,

$$35I_1 + 25I_2 = 30$$

and

$$35I_1 + 56I_2 = 14$$

$\therefore$

$$-31I_2 = 16$$

and

$$I_2 = -0 \cdot 516 \text{ A}.$$

Substituting this value for I_2 in equation (21),

$$7I_1 - 5 \times 0 \cdot 516 = 6$$

$$\therefore \qquad I_1 = 1 \cdot 226 \text{ A.}$$

Total current through $R = 1 \cdot 226 - 0 \cdot 516 = 0 \cdot 71$ A

$$\therefore \qquad \text{terminal voltage} = 0 \cdot 71 \times 5 = 3 \cdot 55 \text{ V}$$

Alternatively „ „ $= 6 - 1 \cdot 226 \times 2 = 3 \cdot 55$ V

or „ „ $= 2 + 0 \cdot 516 \times 3 = 3 \cdot 55$ V.

32. Systems of Distribution. At this stage we shall consider only direct-current (d.c.) systems. The electrical energy is usually generated by dynamos and distributed at a voltage that is maintained approximately constant on any particular system. In fact, one of the Regulations governing the distribution of electricity stipulates that the voltage at a consumer's premises must not vary by more than ± 6 per cent of the declared value. For instance, if a consumer is supplied at a nominal voltage of, say, 230 V, the actual voltage must not exceed 244 V and must not fall below 216 V. If lamps (or other apparatus) are connected in series across the supply mains as in Fig. 28, it is evident that each lamp has to carry the

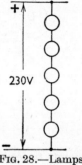

Fig. 28.—Lamps in series.

same current; and if the five lamps of Fig. 28 are exactly similar and the supply voltage is 230 V, the voltage across each lamp is $230/5 = 46$ V.

This system has the disadvantages that (a) all the lamps must have the same current rating and have to be alight simultaneously; (b) if one lamp burns out, the other lamps are extinguished; and (c) if one lamp develops a short-circuit, the supply voltage is divided between the remaining four lamps and the excessive temperature will cause one of them to burn out very soon. Hence the system generally employed is that in which lamps, heaters, motors, etc., are connected in parallel across the supply mains.

In Fig. 29, DD represent two dynamos connected in parallel to bus-bars BB. The bus-bars are two copper bars that extend the whole length of the switchboard, "bus" being an abbreviation of "omnibus," a Latin word meaning "for all." Thus, all the dynamos at the generating station and all the cables connecting the station to various "feeding" points are connected to the bus-bars. The cables radiating from the station are called *feeders*, whereas *distributors* are cables to which the *service mains* supplying the individual consumers are connected. A distributor is connected at one or more

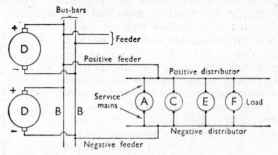

FIG. 29.—A distribution system.

points to feeders, but no service mains are connected to the latter.

In actual practice the distributors are interconnected to form a network that is almost like that of a spider's web. This network is connected to feeders at the most suitable points. Such an arrangement has the advantage that if for some reason a feeder has to be disconnected, the current to the section normally supplied by that feeder can still be supplied through other feeders and distributors.

Example 21. *Two loads, A and B (Fig. 30), taking 50 and 30 A respectively, are connected to a two-wire distributor at distances of 200 and 300 yards respectively from the feeding point, the p.d. at which is 120 V. The resistance of the distributor is 0·01 Ω per 100 yards of* *single conductor. Find:* (a) *the p.d. across each load,* (b) *the cost of the energy wasted in the distributor if the above loads are maintained constant for 10 hours. Assume the cost of energy to be 0·8d per kWh.*

(a) Current in CD and HG (Fig. 30)=30 A

and current in EC and GF=30+50=80 A

Resistance of conductor EC=$0·01 \times \dfrac{200}{100}$=0·02 Ω

and resistance of conductor CD=0·01 Ω

Hence,   p.d. between E and C=80×0·02=1·6 V

Similarly, p.d. between G and F=1·6 V

But   p.d. between E and F=sum of the p.d.'s in circuit ECGF

i.e.   120=1·6+p.d. between C and G+1·6.

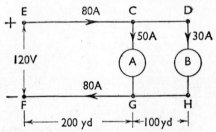

Fig. 30.—Circuit diagram for Example 21.

If the voltage drop in the service main be neglected,
        p.d. across load A=120−3·2=116·8 V

Also

    p.d. between C and D=30×0·01=0·3 V

and p.d. between H and G=0·3 V

But p.d. between C and G=sum of p.d.'s in circuit CDHG

i.e.   116·8=0·3+p.d. between D and H+0·3

so that p.d. across load B=116·8−0·6=116·2 V

(b) Power wasted in conductors EC and FG

$\qquad$ =current ×voltage drops in EC and FG

$\qquad$ =80 ×3·2=256 W

Power wasted in conductors CD and HG

$\qquad$ =30 ×0·6=18 W

∴ total power wasted in distributor

$$=256+18=274 \text{ W}$$
$$=0·274 \text{ kW}$$

and energy wasted in 10 hours

$$=0·274×10=2·74 \text{ kWh}$$

∴ $\qquad$ cost of this energy=2·74 ×0·8=2·192d.

Example 22. *A two-wire ring distributor (i.e. a distributor in which each conductor forms a complete circuit or*

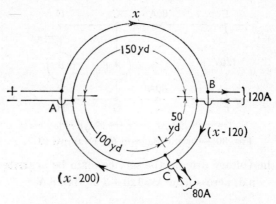

FIG. 31.—Circuit diagram for Example 22.

loop, as in Fig. 31) is 300 yards long and is fed at 240 V at A. At a point B, 150 yards from A, there is a load of 120 A and at C, 100 yards in the opposite direction, there is a load of 80 A. The resistance per 100 yards of single conductor is 0·03 Ω. Find: (a) the current in each section, (b) the p.d.'s at B and C.

(a) Let x amperes be the current from A to B in the positive conductor.

From Kirchhoff's First Law, it follows that the current from B to C in positive conductor

$$=x-120$$

and current from C to A in positive conductor

$$=x-120-80=x-200.$$

Resistance of positive conductor between A and B

$$=0.03 \times \frac{150}{100}=0.045 \ \Omega$$

resistance of positive conductor between B and C

$$=0.03 \times \frac{50}{100}=0.015 \ \Omega$$

and resistance of positive conductor between C and A

$$=0.03 \ \Omega.$$

Hence, voltage drop in positive conductor between A and B

$$=x \times 0.045 \text{ volts,}$$

voltage drop in positive conductor between B and C

$$=(x-120) \times 0.015 \text{ volts}$$

and voltage drop in positive conductor between C and A

$$=(x-200) \times 0.03 \text{ volts.}$$

Since there is no e.m.f. in the loop formed by the positive conductor, it follows from Kirchhoff's Second Law that:

$$x \times 0.045 +(x-120) \times 0.015 +(x-200) \times 0.03=0$$
$$\therefore \qquad x=86.7 \text{ A}$$
$$=\text{current in section AB.}$$

Current in section BC $=86.7-120=-33.3$ A
$$=33.3 \text{ A from C to B in posi-}$$
$$\text{tive conductor}$$

and current in section CA $=86.7-200=-113.3$ A
$$=113.3 \text{ A from A to C in posi-}$$
$$\text{tive conductor.}$$

(b) Voltage drop in positive and negative conductors between A and B

$$=86 \cdot 7 \times 0 \cdot 045 \times 2 = 7 \cdot 8 \text{ V}$$

and voltage drop in positive and negative conductors between A and C

$$=113 \cdot 3 \times 0 \cdot 03 \times 2 = 6 \cdot 8 \text{ V}$$

∴ p.d. across load at B $=240 - 7 \cdot 8 = 232 \cdot 2$ V

and ,, ,, ,, C $=240 - 6 \cdot 8 = 233 \cdot 2$ V.

The difference of 1 V between the p.d.'s across the loads at B and C should agree with the voltage drop calculated from the current in section BC and the resistance of that section, namely $33 \cdot 3 \times 0 \cdot 015 \times 2 = 0 \cdot 999$ V. The very slight discrepancy between the two values is due to the fact that the value of x was limited to three significant figures. This degree of accuracy is sufficient for most practical purposes.

Summary of Important Formulae

For resistances in series,

$$R = R_1 + R_2 + R_3 + \text{ etc.} \quad . \quad . \quad (14)$$

For resistances in parallel,

$$\frac{1}{R} = \frac{1}{R_1} + \frac{1}{R_2} + \frac{1}{R_3} + \text{ etc.} \quad . \quad . \quad (15)$$

For resistances R_1 and R_2 in parallel,

$$I_1 = I \cdot \frac{R_2}{R_1 + R_2} \quad . \quad . \quad . \quad . \quad (16)$$

$$R = \frac{\rho l}{a} \quad . \quad . \quad . \quad . \quad . \quad . \quad (17)$$

$$R = R_0(1 + \alpha t) \quad . \quad . \quad . \quad . \quad (18)$$

For standard annealed copper,

$$\frac{R_2}{R_1} = \frac{234 \cdot 5 + t_2}{234 \cdot 5 + t_1} \quad . \quad . \quad . \quad . \quad (19)$$

and $$t_2 = \frac{R_2}{R_1}(234 \cdot 5 + t_1) - 234 \cdot 5 \quad . \quad . \quad (20)$$

Kirchhoff's First Law. For several conductors meeting at a point,

algebraic sum of currents $= \Sigma I^* = 0$.

Kirchhoff's Second Law. For a closed network,

algebraic sum of e.m.f.'s = algebraic sum of products of currents and their respective resistances

i.e. $$\Sigma E = \Sigma I R.$$

EXAMPLES IV

1. The resistances of two coils A and B are 14 Ω and 18 Ω respectively. Find the combined resistance when they are connected (a) in series, (b) in parallel.

2. A circuit consists of two parallel resistances, 20 Ω and 30 Ω respectively, connected in series with 15 Ω. If the current through the 15-Ω resistance is 3 A, find: (a) the currents through the 20-Ω and 30-Ω resistances respectively, (b) the voltage across the whole circuit, (c) the total power.

3. A circuit consists of two resistors A and B in parallel connected in series with another resistor C. The resistances of A, B and C are 25, 16 and 5 ohms respectively. If the circuit is connected across a 30-volt supply, calculate the current in each resistor.

4. Two resistors, A and B, are connected in parallel across a battery of 20 cells in series. Each cell has an e.m.f. of 2·1 volts and an internal resistance of 0·13 ohm. The resistances of A and B are 20 and 28 ohms respectively. Calculate (a) the current from battery, (b) the currents in A and B, (c) the terminal voltage of battery.

5. A battery of 40 cells in series is to be charged at 8 A from a 230-V supply. Assuming the terminal voltage of each cell under these conditions to be 2·3 V, calculate the value of resistance to be connected in series with the battery. Also, find the cost of maintaining this charging current for 5 hours if the price of electrical energy is 1·5d per kWh.

6. A voltmeter connected across an accumulator reads 2·06 V when the cell is on open circuit. The voltmeter reading immediately falls to 1·92 V when a resistance of 0·2 Ω is connected across the terminals of the cell. Find: (a) the current, (b) the internal resistance of cell, (c) the total electrical power generated in cell, (d) the power in external resistance, (e) the power wasted due to the internal resistance of the cell.

7. A battery of 10 primary cells has an open-circuit e.m.f. of 15 V. When a resistance of 30 Ω is connected across the battery, the terminal p.d. is 12 V. Calculate: (a) the current, (b) the internal resistance per cell, (c) the power in the external circuit.

8. Two metal-filament lamps take 0·8 A and 0·9 A respectively when connected across a 110-V supply. Calculate the value of the

* Σ is the Greek letter *sigma* and is used to represent "algebraic sum of."

current taken when they are connected in series across a 220-V supply, assuming the filament resistances to remain unaltered. Also find the voltage across each lamp.

9. Define the coulomb, the ampere and the volt.

A circuit consisting of three resistances in parallel of 4, 6 and 12 ohms respectively is connected to a cell of internal resistance 1 ohm and e.m.f. 1·5 V. Assuming the e.m.f. of the cell to remain constant, how many coulombs are delivered in one minute?
(U.L.C.I., S1)

10. Three resistors, 18, 20 and 30 ohms respectively, are connected in parallel; two more resistors, 3·6 ohms each, are connected in parallel with each other. The two groups of resistors are then connected in series to a 45-V battery. Draw a circuit diagram and calculate the total current, the current in each resistor, the power absorbed in each of the 3·6-ohm resistors and the potential across the 20-ohm resistor. (E.M.E.U., S1)

11. Two circuits, A and B, are connected in parallel across a 50-volt supply. Circuit A is found to take 120 watts and the total current is 4·2 amperes. Calculate the resistances of A and B and the power absorbed by B.

12. The element of a 500-W electric iron was designed for use on a 200-V supply. Calculate the percentage increase of heat obtained if the iron is to be used on a 240-V supply. It can be assumed that the resistance of the element remains unaltered.

What value of resistance is needed to be connected in series in order that the iron can be operated normally from this 240-V supply?

If the iron is to be re-designed for the 240-V supply, calculate the resistance value of the new element if the power consumption is to remain at 500 watts. (N.C.T.E.C., S1)

13. A battery has a terminal p.d. of 52 V on open circuit and 48 V when connected across 10 Ω. Find its internal resistance.

14. What is the difference between a primary and a secondary cell? Six cells, each having an e.m.f. of 2 V and an internal resistance of 2 ohms, are connected in two groups of three in series, and the two groups connected in parallel to an external resistance of 30 ohms. Sketch the arrangement and calculate the current which will flow through the external resistance. (U.E.I., S1)

15. Resistances of 4 and 6 ohms in parallel are connected to three 1·5-V cells in series, each cell having an internal resistance of 2·2 ohms. Calculate the current in the 4- and the 6-ohm resistances.

Calculate the total current if a 2-V accumulator of negligible resistance is connected in circuit but with polarity opposing that of the three 1·5-V cells. (N.C.T.E.C., S1)

16. (a) Show by means of diagrams what you understand by series and parallel grouping of cells.

(b) A resistance of 10 ohms is connected across the terminals of a battery consisting of four cells in series. Each cell has an e.m.f. of 1·5 V and an internal resistance of 0·5 ohm. Calculate (i) the current in the circuit; (ii) the terminal voltage; (iii) the energy in joules absorbed in the external circuit if the current remains constant for 2 minutes. (E.M.E.U., S1)

17. State Ohm's Law. What is meant by the internal voltage drop (or internal potential drop) of a cell when a current flows through it?

A cell has an e.m.f. of 1·45 V and an internal resistance of 0·5 ohm. Calculate its internal voltage drop and terminal potential difference when it is delivering a current of 0·5 A. (U.L.C.I., S1)

18. Two cells are connected in series and the circuit completed by means of two parallel coils of resistances 7 ohms and 5 ohms respectively, connected in parallel. One cell has an e.m.f. of 1·5 V and an internal resistance of 1·2 ohms and the other cell an e.m.f. of 1·1 V and an internal resistance of 0·7 ohm. Calculate (a) the current in each cell, (b) the current in each coil, (c) the terminal voltage of each cell. (E.M.E.U., S1)

19. Three coils of resistance 8 ohms, 12 ohms and 24 ohms respectively are joined in (a) series, (b) parallel. What is their joint resistance for each grouping? What current would flow in each case if the group were connected to a 44-V supply? (U.L.C.I., S1)

20. Derive expressions for the single equivalent resistances of three resistances r_1, r_2 and r_3 when connected in (a) series, (b) parallel.
A coil of 20 Ω resistance is joined in parallel with a coil of x Ω resistance. This combination is then joined in series with a piece of apparatus A, and the whole circuit connected to 100-V mains. What must be the value of x so that A shall dissipate 600 W with 10 A passing through it? (U.L.C.I., S2)

21. A coil consists of 400 turns of copper wire having a sectional area of 0·005 cm². The mean length per turn is 45 cm, and the resistivity of copper can be taken as 0·02 $\mu\Omega$-m. Find: (a) the resistance of coil, (b) the electrical power when the p.d. across the coil is 20 volts.

22. Find the resistance of one mile of No. 1 S.W.G. aluminium wire, given that the corresponding diameter is 0·30 in and that the resistivity of aluminium is 1·1 $\mu\Omega$-in.

23. A copper rod, ¼ inch diameter and 1 yard long, has a resistance of 513 microhms. If this rod be drawn out to a No. 30 S.W.G. wire, find its new resistance. The area of a No. 30 S.W.G. wire is 0·00012076 in².

24. A copper wire 1 metre long and 1 mm² in cross-section has a resistance of 1/58 Ω. What is the resistance of a copper wire 250 m long and 0·6 cm² in cross-section?

25. A field coil of an electric motor has 1800 turns of copper wire. The cross-sectional area of the wire is 0·02 cm² and the average length per turn is 85 cm. Calculate the resistance of the coil given that the resistivity of copper is 2 microhm-cm at normal working temperature. Also calculate the p.d. required to send 0·7 A through the coil and the corresponding power in watts.

26. The four exciting coils of a certain electric motor are to be connected in series across a 440-V supply. Each coil is to be wound with 3200 turns and the average length of one turn is 28 inches. Calculate the cross-sectional area of the copper wire in order that the current may be 1·3 A, assuming the resistivity of copper under normal working conditions to be 0·8 microhm-inch. Also find the electrical power in kW absorbed by the coils.

27. Calculate the cross-sectional area of a copper conductor, 300 metres long, such that it may carry 500 A with a voltage drop of 8 V. Take the resistivity of copper as 0·019 $\mu\Omega$-m.

28. Define the term "specific resistance." In a test on a 10-cm strip of copper the resistance was found to be 171 microhms. The average cross-sectional area was 9·92 mm². Calculate the specific resistance in (a) centimetre units, (b) inch units. Assume that 1 inch is equivalent to 2·54 cm. (N.C.T.E.C., S1)

29. What is (a) a megohm, (b) a millivolt?

Define resistivity (specific resistance).

The resistance of 25 ft of manganin wire of uniform cross-section 0·002 in² is 2·6 ohms. From these data calculate the resistivity of manganin in microhms per inch cube (or microhm-inch).

(U.L.C.I., S1)

30. Define the term "resistivity." A coil consists of 10,000 turns of copper wire, the mean length per turn being 6 in and the area of cross-section 0·00005 in². Calculate the resistance of the coil, taking the resistivity of copper as 0·7 microhm per inch cube (or microhm-inch). (E.M.E.U., S1)

31. The coil of a relay takes 0·12 A when it is at the room temperature of 15° C and connected across a 60-V supply. After about 3 hours the current is found to have fallen to 0·105 A, the voltage remaining unaltered. Find the average temperature throughout the coil, the wire being of copper having a temperature coefficient of resistance of 1/234·5 at 0° C.

32. A dynamo is run on full load for several hours. At the beginning of the test the temperature was 16° C, the field current was 3 A and the voltage across the field winding was 330 V. At the end of the test the corresponding values of current and voltage were 3·1 A and 425 V. Calculate the temperature rise of the field winding, assuming the temperature coefficient of resistance of copper to be 1/234·5 at 0° C.

33. A coil of copper wire has a resistance of 210 ohms at 18° C. Calculate the resistance of the coil at 70° C, assuming the temperature coefficient to be 0·0043 at 0° C.

34. Taking the temperature coefficient of resistance of copper as 0·004264 at 0° C, calculate the change of resistance of 1 ohm at 20° C when its temperature is raised by 1° C.

35. A tungsten-filament lamp takes 100 watts from a 200-volt supply. The resistance of the filament at 20° C is 34 ohms. Assuming the average temperature coefficient of resistance of tungsten to be 0·005, calculate the temperature of the incandescent filament.

36. If the resistance of a carbon-filament lamp is 270 Ω at 1700° C and 490 Ω at 15° C, calculate the average value of the temperature coefficient of resistance of carbon over this range.

37. Explain the meaning of "temperature coefficient of resistance." A coil of German silver of 0·002 in² cross-section and of length 75 yards, is connected to a d.c. supply at 120 V. Calculate the current flowing when the temperature of the wire is 120° C. The specific resistance of German silver at 15° C is 16·4 × 10⁻⁶ ohm per inch cube. The temperature coefficient of German silver at 15° C is 0·000273 per degree C. (C. & G., El. Inst. Work)

38. A cylindrical rod, 3 inches long and 0·2 inch diameter. has a resistance of 63 microhms at 15° C. If this rod is drawn out to a wire having a uniform diameter of 0·008 inch, calculate its resistance at 60° C. Assume the temperature coefficient of resistance of the material to be 0·0043 at 0° C. (I. Mech. E., Prin. of Elect.)

39. (a) A large power station contains five 30,000-kW generators. Express the total power of the station in megawatts.

(b) A voltmeter requires 20 mA for a full-scale deflection of 250 V. Calculate the resistance and "ohms per volt" of the instrument.

(c) A 660-ft length of cable has an insulation resistance of 4800 megohms. What is the insulation resistance per mile?

(d) A p.d. of 110 V is applied to the field coils of a motor at a temperature of 15° C. The current is 11 A and some time later the current is found to be 9·1 A. Calculate the mean temperature rise of the coils. The temperature coefficient is 1/234·5 at 0° C.

(U.E.I., S2)

40. (a) A cable, 400 yards long, has two copper conductors each 0·1 in diameter; it carries a current of 5 A. Calculate the total voltage drop in the cable at 14° C, if the resistivity of copper is 0·69 microhm per in per in² at 0° C, and its temperature coefficient of resistance is 0·0043 per ° C at 0° C.

(b) A pump driven by a 460-V motor raises 100,000 gallons of water per hour to a height of 70 ft. Assuming efficiencies of 87 per cent and 84 per cent for pump and motor respectively, calculate the current taken by the motor and the cost of energy per hour at 1¼d per kWh. (One gallon of water weighs 10 lb.) (E.M.E.U., S2)

41. A motor is taking 80 amperes from a distribution point 200 yards away. The p.d. at that point is 465 volts, and the cable has a resistance of 0·03 ohm per 100 yards of single conductor. Calculate: (a) the p.d. across motor terminals, (b) the power supplied to motor, (c) the power wasted in cable.

42. An electric motor develops 50 h.p. at an efficiency of 90 per cent. Its terminal voltage is 460 volts. Find the current taken.

If this motor is situated 120 metres from the source of supply and the conductor has a cross-section of 0·5 cm², find the voltage drop in the cable, assuming the resistivity of copper to be 1·8 $\mu\Omega$-cm.

43. An electric motor is connected by a cable to a distribution panel 180 yards away. The section of the conductor is 0·07 in² and the motor is taking 68 A. The voltage at the distribution panel is 460 V. Find: (a) the voltage at the motor terminals, (b) the voltage drop in the cable, (c) the power in kW wasted in cable, (d) the output horsepower of the motor if its efficiency is 88 per cent. Assume the resistivity of copper to be 0·7 microhm-inch.

44. A cable having a resistance of 0·023 ohm per 100 metres of single conductor has a load of 120 A at a point A, 70 metres from the feeding end, and another load of 50 A at a point B, 40 metres beyond A. If the voltage at the feeding point be 242 V, find the voltage across the loads at A and B respectively. Also find the total power wasted in the cable.

45. State Ohm's Law.

A 12-h.p., d.c. motor of 90 per cent efficiency is supplied at 200 V at its terminals. It takes its supply from a generator by means of two conductors, each having a resistance of 0·1 ohm. Calculate the terminal voltage of the generator. What would be the cost of the electrical energy output from the generator terminals used in supplying this motor when working on full load for six hours if electrical energy cost ½d per unit? (U.L.C.I., S1)

46. A two-wire distributor ABCD is fed at A at 240 V. Loads of 50 A, 70 A and 40 A respectively are supplied at B, C and D. B, C and D are respectively 100, 160 and 250 yd from A, and the effective conductor section is 0·3 in² per core between A and C, and 0·2 in² between C and D. Calculate the voltage at each of the three loads. (Resistivity of copper = 0·7 microhm-inch.) (E.M.E.U., S2)

47. A d.c. cable with a cross-section of 0·25 in² per core is 3000 yd long. At 2000, 2400 and 3000 yd from the feeding point, the respective loads are 65, 20 and 15 A. Calculate: (a) the current in each section of the cable, (b) the watts loss in each section of the cable,

3

(c) the p.d. at the feeding point if the 15-A load is kept at 480 V. Assume resistivity of copper to be 0·7 microhm-inch. (U.E.I., S2)

48. A certain two-wire cable has an insulation resistance of 200 MΩ per 100 yd length of cable. If the cable is 3 miles long and is connected to a 230-V supply, find: (a) the insulation resistance of cable, (b) the total leakage current, (c) the corresponding energy wasted in the insulation in one year of 365 days. Neglect any voltage drop in the conductor.

49. A two-conductor cable supplies electrical energy to two consumers A and B, the currents taken being 150 and 200 A respectively. A and B are situated 250 and 400 metres respectively from the feeding point. The resistance of the cable is 0·04 Ω per 1000 metres of single conductor. If the p.d. across the load at B is maintained at 225 V, find: (a) the p.d.'s at A and at the feeding point, (b) the total power wasted in the cable.

50. A two-wire distributor 500 feet long is fed at each end at 115 V. At a distance of 100 feet from one end there is a load of 120 A, and 200 feet from the other end there is a load of 150 A. The resistance per 100 feet of single conductor is 0·01 Ω. Calculate: (a) the current in each section of the distributor, (b) the voltage at each load point, (c) the total power wasted in the cable.

51. A two-wire ring main 3 km long is formed of copper wires, each having a resistance of 0·003 Ω per 100 metres. It is fed at one point at 240 V. At a distance of 800 m in one direction from the feeding point there is a load of 80 A, and 1500 m in the other direction there is a load of 120 A. Calculate: (a) the current in each section, (b) the voltage at each load point, (c) the total power wasted in the ring main.

52. A d.c. distribution cable 350 ft long has two cores, each of 0·1 in^2, and is fed at one end at the constant voltage of 250. A consumer A, whose full load current is 40 A, is connected to the other end of the distribution cable by a service cable 30 ft long having two cores each of 0·06 in^2. Another consumer B, whose full load current is 60 A, is connected to the distribution cable at a point 150 ft from connection A by a service cable 50 ft long with two cores each of 0·06 in^2. Find the potential difference at each consumer's terminals when both are taking full load. Take the resistivity of copper as 0·7 microhm per inch cube. (C. & G., El. Inst. Work)

53. State Kirchhoff's Laws and apply them to the solution of the following problem:

Two batteries, A and B, are connected in parallel. The e.m.f. and internal resistance of battery A are 10 V and 3 Ω respectively; and the corresponding values for battery B are 14 V and 2 Ω respectively. A resistance of 8 Ω is connected across the battery terminals. Find (a) the value and the direction of the current in each battery and (b) the terminal voltage.

(I. Mech. E., Prin. of Elect.)

54. A battery having an e.m.f. of 10 V and an internal resistance of 0·01 Ω is connected in parallel with a second battery of e.m.f. 10 V and internal resistance of 0·008 Ω. The two batteries in parallel are properly connected for charging from a d.c. supply of 20 V through a resistance of 0·9 Ω. Calculate the current taken by each battery and the current from the supply. (N.C.T.E.C., S2)

CHAPTER V

ELECTROMAGNETISM

33. Magnetic Field. Before dealing with the magnetic effect of an electric current, it is necessary to explain what is meant by a magnetic field.

If a permanent magnet be suspended so that it is free to swing in a horizontal plane, as in Fig. 32, it is found that it always takes up a position such that a particular end points towards the earth's North Pole. That end is, therefore, said to be the *north-seeking* end of the magnet; similarly, the other end is the *south-seeking* end. For

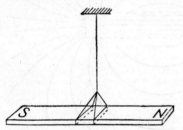

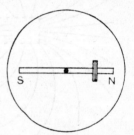

FIG. 32.—A suspended permanent magnet.

FIG. 33.—Compass needle.

short, these are referred to as the *north* (or N) and *south* (or S) *poles* respectively of the magnet. In the case of small compass-needles the north pole is usually indicated by a small crosspiece, as shown in Fig. 33.

If the N pole of another magnet is brought near the N pole of the suspended magnet, the latter is repelled * ;

* These forces of attraction and repulsion can be demonstrated very effectively by means of "Alnico" magnets. "Alnico" is an alloy of iron, aluminium, nickel and cobalt and enables very powerful permanent magnets to be made in short lengths.

whereas attraction occurs if the S pole of the second magnet is brought near the N pole of the suspended magnet. In general we may therefore say that like poles repel each other whereas unlike poles attract each other.

Let us next place a permanent magnet on a table, cover it over with a sheet of smooth cardboard and sprinkle some iron filings uniformly over the sheet.

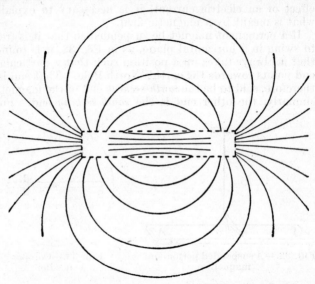

FIG. 34.—Use of iron filings for determining distribution of magnetic field.

Slight tapping of the latter causes the filings to set themselves in curved chains between the poles, as shown in Fig. 34. The shape and density of these chains enable one to form a mental picture of the magnetic condition of the space or "field" around a bar magnet and lead to the idea of *lines of magnetic flux*. Thus, any one of the chains shown in Fig. 34 represents the direction of the magnetic field along the path occupied by that chain. Also, the more intense the magnetic field, the closer together are the chains. Consequently, it has become the practice to refer to the density of a magnetic field as being so many lines of flux per unit area perpendicular to the direction of the flux. The basis upon which the numerical value of the number of lines of flux per square metre is calculated is dealt with in Art. 42.

It is necessary to emphasise at this stage that these lines of magnetic flux have no physical existence; they are purely imaginary and were introduced by Michael Faraday as a means of visualising the distribution and density of a magnetic field.

As to the nature of the magnetic field, all we can say is that it appears to be some form of strain both in the space occupied by the magnet and in that around the magnet—somewhat analogous to the skin of a rubber balloon in that it tends to collapse, and in consequence to keep to the shape that involves the minimum of stress. Thus, if a balloon is dented inwards, say by pressing a finger against it, the skin reacts against the finger, tending to push the latter out of the way. In Art. 39 it is shown that when a magnetic field is dented or distorted by an electric current, the magnetic field reacts in such a way that it tends to push away the conductor carrying the current.

34. Direction of Magnetic Field. The direction of a magnetic field is taken as that in which the north-seeking pole of a magnet points when the latter is suspended in the field. Thus, if a bar magnet NS rests on a table and four compass-needles are placed in positions indicated in Fig. 35, it is found that the needles take up positions such that their axes coincide with the corresponding chain of filings (Fig. 34) and the north poles are all pointing along the dotted line, from the N pole of the bar magnet to its S pole. Hence the lines of magnetic flux are assumed to pass through the magnet, emerge from the N pole and return to the S pole. This may be expressed in another way, thus: if a compass-needle is placed near a magnetised iron rod and if its N pole is repelled from the rod, the direction of the magnetic field in that region is outwards from the rod, and the adjacent surface of the rod has a north polarity.

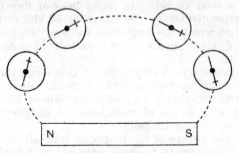

FIG. 35.—Use of compass needles for determining direction of magnetic field.

35. Magnetic Field due to an Electric Current.

In Art. 6 it was demonstrated that one of the characteristics of an electric current is its ability to magnetise the space surrounding it. The discovery of this phenomenon by Oersted at Copenhagen, in 1820, was the first definite demonstration of a relationship between electricity and magnetism. Oersted found that if he placed a wire

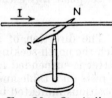

FIG. 36.—Oersted's experiment.

carrying a current of electricity above a magnetic needle (Fig. 36) and in line with the normal direction of the latter, the needle was deflected clockwise or counterclockwise, depending upon the direction of the current. This phenomenon may be better understood from experiments made with the apparatus shown in Fig. 37.* A stout copper wire W passes vertically

* It is usual to represent a current receding from the reader by a cross, as in Fig. 37, and an approaching current by a dot, as on the right-hand conductor in Fig. 51 (c). These conventions are based upon the cross being the back end elevation of the feathers of an arrow and the dot being the front view of the arrow point.

through a hole in a sheet of cardboard or glass G placed horizontally, with a number of compass-needles arranged around W.

With no current through the wire the north-seeking poles of the needles all point towards the earth's north pole. Immediately a current of, say, 10 amperes is switched on, the needles are deflected, and after a number of oscillations they come to rest with their axes lying roughly on a circle having the conductor as its centre—as shown in Fig. 37.

If the current be reversed, all the compass-needles reverse their direction.

Let us now remove the compass-needles and sprinkle plate G as uniformly as possible with iron filings. A current of, say, 20 or 30 amperes is then passed through wire W and the plate tapped gently. It is found that the filings tend to arrange themselves in concentric circles around the wire (Fig. 38), this tendency being most pronounced in the vicinity of the conductor.

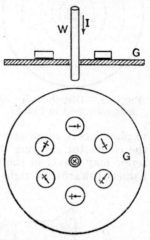

FIG. 37.—Magnetic field of an electric current.

These experiments indicate that a magnetic state or field is produced around a wire carrying an electric current and that the intensity of this field decreases as the distance from the conductor increases.

36. Direction of the Magnetic Field due to an Electric Current. It was pointed out in Art. 34 that the direction of the magnetism in any particular space is always taken as the direction of the N pole of a compass-needle placed in that field. Consequently, from an experiment such as that described in connection with Fig. 37, we can determine the relationship between the direction of the magnetic field and that of the current. Thus, it is seen from Fig. 37 that if we look along the conductor and if the current is flowing away from us, the magnetic field has a clockwise direction.

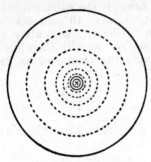

A convenient method of representing this relationship is to grip the conductor with the *right* hand, with the thumb outstretched parallel to the conductor and pointing in the direction of the current; the fingers then point in the direction of the magnetic field around the conductor.

FIG. 38.—Distribution of magnetic field in Fig. 37.

Another way of representing the relationship between the direction of a current and that of its magnetic field is to place a cork-screw or a wood-screw (Fig. 39) alongside the conductor carrying the current. In order that the screw may travel in the same direction as the current, namely towards the right in Fig. 39, it has to be turned

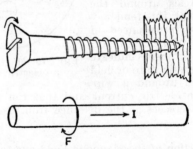

FIG. 39.—Right-hand screw Rule.

clockwise when viewed from the left-hand side. Similarly, the direction of the magnetic field, viewed from the same side, is clockwise around the conductor, as indicated by curved arrow F.

37. Magnetic Field of a Solenoid. A solenoid consists of a number of turns of wire wound in the same direction, so that when the coil is carrying a current, all the turns are assisting one another in producing a magnetic field. Fig. 40 shows a few turns of wire wound spirally through holes in a horizontal board and connected to a battery capable of supplying 15 to 20 amperes. Iron filings are evenly sprinkled over the board and the latter is gently tapped. The filings arrange themselves in concentric rings of the shape shown by the thin dotted lines. The direction of the magnetic field can be determined by

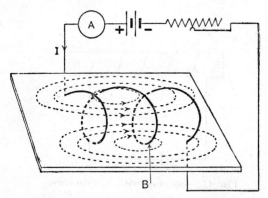

FIG. 40.—Magnetic field of a solenoid.

placing a compass-needle on the board and noting the direction in which its north-seeking pole is pointing. It is found that this direction is that indicated by the arrow-heads on the dotted lines in Fig. 40.

The magnetic field may be intensified by inserting a rod of iron inside the solenoid, as shown in Fig. 41. The magnetic field is again represented by the dotted lines and the arrowheads indicate the direction of the field. The iron core thus becomes magnetised with the polarities shown, and behaves just like a permanent magnet so long as the current is maintained in the coil.

The direction of the magnetic field produced by a
3*

current in a solenoid may be deduced by applying either the grip or the screw rule. Thus, if the solenoid is gripped with the right hand, with the fingers pointing in the direction of the current, then the thumb outstretched parallel to the axis of the solenoid points in the direction of the magnetic field *inside* the solenoid.

The screw rule can be expressed thus: If the axis of the screw is placed along that of the solenoid and if the screw is turned in the direction of the current, it travels

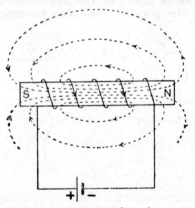

FIG. 41.—Solenoid with an iron core.

in the direction of the magnetic field, namely towards the right in Fig. 40 and 41.

38. Applications of the Magnetic Effect of a Current. The following examples are given to indicate ways in which the magnetic effect of a current may be utilised, and are not intended to be exhaustive.

(a) *Lifting Magnet.* A coil C, usually of insulated copper strip, is wound round a central core A forming part of an iron casting shaped as shown in Fig. 42, where the upper half is a sectional elevation at YY and the lower half is a sectional plan at XX. Over the face of the electromagnet is a disc D of non-magnetic manganese steel which is capable of withstanding considerable impacts when the load L is picked up. The load must be of magnetic material and the dotted lines FF represent the paths of the lines of magnetic flux. The lifting magnet is just a large-scale application of the magnetic experiment described in Art. 6.

(b) *Electric Bell*. Two coils AA (Fig. 43) are wound on an iron core C and connected in series in such a manner

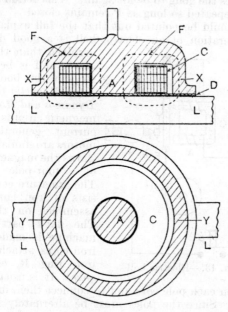

FIG. 42.—Sectional elevation and plan of lifting magnet.

that they help each other in setting up lines of magnetic flux through C and an iron plate or armature B, as indicated by the dotted line. The armature is supported by a flat spring S fixed at the upper end. Attached to B is another flat spring D carrying a contact E which normally rests against an adjustable contact F.

When a push-button P is pressed, the circuit is closed and current flows round coils A and contacts EF. Core

C becomes magnetised, armature B is attracted towards the poles of C and hammer H hits gong G. At the same time, contact E moves away from F, so that the electrical circuit is broken and core C becomes demagnetised. The armature is then brought back to its original position by spring S. The closing of the circuit at EF enables coils A to be energised once more and the attraction of B causes the gong to be hit again. This action continues to be repeated so long as P remains closed.

It should be pointed out that the full explanation of the operation of an electric bell is a good deal more involved than that given above and is beyond the scope of this book.

(c) *Magnetic Circuits of Dynamos and Motors.* The magnetic circuits of direct-current generators and motors are similar. Fig. 44 shows the magnetic circuit of a four-pole machine. The armature core A consists of iron laminations, assembled on the shaft. The fixed part of the machine is made of four iron cores attached to an iron ring R, called the *yoke.* It is usual to place

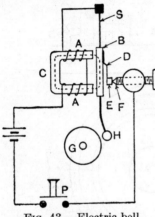

FIG. 43.—Electric bell.

a coil on each pole core and to connect them in series as shown. Since the poles must be alternately N and S, it is essential that the coils should be so connected that the current flows clockwise—when viewed from the armature end of the poles—round the cores which are to be south, and counterclockwise round those which are to be north.

It will be seen from Fig. 44 that the magnetic flux which emerges from N_1 divides, half going towards S_1 and half towards S_2. Similarly, the flux which emerges from N_2 divides equally between S_1 and S_2.

(d) *Telephone Receiver.* A telephone receiver (Fig. 45)

consists of a permanent magnet NS, two soft-iron pole-pieces B pressed on to the ends of the magnet and shaped as shown, two coils CC and a soft-iron disc or diaphragm

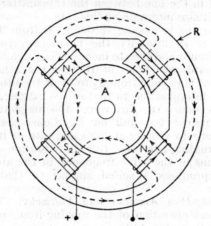

FIG. 44.—Magnetic circuit of a 4-pole dynamo or motor.

D arranged with a small clearance between it and the pole-faces of BB. Terminals T_1, T_2, are connected through the telephone line to the transmitter, so that

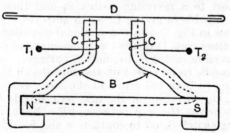

FIG. 45.—Telephone receiver.

the alternating current through CC reverses its direction as many times per second as the vibrations of the sound waves at the transmitter. For instance, if the sound at the transmitter be the middle C of the piano, the vibrations of the air, and therefore of the microphone diaphragm, will be at the rate of 256 per second; and the current in the line between the transmitter and the receiver will also alternate at this rate.

When current is passing through CC from T_1 to T_2, the effect is to intensify the magnetism round the magnetic circuit, and thus to increase the force attracting disc D towards the poles of B. On the other hand, when current is passing from T_2 to T_1, it tries to produce magnetism in opposition to that of the magnet, and the effect is to reduce the flux round the magnetic circuit and thus reduce the pull on D. Consequently, the latter is made to vibrate at the same rate or frequency as the alternating current. But the vibration of D sets up vibrations of the same frequency in the air around and thus produces a sound similar to that at the transmitter.

(e) *Moving-Iron Ammeter and Voltmeter*. The construction and operation of the moving-iron instrument are dealt with in Art. 142.

39. Force on a Conductor carrying Current across a Magnetic Field. Fig. 46 shows a brass or copper rod B suspended by two springs S between the poles P of an electromagnet. Connections are taken from the points of support to a reversing switch S_1 and then on to a battery capable of giving 12 to 15 amperes. (The left-hand view in Fig. 46 shows a sectional elevation at XX.) The exciting coils D of the electromagnet are connected by a reversing switch S_2 to another battery.

Suppose S_2 to be closed on the side shown in Fig. 46. According to both the grip and the screw rules given in Art. 37, the direction of the magnetic flux is from left to right across the gap between PP. Next, close the reversing switch S_1 on to contacts *a* and *b*. It is found that rod B moves downwards, and that the larger the current through B the greater is the force acting on it, as shown by the extension of springs S.

If S_1 be moved over to contacts *bc*, the current in B is reversed and it is found that B is lifted above its normal position, indicating that the direction of the force has been reversed.

The same effect is obtained if S_1 is left in its original position *ab*, but the current in DD reversed by means of S_2. If the currents in B and D are both reversed by operating S_1 and S_2 simultaneously, the direction of the force on B is found to remain unaltered.

These effects can be explained * by the simple apparatus shown in elevation and plan in Fig. 47. Two permanent magnets NS rest on a sheet of paper or glass

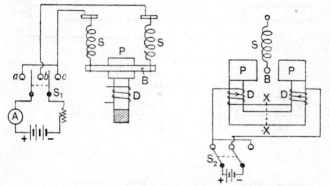

FIG. 46.—Force on conductor carrying current across a magnetic field.

G, and soft-iron pole-pieces P are added just to spread out the magnetic field in the gap between them. Mid-

* Many textbooks give a *left*-hand rule for deducing the direction of the force on a conductor carrying current across a magnetic field. This rule is liable to be confused with the *right*-hand rule, given in Art. 47, for determining the direction of a generated e.m.f. The latter rule is extremely useful and should be memorised. Few students can memorise both rules correctly and it is suggested that the left-hand rule should be forgotten and that the direction of the force on a current-carrying conductor in a magnetic field should be deduced from first principles by drawing separately the magnetic field due to the current in the conductor and that due to the permanent magnet or electromagnet and thus derive the distribution of the resultant magnetic field as in Fig. 47.

way between the pole-pieces is a wire W passing vertically downwards through G and connected through a switch to a 6-volt accumulator, such as a car battery, capable of giving a very large current for a short time.

With the switch open, iron filings are sprinkled over G and the latter is gently tapped. The filings in the space between PP take up the distribution shown in Fig. 47 (b). If the switch is closed momentarily, the

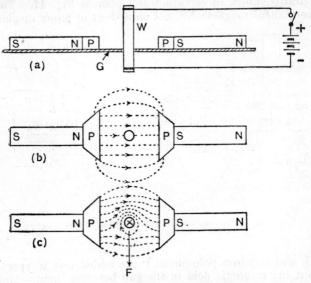

FIG. 47.—Flux distribution with and without current.

filings rearrange themselves as in Fig. 47 (c). It will be seen that the lines of magnetic flux have been so distorted that they partially surround the wire. This distorted field acts like stretched elastic strings bent out of the straight; the lines of flux try to return to the shortest paths between PP, thereby exerting a force F urging the conductor out of the way.

It has already been shown in Art. 36 that a wire W carrying a current downwards in Fig. 47 (a) produces a magnetic field as shown in Fig. 48. If this field is compared with that of Fig. 47 (b), it is seen that on the upper side the two fields are in the same direction, whereas on the lower side they are in opposition. Hence, the combined effect is to strengthen the magnetic field on the upper side and weaken it on the lower side, thus giving the distribution shown in Fig. 47 (c).

By combining diagrams similar to Fig. 47 (b) and 48, it is easy to understand that if either the current in W or the polarity of the magnets NS is reversed, the field is strengthened on the lower side and weakened on the upper side of diagrams corresponding to Fig. 47 (b), so that the direction

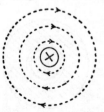

Fig. 48.—Flux distribution due to current in a straight conductor.

of the force acting on W is the reverse of that shown in Fig. 47 (c).

On the other hand, if both the current through W and the polarity of the magnets are reversed, the *distribution* of the resultant magnetic field and therefore the direction of the force on W remain unaltered.

40. Applications of the Mechanical Force on a Conductor carrying Current in a Magnetic Field. The following are only a few typical examples of the mechanical force discussed in the preceding Article.

(a) *Moving-Coil Loudspeaker.* The electromagnet of Fig. 49 is made by winding a coil A on a central iron core. The iron pole-piece B is an annular iron ring arranged to give a uniform airgap between it and the central core. In this space there is a coil C wound on a former carried by a conical diaphragm D, and current is led into and out of C by thin flexible wires. The dotted lines represent the paths of the magnetic flux.

The alternating current supplied by the wireless receiver passes through C, so that at one instant there is a force acting on the wires of C urging the coil and its diaphragm towards the right. At the next instant the current in C will have reversed and the diaphragm will be drawn to the left. Thus the air in the vicinity of D is set in vibration and a corresponding sound is produced.

Many loudspeakers are constructed with a permanent magnet instead of the electromagnet.

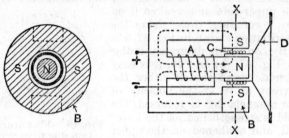

FIG. 49.—Moving-coil loudspeaker.

(b) *The Electric Motor.* Fig. 50 shows a copper disc D supported by a spindle in such a way that its lower edge just dips into a mercury pool M. The portion of

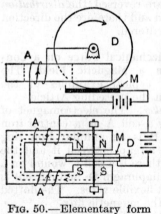

FIG. 50.—Elementary form of electric motor.

the disc that is between the spindle and the mercury is situated in the field of an electromagnet excited by coils AA. One end of a battery is connected to the mercury pool and the other end to coils A and then, via the spindle, to disc D. The latter is therefore carrying current from its spindle to the mercury in a direction that is at right angles to the field of the electromagnet NS. By combining the magnetic field due to this current with that due to the electromagnet, it is found that the resultant field is distorted in such a direction as to exert a torque urging the disc clockwise.

This principle is applied in the rotating mercury meter

used on d.c. supply systems for measuring the amount of electrical energy consumed. It is also the principle of action of the electric motor, though actual machines are much more complicated in construction and are referred to more fully in Chap. XVI.

(c) *Moving-Coil Ammeter and Voltmeter.* The construction and operation of the moving-coil instrument are dealt with in Art. 141.

41. Force between Two Long Parallel Conductors carrying Electric Current. Consider two parallel conductors, A and B, each carrying current towards the paper as shown in Fig. 51. The lines of magnetic flux due to current in A alone are represented by the uniformly-dotted circles in Fig. 51 (a) and those due to B alone are represented by the chain-dotted circles. It is evident that in the space between A and B the two fields tend to neutralise each other, but in the space outside A and B they assist each other. Hence the resultant distribution is somewhat as shown in Fig. 51 (b). Since lines of magnetic flux behave like stretched elastic cords, the effect is to try to move conductors A and B towards each other;

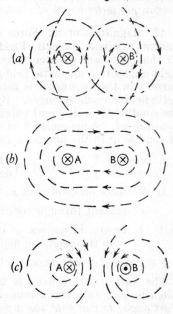

FIG. 51.—Magnetic fields due to current-carrying parallel conductors.

in other words, there is a force of attraction between A and B.

If the current in B is reversed, the magnetic fields

due to A and B assist each other in the space between the conductors and the resultant distribution will be as shown in Fig. 51 (c). The lateral pressure between the lines of flux exerts a force on the conductors tending to repel them from each other.

It is this force between two parallel current-carrying conductors that forms the basis for the definition of the *ampere* given in Art. 11, namely *that current which, when flowing in each of two infinitely long conductors, situated in a vacuum and separated 1 metre between centres, causes each conductor to have a force acting upon it of* 2×10^{-7} *newton per metre length of conductor*.

42. Magnitude of the Force on a Conductor carrying Current across a Magnetic Field. It was shown in Art. 39 that the force on a conductor carrying a current at right angles to a magnetic field is increased when (a) the current in the conductor is increased and (b) the magnetic field is made stronger. By measuring the force on the conductor for different values of current, for different densities of the magnetic field and for different lengths of conductor in the magnetic field, it is found that:

$$\left.\begin{array}{c}\text{force on}\\\text{conductor}\end{array}\right\} \propto \text{current} \times \left(\begin{array}{c}\text{flux}\\\text{density}\end{array}\right) \times \left(\begin{array}{c}\text{length of}\\\text{conductor}\end{array}\right)$$

If F=force on conductor in newtons,

I=current through conductor in amperes

and l=length, in metres, of conductor at right angles to the magnetic field,

F (newtons) $\propto$ flux density $\times l$ (metres) $\times I$ (amperes).

The *unit of flux density* is taken as *the density of a magnetic field such that a conductor carrying 1 ampere at right angles to that field has a force of 1 newton per metre acting upon it*. This unit is termed a *weber per square metre* (Wb/m²) to commemorate a German physicist, Wilhelm Eduard Weber (1804–91), who was the first to develop a system of absolute electrical and magnetic units. Hence, for a flux density of B webers/metre²,

force on conductor $= BlI$ newtons . (23)

For a magnetic field having a cross-sectional area of a metres^2, the *total flux* in *webers* (or Wb) is represented by the Greek capital letter Φ (phi), where

$$\Phi \text{ (in Wb)} = B \text{ (in Wb/m}^2) \times a \text{ (in m}^2)$$

or $\qquad B \text{ (in Wb/m}^2) = \dfrac{\Phi \text{ (in Wb)}}{a \text{ (in m}^2)} \qquad \ldots \ldots \text{ (24)}$

The weber is a large unit and either the *milliweber* (mWb) or the *microweber* (μWb) is often a more convenient unit to employ, where

$$1 \text{ milliweber} = 10^{-3} \text{ weber}$$

and $\qquad 1 \text{ microweber} = 10^{-6} \text{ weber}.$

Example 23. *A conductor carries a current of 800 A at right angles to a magnetic field having a density of 0·5 weber/metre*^{2}*. Calculate the force on the conductor (a) in newtons per metre length and (b) in pounds per yard length.*

(a) From (23),

force per metre length $= 0{\cdot}5 \text{ (Wb/m}^2) \times 1\text{(m)} \times 800\text{(A)}$

$\qquad\qquad\qquad\qquad = 400 \text{ newtons.}$

(b) Since $\quad 1 \text{ newton} = 0{\cdot}225 \text{ lb and } 1 \text{ yd} = 0{\cdot}9114 \text{ m,}$

force per yard length $= 0{\cdot}5 \times 0{\cdot}9114 \times 800 \text{ newtons}$

$\qquad\qquad\qquad\qquad = 400 \times 0{\cdot}9114 \times 0{\cdot}225 = 82{\cdot}3 \text{ lb.}$

Example 24. *The coil of a moving-coil instrument (see Fig. 195) is wound with 42½ turns. The mean width of the coil is 2·5 cm and the axial length of the magnetic field is 2 cm. If the flux density in the airgap is 0·1 Wb/m*^{2}*, calculate the torque (a) in newton-metres and (b) in gram-cm for a current of 15 mA.*

(a) Since the coil has 42½ turns, one side will have 42 wires and the other side will have 43 wires.

From (23), force on the side having 42 wires

$\qquad\qquad = 0{\cdot}1 \text{ (Wb/m}^2) \times 0{\cdot}02 \text{ (m)} \times 0{\cdot}015 \text{ (A)} \times 42$

$\qquad\qquad = 1260 \times 10^{-6} \text{ newton}$

$\therefore$ torque on that side of coil

$\quad = 1260 \times 10^{-6} \times 0{\cdot}0125 = 15{\cdot}75 \times 10^{-6} \text{ newton-metre.}$

Similarly, torque on side of coil having 43 wires

$=15 \cdot 75 \times 10^{-6} \times 43/42 = 16 \cdot 12 \times 10^{-6}$ newton-metre.

$\therefore$ total torque on coil $= 31 \cdot 87 \times 10^{-6}$ newton-metre.

(b) Since 1 newton $= 1/9 \cdot 81$ kg (force)

$= 102$ g (force),

$\therefore$ torque on coil $= 31 \cdot 87 \times 10^{-6} \times 102 \times 100$

$= 0 \cdot 325$ g-cm.

43. Force between Coils carrying Electric Current.   We are now in a position to explain the effect observed in Art. 7, namely, that two co-axial coils, placed one above the other, attract or repel each other, depending upon

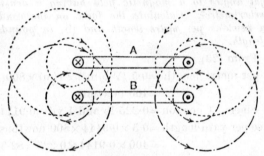

Fig. 52.—Magnetic fields due to currents in A and B separately.

the relative direction of their currents.   Suppose A and B in Fig. 52 to represent the cross-section of two coils carrying currents in the directions shown by the dots and crosses.   Let us first consider the distribution of the magnetic fields due to the coils acting independently. Thus, current through A alone gives the flux distribution represented by the uniformly dotted lines in Fig. 52, while current in the same direction through B alone gives the distribution indicated by the chain-dotted lines.   It will be seen that in the space between the coils the two fields oppose each other, while on the outside they are in the same direction.   Consequently the combined effect is to give the distribution shown in Fig. 53. Since lines of magnetic flux act as if they were in tension, trying to shorten themselves, they tend to draw coils A and B together.

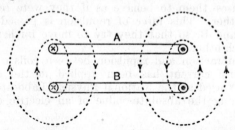

FIG. 53.—Resultant magnetic field when currents in A and B are in the same direction.

On the other hand, if the current through B is reversed, the direction of the arrowheads on the chain-dotted lines in Fig. 52 is reversed. Consequently, the magnetic fields

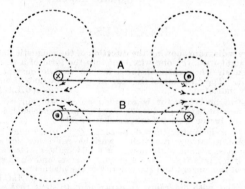

FIG. 54.—Resultant magnetic field when currents in A and B are in opposite directions.

of A and B are in the same direction in the space between the coils and in opposition outside the coils, so that the resultant distribution becomes that shown in Fig. 54. But lines of magnetic flux also exert a lateral pressure on one another—just as stretched rubber cords try to swell when allowed to contract in length, and thereby exert sideways pressure on other rubber cords that are alongside. This lateral pressure between the lines of flux causes them to behave as if they were repelling one another. This force of repulsion is passed on to coils A and B, so that they try to move farther away from each other.

This attraction and repulsion between coils carrying an electric current has been applied in the current balance * used at the National Physical Laboratory for determining the absolute value of an electric current (Art. 11).

Summary of Important Formulae

$$\left.\begin{array}{l}\text{Force on conductor}\\ \text{(in newtons)}\end{array}\right\} = \frac{B \text{ (in Wb/m}^2) \times l \text{ (metres)}}{\times I \text{ (amperes)}} \quad (23)$$

$$B \text{ (in Wb/m}^2) = \frac{\Phi \text{ (webers)}}{a \text{ (square meters)}} \quad . \quad . \quad (24)$$

EXAMPLES V

1. Give a diagram showing the direction of the magnetic field round (a) a straight wire, (b) one wire bent into the form of a circle, (c) a long solenoid, when each of these has an electric current passing through it. The direction of the current and of the lines of force must be clearly indicated. (U.L.C.I., S1)

2. A straight conductor is carrying an electric current. What type of magnetic field is produced? What happens when such a current-carrying conductor is placed in a magnetic field? (U.E.I., S1)

3. Given a horseshoe-shaped piece of soft iron, some insulated copper wire, a battery, a switch, a variable resistance, an ammeter and a compass needle, state how you would make an electromagnet and test it for polarity. Give a circuit diagram and on it show the direction of the current and the polarity of the magnet.
(U.L.C.I., S1)

4. Describe, with diagrams, an experiment to show that a force is produced when a current-carrying conductor is in a magnetic field. What are the relative directions of the magnetic field, current and force? (N.C.T.E.C., S1)

5. Explain what is meant by a "magnetic field" and the "direction of a magnetic field." A long, straight horizontal wire lies along the

* Further particulars, together with an illustration of this balance, can be found in the *Journal* of the Institution of Electrical Engineers, December, 1951.

magnetic meridian and an observer holds a compass needle above and close to the wire. Describe, with sketches, the effect on the needle when a current is passed through the wire (a) flowing from north to south and (b) flowing from south to north, giving reasons for the effects produced.   (E.M.E.U., S1)

6. A straight conductor is carrying a current of 2500 A across a magnetic field of 0·12 Wb/m². Calculate the force on the conductor in (a) newtons/metre and (b) kg/metre.

7. A conductor, 1 foot long, is carrying a current of 60 A at right angles to a magnetic field. The force on the wire is 2 lb. Calculate the density of the magnetic field.

8. The coil of a moving-coil loudspeaker (Fig. 49) has a mean diameter of 3 cm and is wound with 800 turns. It is situated in a radial magnetic field of 0·5 Wb/m². Calculate the force in grams when the current is 12 mA.

9. The coil of a moving-coil instrument is wound with 36½ turns on a square former having a length of 2·5 cm. The flux density in the gap is 0·13 Wb/m². Calculate the torque in gram-cm when the current is 25 mA.

10. The coil of a moving-coil instrument is wound with 50½ turns on a rectangular former. The axial length of the pole shoes is 2·3 cm and the mean width of the coil is 1·7 cm. If the flux density in the gap is 0·12 Wb/m², calculate the current to give a torque of 0·3 g-cm.

11. The armature of a certain electric motor has 900 conductors and the current per conductor is 24 A. The flux density in the airgap under the poles is 0·6 Wb/m². The armature core is 16 cm long and has a diameter of 25 cm. Assume that the core is smooth (i.e. there are no slots and the winding is on the cylindrical surface of the core) and also assume that only two-thirds of the conductors are simultaneously in the magnetic field. Calculate (a) the torque in newton-metres and in pound-feet and (b) the mechanical power developed in kW and in h.p. if the speed is 700 r.p.m.

(*Note.* In the case of slotted cores, the flux density in the slots is very low, so that there is very little torque on the conductors; nearly all the torque is exerted on the teeth.)

12. The flux in the pole of an electric motor is 0·013 weber. If the pole has a circular cross-section and a diameter of 12 cm, calculate the value of the flux density.

13. If the flux density inside a solenoid is 0·08 Wb/m², and the cross-sectional area of the solenoid is 20 cm², calculate the value of the total flux in microwebers.

CHAPTER VI

ELECTROMAGNETIC INDUCTION

44. Induced E.M.F. It was mentioned in Art. 35 that the magnetic effect of an electric current was discovered by Oersted in 1820. The knowledge of this connection between electricity and magnetism caused many scientists of the time, particularly Michael Faraday in England, to try to discover a method of obtaining an electric current from a magnetic field. Failure after failure dogged Faraday's efforts until on August 29th, 1831, he made the great discovery of *electromagnetic induction* with which his name will be for ever associated.

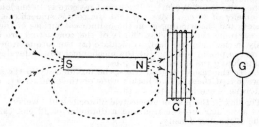

Fig. 55.—Electromagnetic induction.

As far as we are concerned, it will be more convenient to approach this matter experimentally in a different sequence from that followed by Faraday. Let us take a coil C (Fig. 55), wound with a large number of turns, and connect it to a galvanometer G, namely a very sensitive moving-coil ammeter. If a permanent magnet NS is moved up to and along the axis of C, as shown, the moving coil of G is deflected, thereby indicating that there must be an electromotive force induced or generated in coil C. Immediately the movement of NS ceases, the moving coil of G returns to its original position. This effect proves that e.m.f. is induced only while NS is moving relative to C.

Let us now move NS away from C. The galvanometer deflection is found to be in the reverse direction, showing that the direction of the induced e.m.f. depends upon the direction in which NS is moved relative to coil C.

If, next, we hold the magnet stationary but move the coil towards the magnet and then away from it, the deflection of the galvanometer is found to follow exactly the same sequence as it did when the magnet was moved and the coil held stationary. This result shows that the generation of an e.m.f. in C depends only upon the relative movement of the magnet and the coil.

If the permanent magnet be reversed so that its S pole is pointing towards the coil, it is found that a repetition of the movements described above is accompanied by galvanometer deflections similar to those previously obtained, except that their directions are reversed. Thus, the direction of the e.m.f. induced by bringing the S pole up to the coil is the same as that previously obtained when the N pole was moved away from the coil.

The arrowheads on the dotted lines in Fig. 55 represent the direction of the magnetic field in their respective regions. It will be seen that as the magnet is moved towards the coil, the magnetic field of NS also moves across the wires forming the coil; that is, the lines of magnetic flux are said to *cut* the coil. Similarly, when the coil is moved towards the magnet, the lines of magnetic flux are said *to be cut* by the coil. It is this relative movement of the magnetic flux and the coil that causes an e.m.f. to be induced (or generated) in the latter. The above experiments also show that the direction of the induced e.m.f. depends both upon the direction of the magnetic field and upon that in which the coil moves relative to the field.

Let us next bring the magnet up to the coil at different speeds. It is found that the greater the speed the greater is the deflection of the galvanometer and, therefore, the greater must be the e.m.f. induced in the coil.

45. Induced E.M.F. (*continued*). Let us now replace
magnet NS of Fig. 55 by a coil A (Fig. 56) connected
through a switch S to a battery. At the instant when S
is closed, there is a momentary deflection on G; and
when S is opened, G is deflected momentarily in the
reverse direction. On the other hand, if S is kept closed
and coil A moved towards C, the galvanometer is
deflected in the same direction as when S was closed
with A stationary. The withdrawal of A causes a
deflection in the reverse direction. Deflection of G
only continues while there is relative movement between
the two coils.

The dotted lines in Fig. 56 represent the magnetic

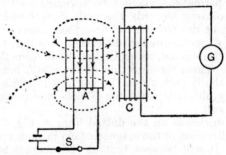

FIG. 56.—Electromagnetic induction.

field due to current in coil A. When S is opened, the
current falls to zero. Consequently, the magnetic field
of A must also disappear; in other words, the lines of
magnetic flux are said to *collapse* towards A, and in so
doing those lines of flux that passed through (or were
linked with) coil C, cut the latter and induce an e.m.f.
in it.

Similarly, when S is closed, the current through A
causes a magnetic field to come into existence; and in
this process the lines of magnetic flux may be regarded
as spreading outwardly from coil A, and many of them
will extend sufficiently to cut coil C and thereby induce
an e.m.f. in it. It will be seen that as far as the e.m.f.
induced in C is concerned, both the closing of S in Fig. 56

and the moving of A towards C, with S closed, have the same effect as moving the magnet towards C in Fig. 55.

The effects observed with the apparatus of Fig. 56 may be accentuated by placing an iron core inside the coils, thereby increasing the number of lines of flux linked with C due to a given current in A. In fact, we may go still further and wind the two coils A and C on an iron ring R, as in Fig. 57. When S is closed, the current in A sets up lines of magnetic flux through R, as indicated by the dotted circles. These lines of flux, in becoming linked with coil C, induce in the latter an e.m.f. which circulates a current causing G to be deflected

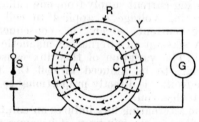

FIG. 57.—Electromagnetic induction.

momentarily. So long as S remains closed, there is no further change of magnetic flux and therefore no e.m.f. induced in C. But immediately S is opened, the magnetic flux decreases and an e.m.f. is induced in C in the reverse direction.

It was by means of apparatus similar to that shown in Fig. 57 that Faraday discovered electromagnetic induction, namely that a change in the value of the magnetic flux through a coil causes an e.m.f. to be induced in that coil.

It should be pointed out that when S (Fig. 57) is closed, the flux which becomes linked with coil C has also to grow in coil A; consequently, an e.m.f. is induced in A as well as in C. Similarly, when S is opened the decrease of flux causes an e.m.f. to be induced in both A and C.

The results obtained from the above experiments on electromagnetic induction may now be summarised thus :

(a) When a conductor cuts or is cut by magnetic flux, an e.m.f. is induced in the conductor.

(b) The direction of the induced e.m.f. depends upon the direction of the magnetic field and upon the direction in which the field moves relative to the conductor.

(c) The magnitude of the e.m.f. is proportional to the rate at which the conductor cuts or is cut by the magnetic flux.

46. The Transformer. It is only a small step from the apparatus shown in Fig. 57 to a transformer. The function of the latter is merely to change the voltage of an alternating-current supply from one value to another. An alternating voltage is applied to coil A and the alternating current which, in consequence, passes through A sets up an alternating magnetic flux in the iron core. The variation of this flux causes an alternating e.m.f. to be induced in coil C. The voltage obtainable from C is directly proportional to the number of turns on that coil.

Since the alternating flux induces an e.m.f. in the iron core as well as in the windings, it becomes necessary to reduce the magnitude of the alternating current circulating in the core. This is done by constructing the latter of iron sheets or laminations, about 0·3 to 0·5 mm thick, insulated from one another by thin layers of varnish or paper (Art. 123). In this way, the currents in the core are confined to their respective laminations; and the effect is to reduce very considerably the area and thereby increase the resistance of the paths of these currents. Consequently, the reduction in the value of these circulating currents involves smaller loss of power and less heating of the core. If the core were made of solid iron, the "eddy" currents would be sufficient to overheat the transformer and reduce its efficiency very considerably.

47. Direction of the Induced E.M.F. The simplest method of determining the direction of the e.m.f. induced or generated in a conductor is to find the direction of the current which that e.m.f. sets up. Thus, in

Fig. 58, AB represents a metal rod with its ends connected through a change-over switch S to a moving-coil
galvanometer G. With S on side *a*, let us move AB
downwards between the poles NS of an electromagnet
and note the direction of G's deflection. Let us then
move S over to *b*, so as to connect G in series with a high
resistance R across a cell C. It is found that in order
that G may again be deflected in the same direction, the
polarity of C must be that shown in Fig. 58; that is,
the current through the galvanometer must be in the
direction indicated by the arrow alongside G. Hence,
the e.m.f. generated in AB must be acting from A towards

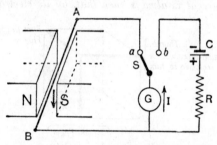

FIG. 58.—Direction of induced e.m.f.

B when the rod is moved downwards through the
magnetic field shown in Fig. 58.

Now arises the problem: how can we remember this
relationship in a form that can be easily applied to any
other case? Two methods are available for this purpose,
namely:

(a) **Fleming's** * **Right-hand Rule.** *If the first finger of
the right hand be pointed in the direction of the magnetic
flux, as in Fig. 59, and if the thumb be pointed in the
direction of motion of the conductor* **relative** *to the magnetic
field, then the middle finger, held at right angles to both
the thumb and the first finger, represents the direction of
the e.m.f.* The manipulation of the thumb and fingers

* John Ambrose Fleming (1849–1945) was Professor of
Electrical Engineering at University College, London.

and their association with the correct quantity present
some difficulty to many students. Easy manipulation
can only be acquired by experience; and it may be
helpful to associate *field* or *flux* with *first* finger, *motion*
of the conductor relative to the field with the *m* in
thu*m*b and e.m.f. with the *e* in *second* finger. If any
two of these are correctly applied, the third is correct
automatically.

(b) **Lenz's Law.** In 1834, almost immediately after
the discovery of induced currents, Heinrich Lenz, a
German physicist (1804–65), gave a simple rule for
determining their direction, namely : *The direction of an
induced current is always such that, by its electromagnetic*

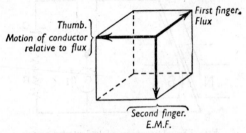

FIG. 59.—Fleming's Right-hand Rule.

*reaction, it tends to prevent the motion responsible for
inducing the current.* In order that we may be able to
determine the direction of the induced e.m.f. whether
the latter is due to the motion of a conductor or of a
magnetic field or due to the variation of the magnetic
flux linked with a circuit, it is convenient to express
Lenz's Law in a generalised form thus : *The direction of
an induced e.m.f. is always such that it tends to set up a
current opposing the change responsible for inducing that
e.m.f.*

Let us consider the application of this law to the
experiment described in connection with Fig. 58. The
current due to the e.m.f. induced in AB tends to set up
a counterclockwise magnetic field around the rod, so
that the resultant field in the vicinity of AB is distorted

in the opposite direction to that shown in Fig. 47 (c). But such a distorted field exerts an upward force upon the conductor, trying to oppose its downward movement and therefore trying to prevent that which is responsible for the generation of the e.m.f. Hence, when Lenz's Law is applied to such an example, it is necessary to find the direction of the current which will distort the field in such a direction as to try and prevent the relative movement of the conductor and the magnetic field. The direction of such a current is also the direction of the generated e.m.f.

Let us also consider the application of Lenz's Law to the ring shown in Fig. 57. By applying either the screw or the grip rule given in Art. 37, we find that when S is closed and the battery has the polarity shown, the direction of the magnetic flux in the ring is clockwise. Consequently, the current in C must be such as to try and produce a flux in a counterclockwise direction, tending to oppose the growth of the flux due to A, namely the flux which is responsible for the e.m.f. induced in C. But a counterclockwise flux in the ring would require the current in C to be passing through the coil from X to Y (Fig. 57). Hence, this must also be the direction of the e.m.f. induced in C.

48. Magnitude of the Generated or Induced E.M.F.

Fig. 60 represents the elevation and plan of a conductor AA situated in an airgap between poles NS. Suppose AA to be carrying a current, I amperes, in direction shown. By applying either the screw or the grip rule of Art. 36 it is found that the effect of this current is to strengthen the field on the right and weaken that on the left of A, so that there is a force of BlI newtons (Art. 42) urging the conductor towards the left, where B is the flux density in webers per square metre and l is the length in metres of conductor in the magnetic field. Hence, a force of this magnitude has to be applied in the opposite direction to move A towards the right.

The work done in moving conductor AA through a distance d metres to position BB in Fig. 60 is $(BlI \times d)$ metre-newtons or joules. If this movement of AA takes place at a uniform velocity in t seconds, the e.m.f. induced in the conductor is constant at, say, E volts. Hence the electrical power generated in AA is IE watts and the electrical energy is IEt watt-seconds or joules. Since the mechanical energy expended in moving the conductor across the gap is all converted into electrical energy,

then $$IEt = BlId$$

$$\therefore \quad E = \frac{Bld}{t} \text{ volts.}$$

But $Bld =$ the total number of magnetic lines in the area shown shaded in Fig. 60 and is therefore the total flux,

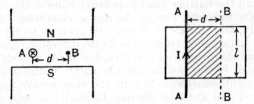

Fig. 60.—Conductor moved across magnetic field.

Φ webers, cut by the conductor when the latter is moved from AA to BB.

Hence $$E \text{ (in volts)} = \frac{\Phi \text{ (in webers)}}{t \text{ (in seconds)}} \quad \cdot \quad \cdot \quad \cdot \quad (25)$$

i.e. the e.m.f., in volts, generated in a conductor is equal to the rate (in webers/second) at which the magnetic flux is cutting or being cut by the conductor; and the *weber* may therefore be defined as *that magnetic flux which when cut by a conductor in 1 second generates an e.m.f. of 1 volt.*

Example 25. *Calculate the e.m.f. generated in the axle of a car travelling at 40 miles per hour, assuming the length of the axle to be 5 feet and the vertical component of the earth's magnetic field to be 40 microwebers/metre².*

Since   1 yard $=0\cdot9144$ metre,

$$\text{speed of car} = \frac{40 \times 1760 \times 0\cdot9144}{3600} = 17\cdot9 \text{ m/sec.}$$

Length of axle $=\frac{5}{3} \times 0\cdot9144 = 1\cdot524$ m,

$\therefore$ flux cut by axle in 1 sec $=40 \times 17\cdot9 \times 1\cdot524$

$$=1090 \ \mu\text{Wb}$$

and e.m.f. generated in axle $=1090$ microvolts.

Example 26. *A 4-pole dynamo has a magnetic flux of 12 milliwebers per pole. Calculate the average value of the e.m.f. generated in one of the armature conductors if the armature is driven at 900 r.p.m.*

Each time a conductor passes a pole, whether it be N or S, it cuts 12 milliwebers; hence, in one revolution, the conductor cuts $4 \times 12 = 48$ milliwebers. Since the conductor is rotating at $900/60 = 15$ revolutions per second,

average e.m.f. generated in one conductor

=flux, in webers, cut per second

=flux, in webers, cut per rev $\times$ r.p.s.

$=0\cdot048 \times 15 = 0\cdot72$ V.

49. Magnitude of E.M.F. induced in a Coil. Suppose the magnetic flux through a coil of T turns to be increased by Φ webers in t seconds due to, say, the relative movement of the coil and a magnet (Fig. 55). Since each of the lines of magnetic flux cuts * each turn, one turn can be regarded as a conductor cut by Φ webers in t seconds; hence, from expression (25), the average

---

* It is immaterial whether we consider the e.m.f. as being due to change of flux linked with a coil or due to the coil cutting or being cut by lines of flux; the result is exactly the same. The fact of the matter is that we do not know what is really happening; but we can calculate the effect by imagining the magnetic field in the form of lines of flux, some of which expand from nothing when the field is increased or collapse to nothing when the field is reduced. In so doing they may be regarded as cutting the turns of the coil, or alternatively may be regarded merely as a change in the number of flux-linkages.

e.m.f. induced in each turn is Φ/t volts. The current due to this e.m.f., by Lenz's Law, tries to prevent the increase of flux, i.e. tends to set up an opposing flux. Thus, if the magnet NS in Fig. 55 is moved towards coil

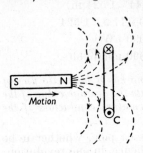

C, the flux passing from left to right through the latter is increased. The e.m.f. induced in the coil circulates a current in the direction represented by the dot and cross in Fig. 61, where—for simplicity—coil C is represented as one turn. The effect of this current is to distort the magnetic field as shown by the dotted lines, thereby tending to push the coil away from the magnet. There must therefore be an equal and opposite force tending to oppose

FIG. 61.—Distortion of magnetic field caused by induced current.

the movement of the magnet.

Owing to the fact that the induced e.m.f. circulates a current tending to oppose the increase of flux through the coil, its direction is regarded as negative; hence

$$\left.\begin{array}{c}\text{average e.m.f.}\\\text{induced in 1 turn}\end{array}\right\} = -\Phi/t \text{ volts}$$

$$= -\left\{\begin{array}{l}\text{average rate of } increase \text{ of}\\\text{flux in webers per second}\end{array}\right.$$

$$\text{and}\quad\left.\begin{array}{c}\text{average e.m.f.}\\\text{induced in coil}\end{array}\right\} = -T\Phi/t \text{ volts} \quad . \quad . \quad (25\text{A})$$

$$= -\left\{\begin{array}{l}\text{average rate of } increase \text{ of}\\\text{flux-linkages per second.}\end{array}\right.$$

Next, let us consider the case of the two coils, A and C, shown in Fig. 57. Suppose that when switch S is closed, the flux in the ring increases by Φ webers in t seconds. Then if coil A has T_1 turns,

average e.m.f. induced in A $= -T_1\Phi/t$ volts.

The minus sign signifies that this e.m.f. is acting in opposition to the e.m.f. of the battery, thereby trying to prevent the growth of the current, an effect that is dealt with in Art. 60.

If coil C is wound with T_2 turns and if all the flux produced by coil A passes through C,

average e.m.f. induced in C $= -T_2\Phi/t$ volts.

In this case the minus sign signifies that the e.m.f. circulates a current in such a direction as to tend to set up a flux in opposition to that produced by the current in coil A, thereby delaying the growth of flux in the ring.

Example 27. *A magnetic flux of* 400 *μWb passing through a coil of* 1200 *turns is reversed in* 0·1 *second. Calculate the average value of the e.m.f. induced in the coil.*

The magnetic flux has to decrease from 400 μWb to zero and then increase to 400 μWb in the reverse direction; hence the *increase* of flux in the original direction is −800 μWb.

Substituting in expression (25A), we have:

$$\text{average e.m.f. induced in coil} = -\frac{1200 \times (-800 \times 10^{-6})}{0·1}$$

$$= 9·6 \text{ V.}$$

This e.m.f. is positive because its direction is the same as the original direction of the current, at first tending to prevent the current decreasing and then tending to prevent it increasing in the reverse direction.

Summary of Important Formulae

$$\left.\begin{array}{l}\text{Average e.m.f. generated} \\ \text{in a conductor}\end{array}\right\} = \Phi/t \text{ volts } . \quad . \quad . \quad (25)$$

where Φ = flux, in webers, cut in t seconds.

$$\left.\begin{array}{l}\text{Average e.m.f. induced in} \\ \text{a coil of } T \text{ turns}\end{array}\right\} = -T\Phi/t \text{ volts } . \quad (25A)$$

where Φ = *increase* of flux, in webers, in t seconds.

EXAMPLES VI

1. Two coils, A and B, are wound on the same iron core. There are 300 turns on A and 2800 turns on B. A current of 4 amperes through A gives rise to 800 microwebers in the core. If this current be reversed in 1/50 second, find the average e.m.f.'s induced in A and B.

2. A coil of 1500 turns gives rise to a magnetic flux of 2500 μWb when carrying a certain current. If this current be reversed in one-fifth of a second, find the average e.m.f. induced in the coil.

3. A current of 8 A through a coil of 3000 turns produces a flux of 0·004 weber. If this current is reduced to 2 A in 0·1 second, calculate the average e.m.f. induced in the coil, assuming the flux to be proportional to the current. What is the direction of the induced e.m.f.?

4. A short coil of 200 turns surrounds the middle of a bar magnet. If the magnet sets up a flux of 80 μWb, find the average e.m.f. induced in the coil when the latter is removed completely from the influence of the magnet in 1/20 second.

5. A coil of 800 turns is wound on an iron core and a certain current produces a flux of 3000 μWb. When the circuit is opened, the residual flux in the iron is 1900 μWb. If this reduction of flux takes place in 0·15 sec, calculate the average value of the induced e.m.f.

6. The field winding of a 6-pole dynamo is separately-excited. The 6 coils are connected in series and each coil is wound with 2500 turns. The flux in each pole is 30 milliwebers. If the field switch is opened at such a speed that the flux falls to the residual value of 1 milliweber in $\frac{1}{3}$ sec, calculate the average value of the e.m.f. induced in the field winding.

7. An all-metal aeroplane having a wing-span of 100 feet is flying horizontally at a speed of 300 m.p.h. Calculate the e.m.f. generated between the tips of the wings, assuming the vertical component of the earth's magnetic field to be 40 μWb/m². Is it possible to measure this e.m.f.?

8. The axle of a certain motor-car is 1½ metres long. Calculate the e.m.f. generated in it when the car is travelling at 140 kilometres/hour. Assume the vertical component of the earth's magnetic field to be 40 μWb/m².

9. A wire, 20 cm long, is moved at a uniform speed of 6 metres/sec at right angles to its length and to a magnetic field. Calculate the density of the magnetic field if the e.m.f. generated in the wire is 0·4 V.

If the wire forms part of a closed circuit having a resistance of 0·1 Ω, calculate the force on the wire (a) in newtons and (b) in grams.

10. The flux through a 100-turn coil increases uniformly from zero to 300 μWb in 2 milliseconds. It remains constant at 300 μWb for the third millisecond and then decreases uniformly to zero during the fourth millisecond. Draw to scale graphs representing the variation of the flux and of the e.m.f. induced in the coil.

11. A copper disc, 30 cm in diameter, is rotated at 200 r.p.m. about a horizontal axis through its centre perpendicular to its plane. If the axis points magnetic north and south, calculate the e.m.f. between the circumference of the disc and the axis. Assume the horizontal component of the flux density due to the earth's field to be 18 μWb/m².

12. A 6-pole motor has a magnetic flux of 0·08 weber per pole and the armature is rotating at 700 r.p.m. Calculate the average e.m.f. generated per conductor.

13. A 4-pole armature is to generate an average e.m.f. per conductor of 1·4 volts, the flux per pole being 0·015 Wb. Calculate the speed at which the armature must be driven.

CHAPTER VII

MAGNETIC CIRCUIT

50. Introductory. Lines of magnetic flux form a complete closed path; for instance, in Fig. 41, the dotted lines represent the flux passing through the iron core and returning through the surrounding air space. Similarly, the dotted lines in Fig. 44 show that *any one line of flux forms a closed loop*, and that in the case of a d.c. machine, part of the line is in air and the remainder in iron. The complete closed path followed by any group of lines of magnetic flux is referred to as a *magnetic circuit*. One of the simplest forms of the magnetic circuit is indicated in Fig. 57, where the iron ring R provides the path for the magnetic flux.

51. Magnetomotive Force ; Magnetising Force. In Art. 19 it was stated that in an electric circuit an electric current is due to the existence of an electromotive force. By analogy, we may say that in a magnetic circuit the magnetic flux is due to the existence of a *magnetomotive force* (m.m.f.) caused by a current flowing through one or more turns. The value of the m.m.f. is proportional to the current and to the number of turns, and in the *rationalized* system of units, the *ampere-turn* is taken as the *unit of m.m.f.* Hence, if a current of I amperes flows through a coil of T turns, as shown in Fig. 62, the magnetomotive force is IT ampere-turns. If the magnetic circuit is homogeneous and of uniform cross-sectional area, the magnetomotive force per metre length of the magnetic circuit is termed the *magnetising force* and is represented by the symbol H. Thus if the mean length of the magnetic circuit of Fig. 62 is l metres,

$$H = IT/l \text{ ampere-turns/metre} \quad . \quad . \quad (26)$$

52. Permeability of Free Space or Magnetic Space Constant. Suppose A in Fig. 63 to represent the cross-section of a long straight conductor, situated in a vacuum and carrying a current of one ampere towards the paper; and suppose the return path of this current

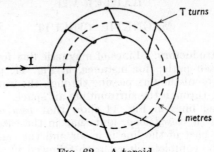

FIG. 62.—A toroid.

to be some considerable distance away from A so that the effect of the return current on the magnetic field in the vicinity of A may be neglected.   The magnetic lines

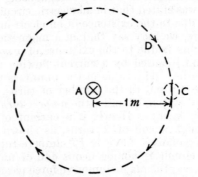

FIG. 63.—Magnetic field at 1-metre radius due to current in a long straight conductor.

of flux surrounding A will therefore be in the form of concentric circles, as already described in Art. 35, and the dotted circle D in Fig. 63 represents the path of one of these lines of flux at a radius of 1 metre.   Since conductor A and its return conductor form 1 turn, the magnetomotive force acting on path D is 1 ampere-turn; and since the length of this line of flux is 2π metres, the magnetising force, H, at a radius of 1 metre is $1/2\pi$ ampere-turn/metre.

If B is the flux density in webers/metre² in the region of line D, it follows from expression (23) that the force per metre length on a conductor C (parallel to A) carrying 1 ampere at right angles to this flux density is given by:

$$\left.\begin{array}{c}\text{Force per}\\ \text{metre length}\end{array}\right\} = B \ (\text{Wb/m}^2) \times 1 \ (\text{m}) \times 1 \ (\text{A}) = B \text{ newtons.}$$

But from the definition of the ampere given in Art. 11, this force is 2×10^{-7} newton,

$$\therefore \left.\begin{array}{c}\text{flux density at 1-m radius}\\ \text{from conductor carrying 1 A}\end{array}\right\} = B = 2 \times 10^{-7} \text{ Wb/m}^2.$$

Hence,

$$\frac{\text{flux density at C}}{\text{magnetising force at C}} = \frac{B}{H} = \frac{2 \times 10^{-7} \text{ Wb/m}^2}{1/2\pi \text{ ampere-turn/m}}$$

$$= 4\pi \times 10^{-7} \text{ M.K.S. units.}$$

The ratio B/H for the above condition is termed the *permeability of free space* or the *magnetic space constant* and is represented by the symbol μ_0. The value of this ratio is almost exactly the same whether the conductor A of Fig. 63 is assumed to be situated in a vacuum (or free space) or in air or in any other non-magnetic material.

Hence, $\mu_0 = \dfrac{B}{H}$ for a vacuum and non-magnetic materials

$$= 4\pi \times 10^{-7} \quad \ldots \ldots \ldots \ldots \quad (27)$$

$$= 12 \cdot 57 \times 10^{-7} \text{ rationalized M.K.S. units}$$

and $\left.\begin{array}{c}\text{ampere-turns/metre for}\\ \text{non-magnetic materials}\end{array}\right\} = \dfrac{B}{\mu_0} = \dfrac{B \ (\text{in Wb/m}^2)}{12 \cdot 57 \times 10^{-7}} \ (28)$

Example 28. *A coil of 200 turns is wound uniformly over a wooden ring having a mean circumference of 60 cm and a uniform cross-sectional area of 5 cm². If the*

4*

current through the coil is 4 A, calculate (a) *the magnetising force,* (b) *the flux density and* (c) *the total flux.*

(a) Mean circumference $= \dfrac{60}{100} = 0\cdot6$ m,

$\therefore$ magnetising force $= \dfrac{4 \times 200}{0\cdot6}$

$= 1333$ ampere-turns/m.

(b) From expression (27):

flux density $= \mu_0 H = 4\pi \times 10^{-7} \times 1333$

$= 0\cdot001675$ Wb/m²

$= 1675$ microwebers/m².

(c) Cross-sectional area $= \dfrac{5}{100 \times 100} = 5 \times 10^{-4}$ m²

$\therefore$ total flux $= 1675 \times 5 \times 10^{-4}$

$= 0\cdot8375 \ \mu$Wb.

Example 29. *Calculate the ampere-turns required to produce a flux of* $0\cdot015$ *weber across an airgap* $0\cdot1$ *inch long, having an effective area of 30 square inches.*

Area of airgap $= 30 \times 6\cdot45 \times 10^{-4} = 0\cdot01935$ m²,

$\therefore$ flux density $= \dfrac{0\cdot015}{0\cdot01935} = 0\cdot775$ Wb/m².

From (28),

magnetising force for gap $= \dfrac{0\cdot775}{12\cdot57 \times 10^{-7}}$

$= 617,000$ ampere-turns/m.

Length of gap $= 0\cdot1 \times 0\cdot0254 = 0\cdot00254$ m,

$\therefore$ total ampere-turns required to send flux across gap

$= 617,000 \times 0\cdot00254 = 1570$.

53. Relative Permeability. In Art. 37 it was shown that the magnetic flux inside a coil is intensified when an iron core is inserted. It follows that if the non-magnetic core of a toroid, such as that shown in Fig. 62, is replaced by an iron core, the flux produced by a given number of ampere-turns is greatly increased; and the ratio of the flux density produced in a material to the flux density produced in a vacuum (or in a non-magnetic core) by the same magnetising force is termed the *relative permeability* and is denoted by the symbol μ_r. For air, $\mu_r = 1$; but for certain nickel-iron alloys (Art. 58), it may be as high as 100,000. Graphs representing the values of μ_r are given in Fig. 67 and 68 for various qualities of iron, and it will be seen that for a given quality, the value of μ_r varies over a wide range.

From (27), B (Wb/m^2) $= \mu_0 H$ for a non-magnetic material; hence,

for a material having a relative permeability μ_r,

$$B = \mu_r \mu_0 H$$

$$\therefore \text{ absolute permeability} = B/H = \mu_r \mu_0 \quad \ldots \quad \ldots \quad (29)$$

54. Reluctance. Let us consider an iron ring having a cross-sectional area of a square metres and a mean circumference of l metres (Fig. 62), wound with T turns carrying a current I amperes;

then total flux $= \Phi =$ flux density $\times$ area $= Ba$. (30)

and m.m.f. = magnetising force $\times$ length $= Hl$ (31)

Dividing (30) by (31), we have:

$$\frac{\Phi}{\text{m.m.f.}} = \frac{Ba}{Hl} = \mu_r \mu_0 \times \frac{a}{l}$$

$$\therefore \qquad \Phi = \frac{\text{m.m.f.}}{\dfrac{l}{\mu_r \mu_0 a}} \quad \ldots \quad \ldots \quad (32)$$

This expression is similar in form to: $I = \dfrac{\text{e.m.f.}}{\rho l/a}$ for the electric circuit. The denominator, $\dfrac{l}{\mu_r \mu_0 a}$, in expression (32) is termed the *reluctance* of the magnetic circuit and is similar in form to $\rho l/a$ for the resistance of a conductor except that the absolute permeability, $\mu_r \mu_0$, for the magnetic material corresponds to the reciprocal of the resistivity, namely the conductivity of the electrical

material.   Since the m.m.f. is equal to the number of
ampere-turns acting on the magnetic circuit,

$$\therefore \quad \text{magnetic flux} = \frac{\text{no. of ampere-turns}}{\text{reluctance}} \quad . \quad . \quad (33)$$

$$\text{where reluctance} = \frac{l}{\mu_r \mu_0 a} \quad . \quad . \quad . \quad . \quad . \quad . \quad (34)$$

$$= \frac{l}{\mu_0 a} \text{ for non-magnetic materials.}$$

The symbol for reluctance is S but no name has been
attached to the unit of reluctance.

55. Comparison of the Electric and Magnetic Circuits.
It is helpful to tabulate side by side the various electric
and magnetic quantities and their relationships, thus:

Electric circuit		Magnetic circuit	
Quantity	Unit	Quantity	Unit
E.M.F. . .	volt	M.M.F. . .	ampere-turn
		Magnetising force	amp-turn/m
Current . .	ampere	Magnetic flux .	weber
Current density	ampere/m²	Magnetic flux density	weber/m²
Resistance	ohm	Reluctance	—
$\left(= \rho \cdot \dfrac{l}{a} \right)$		$\left(= \dfrac{1}{\mu_r \mu_0} \cdot \dfrac{l}{a} \right)$	
Current = e.m.f./resistance		Flux = m.m.f./reluctance	

One important difference between the electric and
magnetic circuits is the fact that energy must be supplied
to *maintain* the flow of electricity in a circuit, whereas
the magnetic flux, once it is set up, does not require
any further supply of energy.   For instance, once the
flux produced by a current in a solenoid has attained its
maximum value, the energy subsequently absorbed by
that solenoid is all dissipated as heat due to the resistance
of the winding.

56. Composite Magnetic Circuit. Suppose a magnetic circuit to consist of two specimens of iron, A and B, arranged as in Fig. 64. If l_1 and l_2 are the mean lengths in metres of the magnetic circuits of A and B respectively,

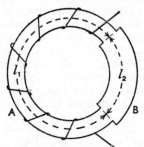

FIG. 64.—Composite magnetic circuit.

a_1 and a_2 their cross-sectional areas in square metres and μ_1 and μ_2 their relative permeabilities,

then reluctance of $A = \dfrac{l_1}{\mu_1 \mu_0 a_1}$

and reluctance of $B = \dfrac{l_2}{\mu_2 \mu_0 a_2}$.

Since A and B are magnetically in series, i.e since the same flux passes through the two specimens, assuming the magnetic leakage to be negligible,

total reluctance of magnetic circuit $= \dfrac{l_1}{\mu_1 \mu_0 a_1} + \dfrac{l_2}{\mu_2 \mu_0 a_2}$

and total flux $= \Phi = \dfrac{\text{m.m.f. of coil}}{\text{total reluctance}}$

$$= \dfrac{I\,T}{\dfrac{l_1}{\mu_1 \mu_0 a_1} + \dfrac{l_2}{\mu_2 \mu_0 a_2}} \quad . \quad . \quad . \quad . \quad (35)$$

57. Determination of the Magnetisation Curve for an Iron Ring. (a) *By means of a Ballistic Galvanometer.*

Fig. 65 shows an iron ring of uniform cross-section. It is uniformly wound with a coil P which is connected through a reversing switch RS, a variable resistance R_1 and an ammeter A to a battery B. Another coil S is connected through a resistance R to a ballistic galvanometer BG. The latter consists merely of a coil suspended or pivoted so that it can move between the poles of a permanent magnet, but the coil is wound on a non-metallic former, such as wood, so that there is very little damping when the coil has a high resistance in series. It is usual to provide a key or switch K, which, when closed, short-circuits the galvanometer, thereby enabling the e.m.f. induced in the moving-coil by its

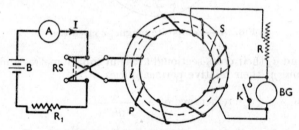

FIG. 65.—Measurement of relationship between flux density and ampere-turns/metre.

movement in the magnetic field to circulate enough current to prevent any oscillation.

The theory of the ballistic galvanometer is well beyond the scope of this volume and it will therefore be necessary to assume that the first deflection or "throw" of the ballistic galvanometer is proportional to the quantity of electricity through the galvanometer, so long as the time taken for this charge to flow is short compared with the time of one oscillation.

When the current through P is reversed by means of RS, the reversal of the flux induces an e.m.f. in S and sends a current through BG. But this current is of very short duration since it ceases immediately the flux has reached its full value in the reversed direction.

If θ=first deflection of the galvanometer when a current of I amperes through P is reversed

and k=ballistic constant of the galvanometer

=quantity of electricity in coulombs per unit of first deflection,

$\therefore$ $\left. \begin{array}{l} \text{quantity of electricity} \\ \text{through galvanometer} \end{array} \right\} = k\theta$ coulombs   (36)

If Φ=flux produced in ring by I amperes through P

and t=time, in seconds, of reversal of flux,

then   change of flux=2Φ webers

and   rate of change of flux=$2\Phi/t$ webers per second.

If T_s=no. of turns on coil S,

$$\text{average e.m.f. induced in S} = \frac{2\Phi}{t} \times T_s \text{ volts.}$$

If R=total resistance of the secondary circuit,

average current through BG

$$= \frac{2\Phi \times T_s}{t \times R} \text{ amperes}$$

and quantity of electricity through BG

$$= \text{average current} \times \text{time}$$

$$= \frac{2\Phi T_s \times t}{tR} = \frac{2\Phi T_s}{R} \text{ coulombs} \quad (37)$$

Equating (36) and (37), we have:

$$k\theta = \frac{2\Phi T_s}{R}$$

$\therefore$ $$\Phi = \frac{k\theta R}{2T_s} \text{ webers.}$$

If a=cross-sectional area of core in square metres,

flux density in core=$B=\Phi/a$

$$= \frac{k\theta R}{2aT_s} \text{ webers/m}^2.$$

If T_p=no. of turns on coil P

and l=mean circumference of ring in metres,

then magnetising force=$H=IT_p/l$ ampere-turns/metre.

This test is repeated with different values of the current; and from the data thus obtained we can plot the flux density against the magnetising force.

(b) *By means of a Fluxmeter.* A fluxmeter is a special type of ballistic galvanometer. The moving system is either pivoted or suspended by a silk fibre, and the current is led into and out of the coil by fine wires or ligaments so arranged as to exert negligible control over the position of the moving coil. The pointer movement is rendered dead-beat (Art. 139) by electromagnetic damping.

The fluxmeter is connected directly across the secondary coil S in Fig. 65. When the current through coil P is reversed, the deflection on the fluxmeter is proportional to the change of flux and to the number of turns on S, i.e. to the change of flux-linkages with coil S. Thus, if the flux is reversed from Φ to $-\Phi$ and if T_s is the number of turns on S,

$$\left. \begin{array}{c} \text{change of flux-linkages} \\ \text{with coil S} \end{array} \right\} = \left\{ \begin{array}{c} \text{change of flux} \times \\ \text{no. of turns on S} \end{array} \right.$$

$$=2\Phi T_s \quad . \quad . \quad . \quad (38)$$

If θ=corresponding deflection on fluxmeter

and c=fluxmeter constant

=no. of weber-turns per unit of scale deflection,

then   change of flux-linkages with S=$c\theta$. . (39)

Equating (38) and (39), we have:

$$2\Phi T_s=c\theta$$

∴ $$\Phi=\frac{c\theta}{2T_s} \text{ webers.}$$

The values of the flux density, etc., can then be calculated exactly as described for the preceding method.

Curves showing the relationship between the flux

density and the magnetising force obtained for different
qualities of iron by one of the above methods are shown
in Fig. 66; and the curves in Fig. 67 and 68 represent
the corresponding values of the relative permeability
plotted against the magnetising force and the flux
density respectively. In actual practice it is found that
the magnetic property of different specimens of iron of
the same chemical composition may vary considerably,

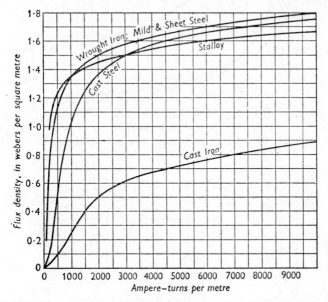

FIG. 66.—Variation of flux density with ampere-turns/metre
for cast steel, etc.

being very dependent upon heat and mechanical treat-
ments. The data for mild steel, wrought iron and the
sheet steel usually employed for the armature cores of
d.c. machines are so similar that they can be represented
by a common graph. "Stalloy" is an alloy of iron and
silicon commonly used in the construction of transformers
and a.c. machines.

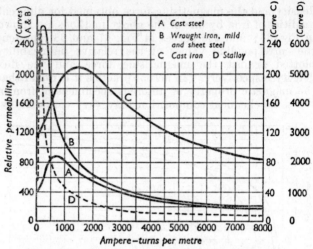

FIG. 67.—Variation of relative permeability with
ampere-turns/metre for cast steel, etc.

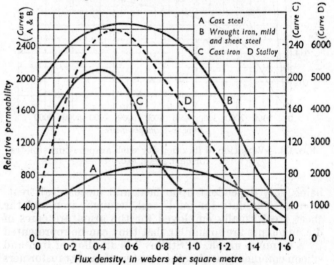

FIG. 68.—Variation of relative permeability with flux
density for cast steel, etc.

Example 30. *A mild-steel ring having a cross-sectional area of 5 cm² and a mean circumference of 40 cm has a coil of 200 turns wound uniformly around it. Calculate the current required to produce a flux of 800 microwebers in the ring.*

$$\text{Flux density in ring} = \frac{800 \times 10^{-6}}{5 \times 10^{-4}} = 1 \cdot 6 \text{ Wb/m}^2.$$

From Fig. 66, the number of ampere-turns/metre to produce a flux density of $1 \cdot 6$ Wb/m² in mild steel = 3500.

$\therefore$ total ampere-turns required = $3500 \times 0 \cdot 4 = 1400$

and $\text{magnetising current} = \dfrac{1400}{200} = 7$ A.

Example 31. *If the mild-steel ring of Example 30 is cut radially at diametrically opposite points and a sheet of*

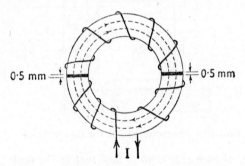

0·5 mm   0·5 mm

I

Fig. 69.—Magnetic circuit for Example 31.

brass 0·5 mm thick inserted in each gap, as indicated in Fig. 69, find the ampere-turns required to produce a flux density of 1·6 Wb/m². Assume that there is no magnetic leakage or fringing, i.e. that all the flux passes round the iron core and directly across the brass strips.

From Example 30, the number of ampere-turns required for the steel is 1400.

From expression (28), the ampere-turns/metre for the non-magnetic gaps $=\dfrac{1\cdot6}{4\pi\times10^{-7}}=1\cdot274\times10^6$

$\therefore$ total ampere-turns for the 2 gaps $\Big\}=1\cdot274\times10^6\times0\cdot001$

$=1274.$

Hence,   total ampere-turns $=1400+1274=2674.$

Example 32. *A core is built of a number of steel laminations stamped out as shown in Fig. 70, in which the lower figure represents a sectional plan at XX. The*

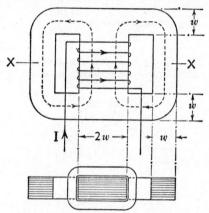

Fig. 70.—Magnetic circuit for Example 32.

width, w, of each side limb is half that of the centre limb. The iron in the latter has a cross-sectional area of 9 cm² and is wound with 150 turns of insulated wire. If the mean length of the flux path is 35 cm, find the current required to set up a flux of 1·2 milliwebers in the centre limb.

A current in the direction indicated by the arrowheads on the conductors in Fig. 70 produces a magnetic flux which is upwards in the centre limb. This flux divides, one half returning via one outer limb and the other half via the other limb, as represented by the dotted lines. Since the area of each outer limb is half that of the centre limb, we may assume the flux density to be the same in every part of the magnetic circuit.

Hence, flux density $= \dfrac{\text{total flux in centre limb}}{\text{cross-sectional area of centre limb}}$

$$= \frac{0 \cdot 0012}{0 \cdot 0009} = 1 \cdot 333 \text{ Wb/m}^2.$$

From Fig. 66 the ampere-turns/m for this flux density in sheet steel $= 900$,

$\therefore$ total ampere-turns required $= 900 \times 0 \cdot 35 = 315$

and   magnetising current $= \dfrac{315}{150} = 2 \cdot 1$ A.

It will be noticed that the flux paths in the side limbs are in parallel and that the ampere-turns which send the flux through one side limb must be responsible for sending flux through the other side limb. This is a case where it may be helpful to compare the magnetic circuit of Fig. 70 with the equivalent electric circuit shown in Fig. 71. The

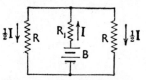

FIG. 71.—Electric circuit equivalent to Fig. 70.

current I from battery B divides equally through the two equal resistances R, R; and the p.d. across the right-hand R is exactly the same p.d. as that which is across the left-hand R.

If R_1 be the resistance of the middle portion of the circuit, it follows from Kirchhoff's Second Law that for both the right- and the left-hand loops

total e.m.f. of battery $= I \times R_1 + \tfrac{1}{2}I \times R.$

Similarly, in the magnetic circuit of Fig. 70, the total ampere-turns are those required to send flux round either of the paths shown dotted.

Example 33. *The magnetic circuit of a 2-pole dynamo is shown in Fig. 72. The armature A is of the smooth-*

*core type, i.e. it has no slots, the armature winding being on
the surface.   Each gap G has a radial length of 0·4 cm
and a cross-sectional area of 60 cm². Each pole core P
has a radial length of 7 cm and a cross-sectional area of
50 cm² and is made of wrought iron.   The yoke Y is of
cast steel, having a cross-sectional area of 15 cm².   The
estimated mean length of the flux paths in the yoke is 42 cm
and that in the armature is 10 cm.   The cross-sectional*

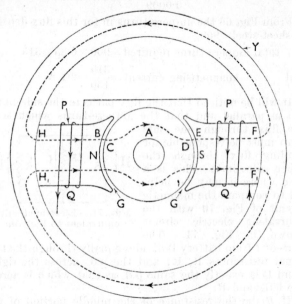

FIG. 72.—Magnetic circuit for Example 33.

*area of each side of the armature core is 12 cm².   Find the
number of turns to be wound on each pole in order that 3A
may set up a flux of 3 milliwebers per pole.   Assume the
flux in the pole cores and yoke to be the same as that in the
armature.*

The simplest procedure is to consider the path taken
by any one line of flux, follow that line round the whole

of its magnetic circuit and calculate the ampere-turns required for each component of that circuit. For instance, let us start at point B in Fig. 72 and follow line BCDEFHB, then:

total ampere-turns $= \begin{cases} \text{sum of ampere-turns for BC, CD,} \\ \text{DE, EF, FH, and HB.} \end{cases}$

It is evident from Fig. 72 that the same ampere-turns will also set up flux round loop H_1F_1.

Path BC. Flux density in gap $= \dfrac{0 \cdot 003}{0 \cdot 006} = 0 \cdot 5$ Wb/m^2.

From expression (28),

ampere-turns/metre for gap $= \dfrac{0 \cdot 5 \times 10^7}{12 \cdot 57} = 0 \cdot 398 \times 10^6$

∴ ampere-turns to send flux from B to C $\Big\}$ $= 0 \cdot 398 \times 10^6 \times 0 \cdot 4 \times 10^{-2}$

$= 1592.$

Path CD. Since the flux divides equally between the two sides of the core,

flux density in armature $= \dfrac{0 \cdot 003}{0 \cdot 0012 \times 2} = 1 \cdot 25$ Wb/m^2.

From graph for sheet steel in Fig. 66,

ampere-turns/m $= 700$

∴ ampere-turns to send flux from C to D $\Big\}$ $= 700 \times 0 \cdot 1 = 70.$

Path DE. No. of ampere-turns required to send the flux from D to E is the same as that for path BC, namely, 1592.

Path EF. Flux density in pole core

$$= \dfrac{0 \cdot 003}{0 \cdot 005} = 0 \cdot 6 \text{ Wb/m}^2.$$

From graph for wrought iron in Fig. 66,

ampere-turns/m $= 200$

∴ ampere-turns to send flux from E to F $\Big\}$ $= 200 \times 0 \cdot 07 = 14.$

Path FH. Since the flux divides equally between the upper and lower yokes,

$$\text{flux density in yoke} = \frac{0{\cdot}003}{0{\cdot}0015 \times 2} = 1{\cdot}0 \text{ Wb/m}^2.$$

From graph for cast steel in Fig. 66,

$$\text{ampere-turns/m} = 900$$

$$\therefore \left.\begin{array}{l}\text{ampere-turns to send flux} \\ \text{from F to H}\end{array}\right\} = 900 \times 0{\cdot}42 = 378.$$

Path HB. No. of ampere-turns required to send the flux from H to B is the same as that for path EF, namely 14.

Hence, total ampere-turns for the whole magnetic circuit

$$= 1592 + 70 + 1592 + 14 + 378 + 14 = 3660.$$

The above calculations can be conveniently tabulated thus:

Components of magnetic circuit	Total area (m²)	Total length (m)	Flux density (Wb/m²)	Ampere-turns/m	Total ampere-turns
Airgaps .	0·006	0·008	0·5	398,000	3184
Armature .	0·0024	0·1	1·25	700	70
Pole cores	0·005	0·14	0·6	200	28
Yoke . .	0·003	0·42	1·0	900	378

Total ampere-turns for whole magnetic circuit $= 3660$

Since the current is to be 3 A,

total no. of turns on coils QQ $= 3660/3 = 1220$.

These can be arranged as 610 turns on each pole core.

58. Hysteresis. If we take a closed iron ring which has been completely demagnetised * and measure the flux density with increasing values of the magnetising

* The simplest method of demagnetising is to reverse the magnetising current a large number of times, the maximum value of the current at each reversal being reduced until it is ultimately zero.

force, the relationship between the two quantities is represented by curve OAC in Fig. 73. If the magnetising force is then reduced, the flux density follows curve CD; and when the magnetising force has been reduced to zero, the flux density remaining in the iron is OD and is referred to as the *remanent flux density*.

If the magnetising force is then increased in the reverse direction, the flux density decreases, until at some value OE the flux has been reduced to zero. The magnetising

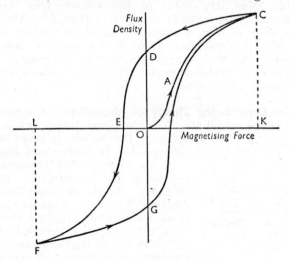

FIG. 73.—Hysteresis loop.

force OE required to wipe out the residual magnetism is termed the *coercive force*. Further increase of the magnetising force causes the flux density to grow in the reverse direction as represented by curve EF. If the reversed magnetising force OL is adjusted to the same value as the maximum magnetising force OK in the initial direction, the final flux density LF is the same as KC.

If the magnetising force is varied backwards from OL to OK, the flux density follows a curve FGC similar to curve CDEF, and the closed figure CDEFGC is termed the *hysteresis loop*.

It is a remarkable fact that for practically every quality of magnetic material, ranging from the hardest of steels, such as those used in the construction of permanent magnets, to the most easily magnetisable materials, such as nickel-iron alloys, the ratio of the residual flux density OD to the maximum flux density KC usually lies between about 0·6 and 0·75. On the other hand, the value of the *coercive force* varies enormously for different materials. Thus, for "Alnico" (an alloy of iron, aluminium, nickel and cobalt used largely for permanent magnets) the coercive force is about 60,000 ampere-turns/metre; whereas for "Mumetal" (nickel, iron and copper), the value is about 3 ampere-turns/metre.

59. Current-ring Theory of Magnetism.

A question frequently asked is: Why does iron retain any magnetism? One answer is based on a theory—due to Weber and Ewing—which assumes that the iron is composed of innumerable little magnets. When the iron is not magnetised, these magnets form small self-contained groups or circuits, somewhat as indicated by the arrows in Fig. 74 (a), the arrowheads representing N poles. When the specimen is magnetised, for instance by being placed inside a solenoid carrying a current, these little magnets are assumed to align themselves as in Fig. 74 (b); and the tenacity with which they tend to retain any particular arrangement is supposed to explain the hysteresis effect.

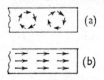

FIG. 74. — Illustrating a theory of magnetism.

Though this theory can be made to account for a number of magnetic phenomena, it has little—if any—justification in fact and it does not attempt to explain the initial magnetism of the molecule. A much more helpful theory is that originally suggested by Ampère and extended by Ewing and Evershed. It is impossible to go fully into this theory; but briefly, each atom of the iron is a tiny electromagnet, the magnetism being produced by the rotation of electrons (i.e. negative charges of electricity) around the nucleus of the atom at extremely high speed. Since a current in a conductor consists of moving electrons (Art. 69), the electrons revolving around the nucleus of the atom may be regarded as forming current-rings in the iron.

When the iron is not magnetised, these current-rings are arranged in small self-contained stable groups, each group giving rise to a local magnetic flux which acts as a magnetic bond for the group but which has no influence outside that group—somewhat similar to the flux in the iron ring of Fig. 65.

If the iron is placed in a solenoid carrying a current, the current-rings in the iron behave like coils carrying current in a magnetic field and turn round so that their axes point more or less in the direction of the magnetic field due to the solenoid. When the current in the solenoid is reduced to zero, the current-rings in the iron tend to remain in the new position, that is, with their axes pointing more or less in the same direction. Consequently, the remanent flux is maintained by the magnetising effect of these current-rings inside the iron. The stronger the magnetising effect applied by the solenoid, the more completely will the axes of the current-rings in the iron be pointing in the same direction and the greater is the remanent flux in the iron.

It will thus be seen that the permanent magnet may be regarded as a special case of an electromagnet; that is, instead of the flux being produced by current passing round the magnet, it is produced by a very large number of minute electrons circulating around the atoms of which the iron is composed.

Summary of Important Formulae

Magnetomotive force $= F = IT$ ampere-turns.

Magnetising force $= H = IT/l$ ampere-turns/metre (26)

Permeability of free space or magnetic space constant $\Big\} = \mu_0 = \begin{cases} B/H \text{ for vacuum} \\ \text{or non-magnetic} \\ \text{materials} \end{cases}$

$$= 4\pi \times 10^{-7} \text{ M.K.S. units} \quad . \quad (27)$$

$$\left.\begin{array}{c}\text{Ampere-turns/metre for}\\ \text{non-magnetic materials}\end{array}\right\} = \frac{B \text{ (in Wb/m}^2)}{4\pi \times 10^{-7}} \quad . \quad (28)$$

$$\text{Absolute permeability} = B/H = \mu_r\mu_0 \quad . \quad . \quad (29)$$

$$\text{Magnetic flux} = \Phi = \frac{IT}{\text{reluctance}} \quad . \quad (33)$$

$$\text{Reluctance} = S = \frac{l}{\mu_r\mu_0 a} \quad . \quad . \quad . \quad (34)$$

For a composite magnetic circuit,

$$\Phi = \frac{IT}{\dfrac{l_1}{\mu_1\mu_0 a_1} + \dfrac{l_2}{\mu_2\mu_0 a_2} +} \quad . \quad . \quad (35)$$

EXAMPLES VII

Data of B–H, when not given in question, should be taken from Fig. 66.

1 A long straight conductor, situated in air, is carrying a current of 200 A, the return conductor being some distance away. Calculate (a) the magnetising force and (b) the flux density at a radius of 10 cm.

2. The flux density at a distance of 6 cm from the centre of a long straight conductor C is 0.02 Wb/m^2. Assuming the return conductor to be some distance away, calculate the current in conductor C.

3. Two straight parallel conductors, situated in air and spaced 10 cm between centres, carry currents of 1000 A in opposite directions. Calculate (a) the magnetising force and (b) the flux density at points on a straight line joining the two conductors (i) midway between the conductors and (ii) 3 cm from one conductor.

Also, calculate the magnetising force and the flux density at the same two points if the conductors are each carrying 1000 A in the same direction.

4. The airgap in a certain magnetic circuit is 0.12 cm long and 25 cm^2 in cross-section. Calculate (a) the reluctance of the gap, (b) the ampere-turns required to send a flux of 800 μWb across the gap and (c) the magnetising force in the gap.

5. The airgap in a certain magnetic circuit is 0.06 inch long and has a cross-sectional area of 5 in^2. If there are 600 ampere-turns available to send the flux across this gap, calculate (a) the magnetising force and (b) the total flux.

6. An iron magnetic circuit has a uniform cross-sectional area of 4 cm^2 and a length of 70 cm. For a flux density of 1.5 Wb/m^2, calculate (a) the reluctance of the circuit and (b) the total ampere-turns required. Assume the value of the relative permeability for this flux density to be 2500.

7. An iron magnetic circuit has a uniform cross-section of 7·5 cm² and a length of 20 cm. A coil of 100 turns is wound uniformly over the circuit. With a current of 1 A the total flux is 450 μWb, and with 3 A the flux is 900 μWb. Calculate the values of (a) the magnetising force and (b) the relative permeability of the iron for each value of flux.

8. In a certain magnetic circuit having a length of 25 in and a cross-section of 0·5 in², an m.m.f. of 300 ampere-turns produces a flux of 400 μWb. Calculate (a) the reluctance of the magnetic circuit and (b) the relative permeability of the core.

9. A coil is wound uniformly with 300 turns over an iron ring having a mean circumference of 40 cm and a cross-section of 5 cm². If the coil has a resistance of 8 Ω and is connected across a 20-V d.c. supply, calculate (a) the m.m.f. of the coil, (b) the magnetising force, (c) the total flux and (d) the reluctance of the ring. Assume the value of the relative permeability to be 900.

10. A ring specimen of iron has a cross-sectional area of 5 cm² and a mean circumference of 40 cm. It is uniformly wound with two coils, A and B, having 100 and 300 turns respectively. Coil B is connected to a ballistic galvanometer having a constant of 2×10^{-8} coulomb per division and the total resistance of the secondary circuit is 0·15 MΩ. When a current of 2·5 A through coil A is reversed, the first deflection of the galvanometer is 150 divisions. Calculate (a) the flux density in the ring and (b) the corresponding value of the relative permeability.

11. A coil P of 200 turns is wound uniformly on an iron ring having a cross-sectional area of 4 cm² and a mean diameter of 30 cm. Another coil Q of 20 turns, wound on the ring, is connected to a fluxmeter having a constant of 150 microweber-turns per division. When a current of 1·5 A through P is reversed, the fluxmeter deflection is 78 divisions. Calculate (a) the flux density in the ring and (b) the corresponding value of the relative permeability.

12. A wooden ring with a mean circumference of 80 cm and a cross-sectional area of 6 cm² is uniformly wound with a coil P of 400 turns. Another coil Q of 800 turns, wound on the ring, is connected to a fluxmeter having a constant of 300 microweber-turns per division. Calculate the fluxmeter deflection when a current of 5 A through P is reversed.

13. A cast-steel ring having a cross-sectional area of 4 cm² and a mean diameter of 15 cm is wound with 60 turns. Calculate the current required to set up a flux of 500 μWb.

14. A cast-iron ring has a mean diameter of 10 inch and a cross-sectional area of 2 in². It is wound with 140 turns of wire. Calculate the total flux due to a current of 6 A.

15. An iron ring having a mean circumference of 30 cm and a cross-sectional area of 4 cm² is wound with a coil of 80 turns. From the following data calculate the current required to set up a flux of 520 μWb:

| Flux density, Wb/m² | . | 1·0 | 1·2 | 1·4 |
| Ampere-turns/metre | . | 350 | 600 | 1250 |

16. If a radial saw-cut, 0·7 mm wide, is made in the ring of Q. 15, calculate the current required to set up the same flux of 520 μWb. Neglect any magnetic leakage and fringing.

17. An iron ring has internal and external diameters of 10 and 12 cm respectively and the axial thickness of the ring is 1·5 cm. The ring is uniformly wound with 300 turns. Calculate the current required to set up a flux of 200 μWb, given the following data:

Flux density, Wb/m²	1·2	1·3	1·4	1·5
Relative permeability	2000	1560	1150	750

If a radial gap, 0·3 mm wide, is made in the ring, calculate (a) the current required to maintain the same flux of 200 μWb and (b) the corresponding reluctance of the magnetic circuit.

18. A U-shaped wrought-iron electromagnet has an armature of the same material across the ends, leaving an airgap of 0·15 mm between each end and the armature. The cross-sectional area of the core and armature is 6 cm² and the total length of iron path is 50 cm. The electromagnet is wound with 300 turns. Calculate the current required to set up a flux of 750 μWb.

19. One portion of a wrought-iron ring has a cross-sectional area of 4 cm² and an effective length of 20 cm, the corresponding values for the remainder of the ring being 3 cm² and 12 cm respectively. The ring is wound with 150 turns. Calculate the current required to set up a flux of 480 μWb.

20. The two halves of a ring of uniform cross-section consist of cast iron and cast steel respectively. The cross-sectional area is 3·5 cm² and the mean circumference of the ring is 60 cm. The butt-joints between the two halves are equivalent to a single radial airgap 0·2 mm wide. Calculate the ampere-turns necessary to set up a flux of 200 μWb.

21. A magnetic system is made of wrought iron arranged as in Fig. A. The centre limb has a cross-sectional area of 6 cm² and each of the outer limbs has a cross-sectional area of 4 cm². Each airgap has an area of 4 cm² and a length of 0·2 cm. If the coil is wound with 500 turns, calculate the current required to set up a flux of 900 μWb in the centre limb, assuming no magnetic leakage. The mean lengths of the various magnetic paths are indicated on the diagram.

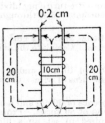

Fig. A.

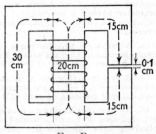

Fig. B.

22. A cast-iron magnetic core has the dimensions shown in Fig. B. There is an airgap 0·1 cm long in one limb, and a coil of 200 turns is wound on the centre limb. The area of each side limb is 10 cm² and that of the centre limb is 13 cm². Calculate the exciting current required to set up a flux density of 0·2 Wb/m² in the airgap. Neglect any leakage and fringing of the flux.

23. The magnetic circuit of a 4-pole machine has the following dimensions:

Area of airgap, 130 cm^2
Effective length of gap, 0·3 cm
Cross-sectional area of armature core, 40 cm^2
Mean length of path of flux in armature, 12 cm
Cross-sectional area of pole core, 80 cm^2
Radial length of pole core, 10 cm
Cross-sectional area of yoke, 45 cm^2
Mean length of path of flux in yoke, 33 cm
Number of turns wound on each pole core, 1500.

The yoke and pole cores are of cast steel.
Calculate the current required to set up a flux of 0·01 weber, neglecting the effect of magnetic leakage and of the armature slots.

CHAPTER VIII

INDUCTANCE IN A D.C. CIRCUIT

60. Inductive and Non-inductive Circuits. Let us consider what happens when a coil C (Fig. 75) and a resistor R, connected in parallel, are switched across a battery B. C consists of a large number of turns wound on an iron core D (or it may be the field winding of a dynamo or motor), and R may be an element of an

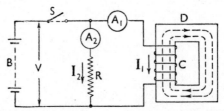

FIG. 75.—Inductive and non-inductive circuits.

electric heater connected in series with a *centre-zero* ammeter A_2.

When switch S is closed it is found that the current I_2 through R increases instantly to its final value, whereas the current i_1 * through C takes an appreciable time to grow—as indicated in Fig. 76. The final value, I_1, is equal to $\dfrac{\text{battery voltage V}}{\text{resistance of coil C}}$. In Fig. 76, I_2 has been shown a little larger than I_1, but this is of no importance.

When S is opened, current through C decreases comparatively slowly, but the current through R instantly reverses its direction and becomes the same current as i_1; in other words, the current of C is circulating round R.

* A small letter is used to denote a quantity that is varying from instant to instant.

Let us now consider the reason for the difference in the behaviour of the currents in C and R.

The growth of current in C is accompanied by an increase of flux—shown dotted—in the iron core D. But it has been pointed out in Art. 47 that any change in the flux linked with a coil is accompanied by an e.m.f. induced in that coil, the direction of which—according to Lenz's Law—is always such as to oppose the change responsible for inducing the e.m.f., namely the growth of current in C. In other words, the induced e.m.f. is a back e.m.f. and is acting in opposition to the current and, therefore, to the applied voltage.

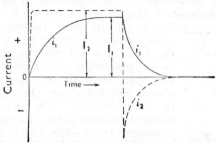

Fig. 76.—Variation of switch-on and switch-off currents.

In circuit R, the flux is so small that its back e.m.f. is negligible.

When switch S is opened, the currents in both C and R tend to decrease; but any decrease of i_1 is accompanied by a decrease of flux in D and therefore by an e.m.f. induced in C in such a direction as to oppose the decrease of i_1. Consequently the induced e.m.f. is now acting in the same direction as the current. But it is evident from Fig. 75 that after S has been opened, the only return path for C's current is that via R; hence the reason why i_1 and i_2 are now one and the same current.

If the experiment is repeated without R it is found that the growth of i_1 is unaffected; but when S is opened there is considerable arcing at the switch due to the maintenance of the current across the gap by the e.m.f. induced in C. The more quickly S is opened, the

5

more rapidly does the flux in D have to collapse and the greater is the e.m.f. induced in C. This is the reason why it is dangerous to break quickly the full excitation of an electromagnet such as the field winding of a d.c. machine. The field circuit of a machine arranged for separate excitation (Art. 125 and 136) should be controlled by a special switch which inserts a suitable resistance in parallel with the field winding before disconnecting the supply.

Any circuit in which a change of current is accompanied by a change of flux, and therefore by an induced e.m.f., is said to be *inductive* or to possess *self-inductance* or merely *inductance*. It is impossible to have a perfectly *non-inductive* circuit, i.e. a circuit in which no

FIG. 77.—Non-inductive coil.

flux is set up by a current; but for most purposes a circuit which is not in the form of a coil may be regarded as being practically non-inductive—even the open helix of an electric fire is almost non-inductive. In cases where the inductance has to be reduced to the smallest possible value—for instance, in resistance boxes—the wire is bent back on itself, as shown in Fig. 77, so that the magnetising effect of one conductor is neutralised by that of the adjacent conductor. The wire can then be coiled round an insulator S without increasing the inductance.

61. Unit of Inductance. The unit of inductance is termed the *henry*, in commemoration of a famous American physicist, Joseph Henry (1797–1878), who, quite independently, discovered electromagnetic induction within a year after it had been discovered in this country by Michael Faraday in 1831. *A circuit has an inductance of 1 henry (or 1 H) if an e.m.f. of 1 volt is induced in the circuit when the current changes at the rate of 1 ampere per second.* If either the inductance or the rate of change of current be doubled, the induced e.m.f. is doubled. Hence we may generalise by saying that if a circuit has an inductance of L henrys and if the current *increases* at a uniform rate from i_1 to i_2 amperes in t seconds :

average rate of increase of current $\Big\} = \dfrac{i_2 - i_1}{t}$ amperes/second,

and average induced e.m.f. $\Big\} = -L \times$ rate of increase of current

$$= -L \times \frac{i_2 - i_1}{t} \text{ volts} \quad . \quad . \quad (40)$$

The minus sign indicates that the direction of the induced e.m.f. is opposite to that of the current increase.

Example 34. *If the current through a coil having an inductance of 0·5 henry is reduced from 5 A to 2 A in 0·05 second, calculate the mean value of the e.m.f. induced in the coil.*

Average rate of *increase* of current

$$= \frac{2 - 5}{0 \cdot 05} = -60 \text{ amperes/second}$$

From (40), average e.m.f. induced in coil

$$= -0 \cdot 5 \times (-60) = 30 \text{ V.}$$

The direction of the induced e.m.f. is the same as that of the current, opposing its decrease.

62. Inductance in Terms of Flux-linkages per Ampere. Suppose a current of I amperes through a coil of T turns to produce a flux of Φ webers, and suppose the corresponding inductance of the coil to be L henrys.

If this current be reversed to $-I$ amperes in t seconds, the change of current is $2I$, and

average e.m.f. induced in coil $= L \times \dfrac{2I}{t}$ volts . (41)

The sign is positive because the e.m.f. is acting in the direction of the original current, at first trying to prevent the current decreasing to zero and then opposing its growth in the reverse direction.

In Art. 49 it was explained that the e.m.f., in volts, induced in 1 turn = rate of change of flux in webers/second.

Since the flux changes from Φ to $-\Phi$ in t seconds

$\therefore$ average e.m.f. induced in 1 turn $= \dfrac{2\Phi}{t}$ volts

and average e.m.f. induced in coil $= T \times$ e.m.f. per turn

$$= \frac{2\Phi T}{t} \text{ volts . (42)}$$

Equating expressions (41) and (42) we have:

$$L \times \frac{2I}{t} = \frac{2\Phi T}{t}$$

$$\therefore \qquad L = \frac{2\Phi T}{2I} \text{ henrys}$$

$$= \frac{\text{change of flux-linkages}}{\text{change of current}} \quad . \quad (43)$$

The term "flux-linkages" merely means the product of the flux in webers and the number of turns through which that flux passes or with which the flux is linked. Thus if a coil of 20 turns has a flux of 0·1 weber through it, the flux-linkages $= 0·1 \times 20$ weber-turns.

Expression (43) gives us an alternative method of defining the unit of inductance, namely: *A coil possesses an inductance of 1 henry when a change of 1 ampere produces a change of 1 weber-turn.*

Example 35. *A coil of 800 turns is wound on a wooden former and a current of 5 A through the coil produces a magnetic flux of 200 μWb. Calculate (a) the inductance of the coil and (b) the average value of the e.m.f. induced in the coil when the current is reversed in 0·2 second.*

(a) Since the relative permeability of wood is unity, the flux is proportional to the current.   Hence, from (43), we have:

$$\text{inductance} = \frac{200 \times 10^{-6} \times 800}{5} = 0·032 \text{ H.}$$

(b) From (41), we have:

$$\left.\begin{array}{l}\text{average e.m.f.} \\ \text{induced in coil}\end{array}\right\} = 0·032 \times \frac{5 \times 2}{0·2} = 1·6 \text{ V,}$$

or alternatively, from (42), we have:

$$\left.\begin{array}{l}\text{average e.m.f.}\\\text{induced in coil}\end{array}\right\} = \frac{2 \times 200 \times 10^{-6} \times 800}{0 \cdot 2} = 1 \cdot 6 \text{ V.}$$

63. Factors determining the Inductance of a Coil.
Let us first consider a coil uniformly wound on a *non-magnetic* ring of uniform section—similar to that of Fig. 62. From expression (27), it follows that the flux density, in webers/m², in such a ring is $4\pi \times 10^{-7} \times$ the ampere-turns/m. Consequently if l be the length of the magnetic circuit in meters and a its cross-sectional area, in square metres, then for a coil of T turns with a current I amperes:

$$\text{number of ampere-turns/m} = \frac{IT}{l}$$

and   total flux $= \Phi =$ flux density $\times a$

$$= 4\pi \times 10^{-7} \times \frac{IT}{l} \times a$$

Substituting for Φ in expression (43) we have:

$$\text{inductance} = L = 4\pi \times 10^{-7} \times \frac{aT^2}{l} \text{ henrys} \quad . \quad (44)$$

Hence the inductance is proportional to the square of the number of turns and to the sectional area, and inversely proportional to the length of the magnetic circuit.

If the coil is wound on a closed iron circuit, such as a ring, the problem of defining the inductance of such a coil becomes involved due to the fact that the variation of flux is no longer proportional to the variation of current. Suppose the relationship between the magnetic flux and the magnetising current to be as shown in Fig. 78; then if the iron has initially no residual magnetism, an increase of current from O to OA causes the flux to increase from O to AC, but when the current is subsequently reduced to zero, the decrease of flux is only ED. If the current is then increased to OG in the reverse direction, the change of flux is EJ. Consequently, we can have an infinite number of inductance values, depending upon the particular variation of current that we happen to consider.

Since we are usually concerned with the effect of an inductance in an a.c. circuit, where the current varies from a maximum in one direction to the same maximum in the reverse direction, it is convenient to consider the value of the inductance as being the ratio of the change

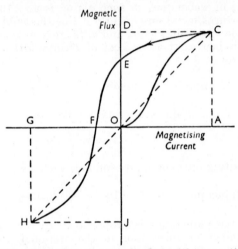

FIG. 78.—Variation of magnetic flux with magnetising current for a closed iron circuit.

of flux-linkages to the change of current when the latter is reversed.   Thus, for the case shown in Fig. 78:

$$\text{inductance of coil} = \frac{DJ}{AG} \times \text{number of turns.}$$

This value of inductance is the same as if the flux varied linearly along the dotted line COH in Fig. 78.

If μ_r represents the value of the relative permeability corresponding to the maximum value AC of the flux, then the inductance of the iron-cored coil, as defined above, is μ_r times that of the same coil with a non-magnetic core. Hence, from expression (44), we have:

inductance of iron-cored coil (for reversal of flux)

$$=4\pi \times 10^{-7} \times \frac{aT^2}{l} \times \mu_r \text{ henrys} \quad . \quad . \quad . \quad (45)$$

The variations of the relative permeability with the magnetising force for various qualities of iron are shown in Fig. 67; hence it follows from expression (45) that as the value of an alternating current through a coil having a closed iron circuit is increased, the value of the inductance increases to a maximum and then decreases, as

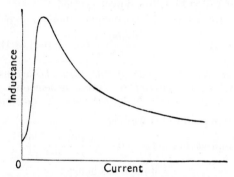

FIG. 79.—Inductance of an iron-cored coil.

shown in Fig. 79. It will now be evident that when the value of the inductance of such a coil is stated, it is also necessary to specify the current variation for which that value has been determined.

Example 36. *A ring of "Stalloy" stampings having a mean circumference of 40 cm and a cross-sectional area of 5 cm^2 is wound with 200 turns. Calculate the inductance of the coil corresponding to a reversal of a magnetising current of* (a) 1 A, (b) 10 A.

(a) Ampere-turns/m $= \dfrac{1 \text{ A} \times 200 \text{ turns}}{0 \cdot 4 \text{ m}} = 500.$

From Fig. 66:

corresponding flux density $=1\cdot22$ Wb/m²

$\therefore$ total flux $=1\cdot22\times0\cdot0005=0\cdot00061$ Wb.

From (43):

$$\text{inductance}=\frac{2\times0\cdot00061\times200}{2\times1\cdot0}$$

$$=0\cdot122 \text{ henry.}$$

(b) Ampere-turns/m $=\dfrac{10\times200}{0\cdot4}=5000.$

From Fig. 66:

corresponding flux density $=1\cdot58$ Wb/m²

$\therefore$ total flux $=1\cdot58\times0\cdot0005=0\cdot00079$ Wb

and   inductance $=\dfrac{2\times0\cdot00079\times200}{2\times10}=0\cdot0158$ H.

Example 37. *If a coil of 200 turns be wound on a non-magnetic core having the same dimensions as the "Stalloy" ring of Example 36, calculate its inductance.*

From expression (44) we have:

$$\text{inductance}=4\pi\times10^{-7}\times\frac{0\cdot0005\times(200)^2}{0\cdot4}$$

$$=0\cdot0000628 \text{ henry}$$

$$=0\cdot0628 \text{ millihenry (or mH)}$$

$$=62\cdot8 \text{ microhenrys (or } \mu\text{H).}$$

A comparison of this inductance with the values obtained in Example 36 for a coil of the same dimensions shows why an iron core is used when a large inductance is required.

64. Iron-cored Inductor in a D.C. Circuit.   Inductors are extensively used in the d.c. circuits of radio receivers —and of rectifiers generally—for smoothing out any variation in the direct current obtained from an a.c. supply.   Let us therefore consider an iron ring, similar to that of Fig. 65, wound with T turns, and assume the relationship between the flux and the magnetising current to be represented by the curve OBD of Fig. 80. It is seen that if the current is increased from OA to OC, the flux is increased from AB to CD. If this increase takes place in t seconds, then:

induced e.m.f.

$$= -\text{number of turns} \times \text{rate of increase of flux}$$

$$= -T \times \frac{(CD - AB)}{t} \text{ volts} \quad \ldots \ldots \quad (46)$$

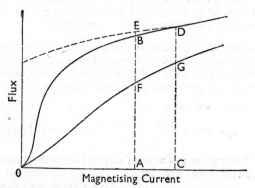

Fig. 80.—Effect of inserting airgap in an iron core.

Let L_e be the effective inductance of the coil over this range of flux variation, then:

$$\text{induced e.m.f.} = -L_e \times \frac{(OC - OA)}{t} \text{ volts} \quad . \quad (47)$$

Equating (46) and (47) we have:

$$L_e \times \frac{(OC - OA)}{t} = T \times \frac{(CD - AB)}{t}$$

$$\therefore \qquad L_e = T \times \frac{CD - AB}{OC - OA} \quad . \quad . \quad (48)$$

$$= T \times \text{slope of curve BD.}$$

From Fig. 80 it is evident that the slope of the curve is very small when the iron is saturated. This effect is accentuated by hysteresis; thus if the current is reduced

5*

from OC to OA, the flux decreases from CD only to AE, so that the effective inductance is still further reduced.

If a short radial airgap were made in the iron ring, the flux produced by current OA would be reduced to some value AF. For the reduced flux density in the iron the total ampere-turns required for the iron and the gap are approximately proportional to the flux; and for the same increase of current, AC, the increase of flux = CG−AF. As (CG−AF) may be much greater than (CD−AB), we have the curious result that the effective inductance of an iron-cored coil in a d.c. circuit may be increased by the introduction of an airgap.

Example 38. *A mild-steel ring is wound with 200 turns. When the current is reduced from 7 to 5 A, the flux decreases from 800 to 760 μWb. Calculate the effective inductance of the coil over this range of current variation.*

From (48) we have:

$$L_e = 200 \times \frac{(800-760)\times 10^{-6}}{(7-5)} = 0\cdot 004 \text{ henry.}$$

65. Derivation of Curve of Current Growth in an Inductive Circuit.

In Art. 60 the growth of current in an inductive circuit was discussed qualitatively; we shall now consider how to derive the curve showing the growth of current in a circuit of known resistance and inductance (assumed constant).

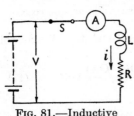

FIG. 81.—Inductive circuit.

When dealing with an inductive circuit it is convenient to separate the effects of inductance and resistance by representing the inductance L as an inductor or coil having no resistance and the resistance R as a resistor having no inductance, as shown in Fig. 81. It is evident from the latter that the current ultimately reaches a steady value I (Fig. 82) where $I = V/R$.

Let us consider any instant A during the growth of the current. Suppose the current at that instant to be

i amperes, represented by AB in Fig. 82. The corresponding p.d. across R is Ri volts. Also at that instant the rate of change of the current is given by the slope

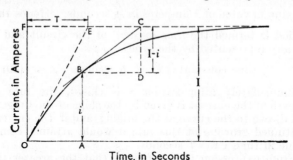

FIG. 82.—Growth of current in an inductive circuit.

of the curve at B, namely the slope of the tangent to the curve at B.

But the slope of $BC = \dfrac{CD}{BD} = \dfrac{I-i}{BD}$ amperes/second.

Hence e.m.f. induced in L at instant A

$$= -L \times \text{rate of increase of current}$$
$$= -L \times \frac{I-i}{BD} \text{ volts.}$$

The total applied voltage V is absorbed partly in providing the voltage drop across R and partly in neutralising the e.m.f induced in L:

i.e. $$V = Ri + L \times \frac{I-i}{BD}.$$

Substituting RI for V, we have:

$$RI = Ri + L \times \frac{I-i}{BD}$$

$\therefore$ $$R(I-i) = L \times \frac{I-i}{BD}$$

hence $$BD = \frac{L}{R}.$$

In words, this expression means that the rate of growth of current at any instant is such that if the current continued increasing at that rate, it would reach its maximum value of I amperes in $\dfrac{L}{R}$ seconds. Hence this period is termed the *time constant* of the circuit and is usually represented by the symbol T:

i.e.   time constant $= T = L/R$ seconds . . (49)

Immediately after switch S is closed, the rate of growth of the current is given by the slope of the tangent OE drawn to the curve at the origin; and if the current continued growing at this rate it would attain its final value in time FE $= T$ seconds.

From expression (49) it follows that the greater the inductance and the smaller the resistance, the larger is the time constant and the longer it takes for the current to reach its final value. Also this relationship can be used to deduce the curve representing the growth of current in an inductive circuit, as illustrated by the following example.

Example 39. *A coil having a resistance of 4 Ω and a constant inductance of 2 H is switched across a 20-V d.c. supply. Deduce the curve representing the growth of the current.*

From (49), time constant $= T = \dfrac{2 \text{ H}}{4 \text{ }\Omega} = 0{\cdot}5$ second.

Final value of current $= I = \dfrac{20}{4} = 5$ A.

With the horizontal and vertical axes suitably divided, as in Fig. 83, draw a horizontal dotted line at the level of 5 A. Along this line mark off a period MN $= T = 0{\cdot}5$ second, and join ON.

Take any point P relatively near the origin and draw a horizontal dotted line PQ $= T = 0{\cdot}5$ second, and at Q draw a vertical dotted line QS. Join PS.

Repeat the operation from a point X on PS, Z on XY, etc.

A curve touching OP, PX, XZ, etc., represents the growth of the current. The greater the number of points used in the construction, the more accurate is the curve.

66. Energy Stored in the Magnetic Field. If the current in a coil having a *constant* inductance of L henrys grows at a uniform rate from zero to I amperes in t seconds, the average value of the current is $\frac{1}{2}I$ and the e.m.f. induced in the coil is $-\left(L \times \dfrac{I}{t}\right)$ volts. The value of the applied voltage required to neutralise this back e.m.f. is therefore $\dfrac{LI}{t}$ volts. The product of the current

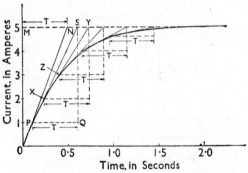

Fig. 83.—Graph for Example 39.

and the component of the applied voltage to neutralise the induced e.m.f. represents the power absorbed by the magnetic field associated with the coil.

Hence average power absorbed by the magnetic field

$$= \tfrac{1}{2}I \times \frac{LI}{t} \text{ watts}$$

and total energy absorbed by the magnetic field

$$= \text{average power} \times \text{time}$$

$$= \tfrac{1}{2}I \times \frac{LI}{t} \times t$$

$$= \tfrac{1}{2}LI^2 \text{ joules} \quad . \quad . \quad . \quad . \quad (50)$$

When an inductive circuit is opened, the current has to die away and the magnetic energy has to be dissipated. If there is no resistance in parallel with the circuit, the energy is largely dissipated as heat in the arc at the switch.   With a parallel resistance as described in Art. 60, the energy is dissipated as heat generated by the decreasing current in the total resistance of the circuit round which that current is flowing.

67. Mutual Inductance.   If two coils A and C are placed relatively to each other as in Fig. 84, then when S is closed, some of the flux produced by the current in

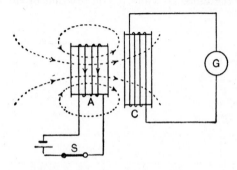

FIG. 84.—Mutual inductance.

A becomes linked with C and the e.m.f. induced in C circulates a momentary current through galvanometer G. Similarly when S is opened the collapse of the flux induces an e.m.f. in the reverse direction in C.   Since a change of current in one coil is accompanied by a change of flux and therefore by an e.m.f. induced in the other coil, the two coils are said to have *mutual inductance*.

The unit of mutual inductance is the same as for self-inductance, namely the *henry*; and two coils have a mutual inductance of 1 henry when an e.m.f. of 1 volt is induced in one coil due to the current in the other coil changing at the rate of 1 ampere/second.

If two coils, A and C, have a mutual inductance of

M henrys and if the current in coil A increases uniformly from i_1 to i_2 amperes in t seconds:

$$\text{e.m.f. induced in coil C} = -M \times \frac{(i_2 - i_1)}{t} \text{ volts}$$

$$= -M \times \text{rate of increase of current in coil A.}$$

The minus sign indicates that the induced e.m.f. tends to circulate a current in such a direction as to oppose the increase of flux due to the growth of current in the first coil.

If Φ_1 and Φ_2 represent the flux in webers linked with the secondary circuit C due to currents i_1 and i_2 amperes respectively in the primary circuit A and if T_2 represents the number of secondary turns:

$$\text{e.m.f. induced in C} = -\frac{\Phi_2 - \Phi_1}{t} \cdot T_2 \text{ volts.}$$

Hence, $$M\left(\frac{i_2 - i_1}{t}\right) = \frac{\Phi_2 - \Phi_1}{t} \cdot T_2$$

$$\therefore \quad M = \frac{\Phi_2 - \Phi_1}{i_2 - i_1} \cdot T_2 \text{ henrys}$$

$$= \frac{\text{change of flux-linkages with secondary}}{\text{change of current in primary}} . \quad (51)$$

Example 40. *Two coils have a mutual inductance of 0·3 henry. If the current in one coil is varied from 5 to 2 A in 0·4 second, calculate:* (a) *the e.m.f. induced in the second coil;* (b) *the change of flux linked with the latter, assuming that it is wound with 200 turns.*

(a) Average rate of increase of current in one coil

$$= \frac{(2-5) \text{ A}}{0·4 \text{ second}} = -7·5 \text{ amperes/second}$$

$\therefore$ average e.m.f. induced in other coil

$$= -0·3 \text{ henry} \times (-7·5) \text{ amperes/second}$$

$$= 2·25 \text{ V.}$$

(b) If Φ be the change of flux linked with the second coil:

$$\text{e.m.f. induced in that coil} = \frac{\Phi \times \text{number of turns}}{\text{time in seconds}}$$

i.e. $$2 \cdot 25 = \frac{\Phi \times 200}{0 \cdot 4}$$

$$\therefore \qquad \Phi = 0 \cdot 0045 \text{ weber.}$$

Summary of Important Formulae

$$\text{Induced e.m.f.} = -\left\{ \begin{array}{l} L \times \text{rate of increase of} \\ \text{current} \end{array} \right. \qquad (40)$$

$$\left. \begin{array}{l} \text{Self-inductance} \\ \text{(in henrys)} \end{array} \right\} = L = \frac{\text{change of flux-linkages}}{\text{change of current}} \quad (43)$$

$$\left. \begin{array}{l} \text{Inductance of coil} \\ \text{(in henrys)} \end{array} \right\} = 4\pi \times 10^{-7} \times \frac{aT^2}{l} \times \mu_r \quad . \quad . \quad (45)$$

$$\left. \begin{array}{l} \text{Time constant of} \\ \text{inductive circuit} \end{array} \right\} = T = \frac{L \text{ (henrys)}}{R \text{ (ohms)}} \text{ seconds} \quad . \quad (49)$$

$$\left. \begin{array}{l} \text{Magnetic energy stored in an} \\ \text{inductor having constant} \\ \text{inductance} \end{array} \right\} = \tfrac{1}{2}LI^2 \text{ joules} \quad . \quad (50)$$

Mutual inductance (in henrys)

$$= \frac{\text{change of flux-linkages with secondary}}{\text{change of current in primary}} \quad . \quad (51)$$

EXAMPLES VIII

1. A 1500-turn coil surrounds a magnetic circuit which has a reluctance of 6×10^6 M.K.S. units. What is the inductance of the coil?

2. Calculate the inductance of a circuit in which 30 V are induced when the current varies at the rate of 200 A/sec.

3. At what rate is the current varying in a circuit having an inductance of 50 mH when the induced e.m.f. is 8 V?

4. What is the value of the e.m.f. induced in a circuit having an inductance of 700 μH when the current varies at a rate of 5000 A/second?

5. A certain coil is wound with 50 turns and a current of 8 A produces a flux of 200 μWb. Calculate (a) the inductance of the coil corresponding to a reversal of the current, (b) the e.m.f. induced when the current is reversed in 0·2 second.

6. A toroid is wound with 300 turns on an ebonite ring having a cross-sectional area of 4 cm² and a mean circumference of 35 cm. Calculate (a) the inductance of coil, (b) the induced e.m.f. when the current is reduced at the rate of 200 amperes/second.

7. A coil wound with 500 turns has a resistance of 2 Ω. It is found that a current of 3 A produces a flux of 500 μWb. Calculate (a) the inductance and the time constant of the coil, (b) the average e.m.f. induced in the coil when the flux is reversed in 0·3 second.

8. If the coil referred to in Question 7 is switched across a 10-V d.c. supply, derive a curve showing the growth of the current, assuming the inductance to remain constant.

9. A coil having an inductance of 2 henrys and a resistance of 5 Ω is switched across a 20-V d.c. supply. Derive the curve of current growth in the coil and estimate the value of the current after 0·5 second.

10. The field winding of a dynamo has a resistance of 80 Ω and an inductance of 90 henrys. It has a resistance of 70 Ω connected permanently in parallel. With a current of 6 A in the field winding, the combined circuits are disconnected from the supply. Derive a curve showing the variation of the field current with time.

11. A coil having a resistance of 20 Ω and an inductance of 4 H is connected across a 50-V d.c. supply. Determine (a) the initial rate of growth of the current, (b) the value of the current after 0·1 second, (c) the time required for the current to grow to 1·5 A, and (d) the energy stored in the magnetic field when the current has attained its steady value.

12. The current through a certain coil is increased uniformly from 0 to 10 A in 0·1 second. It is then increased uniformly from 10 to 20 A in 0·3 second and subsequently decreased uniformly from 20 A to zero in 0·4 second. If the inductance of the coil remains constant at 2 H and if the resistance is negligible, plot graphs to scale representing the variation of (a) the current, (b) the e.m.f. induced in the coil and (c) the voltage applied to the coil.

13. A certain circuit has a resistance of 10 Ω and a constant inductance of 3 H. The current through this circuit is increased uniformly from 0 to 5 A in 0·6 second, maintained constant at 5 A for 0·1 second and then reduced uniformly to zero in 0·3 second. Draw to scale graphs representing the variation of (a) the current, (b) the induced e.m.f. and (c) the resultant applied voltage.

14. Explain what is understood by the term e.m.f. of self-induction.

The current in a circuit consisting of an inductor of 0·1 H which has a resistance of 50 ohms is increasing uniformly from zero at a rate of 5 A/sec. Draw to scale graphs of this current and of the voltage across the circuit for the first 1/100 of a second. If the coil is suddenly short-circuited at the end of this period, calculate the total energy which will have to be dissipated.

(C. & G., Telecom. Prin. II)

15. A coil consists of two similar sections wound on a common core. Each section has an inductance of 0·1 H. Calculate the inductance of the coil when the sections are connected (a) in series, (b) in parallel.

16. A wooden ring with a mean diameter of 16 cm and a sectional area of 2 cm², is uniformly wound with 500 turns. A secondary winding of 400 turns is uniformly wound over the primary. Calculate the inductance of the primary, the inductance of the secondary, the mutual inductance between the primary and secondary and the inductance obtained by connecting the two windings in series.

What would be the effect on these values of using a dust core with a permeability of 10, instead of the wooden ring? (Joint Section A)

17. Derive an expression for the energy stored in the magnetic field of a coil having an inductance of L henrys when the current through the coil is I amperes.

A coil, having an inductance of 2 henrys and a resistance of 5 ohms, is connected across a 20-V d.c. supply. Explain briefly why the current does not instantly reach its final value and calculate the energy stored in the magnetic field when the current has attained its final value. The unit in which the energy is expressed should be stated.   (I. Mech. E., Prin. of Elect.)

18. If two coils have a mutual inductance of 400 μH, calculate the e.m.f. induced in one coil when the current in the other coil varies at a rate of 30,000 A/second.

19. If an e.m.f. of 5 V is induced in a coil when the current in an adjacent coil varies at a rate of 80 A/sec, what is the value of the mutual inductance of the two coils?

20. If the mutual inductance between two coils is 0·2 henry, calculate the e.m.f. induced in one coil when the current in the other coil is increased from 0·5 to 3 A in 0·05 second.

21. If the toroid of Question 6 has a second winding of 80 turns wound over the ebonite ring and inside the first winding of 300 turns, calculate the mutual inductance.

22. When a current of 2 A through a coil P is reversed, a deflection of 36 divisions is obtained on a fluxmeter connected to a coil Q. If the fluxmeter constant is 150 microweber-turns/division, what is the value of the mutual inductance of coils P and Q?

23. Explain what is meant by mutual inductance and state the practical unit in which its value is expressed.

Two coils, A and B, of 600 and 100 turns respectively, are wound uniformly around a wooden ring having a mean circumference of 30 cm. The cross-sectional area of the ring is 4 cm². Calculate (a) the mutual inductance of the coils and (b) the e.m.f. induced in coil B when a current of 2 A in coil A is reversed in 0·01 second.

                              (I. Mech. E., Prin. of Elect.)

CHAPTER IX

ELECTROSTATICS

68. Electrification by Friction. The fact that amber, when rubbed, acquires the property of attracting light bodies was referred to over 2500 years ago by a Greek philosopher, named Thales, as a phenomenon that was quite familiar even at that time; but it was not until about A.D. 1600 that Dr. Gilbert of Colchester discovered that other bodies, such as glass, could also be electrified by rubbing.

If a glass rod be rubbed with silk and placed on a stirrup hung from a wooden stand (Fig. 85), and if the end of another similarly rubbed glass rod be brought near one end of the suspended rod, they are found to repel each other. But if an ebonite rod rubbed with fur is brought near the suspended glass rod, attraction takes place. Similarly, if an excited ebonite rod be supported on the stirrup, the approach of another ebonite rod causes repulsion, whereas a glass rod causes attraction.

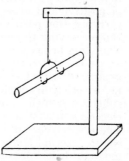

FIG. 85.—Attraction and repulsion of electric charges.

The glass and the ebonite appear to be charged with different kinds of electricity; and the above experiments show that bodies charged with the same kind of electricity repel, while bodies charged with opposite kinds of electricity attract one another.

About 1750 Benjamin Franklin, in America, suggested that electricity was some form of fluid which passed from one body to the other when they were rubbed together, and that in the case of glass rubbed with silk,

147

the electric fluid passed from the silk into the glass so that the glass contained a "plus" or "positive" amount of electricity. On the other hand, when ebonite was rubbed with fur, the electric fluid passed from the ebonite to the fur, leaving the ebonite with a "minus" or "negative" amount of electricity. Franklin's one-fluid theory has long since been discarded, but his convention still remains: thus, the glass is said to be positively charged and the ebonite negatively charged, and it is this convention which governs the signs used for the terminals of dynamos and batteries.

69. Electrons and Protons. The modern conception of electricity, shorn of the complexities that have grown around it, may be briefly stated thus: An atom of any material under normal conditions contains equal amounts of positive and negative electric charges. The particles carrying the positive charges are termed *protons* and those carrying the negative charges are termed *electrons*. The atom behaves as if the protons were concentrated at its centre and surrounded—at distances relatively great compared with their diameter—by planetary electrons, i.e. by electrons circling around the nucleus. In certain substances, such as metals, at least one of the outermost electrons in each atom is very loosely held to the atom. These electrons are termed *free* electrons and only a slight external influence is required to cause them to move or drift from one atom to another. In the experiments described in Art. 68, the friction between the glass and the silk causes some of the electrons to be extracted from the glass, leaving the latter with a deficiency of negative charge, or in other words, with an excess of positive charge. The silk will, of course, have acquired a corresponding excess of negative charge. On the other hand, friction between ebonite and fur causes electrons to be extracted from the fur to attach themselves to the ebonite so that the latter becomes negatively charged.

The simplest method of causing the free electrons to move from atom to atom in a desired direction is to introduce a source of electromotive force into the circuit. In Fig. 86, DE represents an enlarged view of a metal conductor forming part of a closed circuit which includes a battery B. The circles with crosses represent atoms which have lost one or more of their free electrons, such atoms being termed *positive ions*, and the small black circles represent the free electrons moving from left to right. This procession or drift of the electrons takes place round the whole circuit, including battery B; i.e. the number of electrons emerging per second from the negative terminal of B is exactly the same as that entering the positive terminal per second. It follows that an electric current in a metal conductor consists of a movement of electrons from a point at the *lower* potential to a point at the *higher* potential, namely in the opposite direction to that taken as the conventional

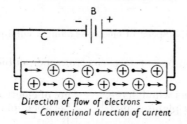

Direction of flow of electrons ⟶
⟵ Conventional direction of current

Fɪɢ. 86.—Movement of electrons in a conductor.

direction of the current. The latter was universally adopted long before the discovery of the electron and so we continue to say that an electric current flows from a point at the *higher* potential to that at the *lower* potential.

It has been found experimentally that the charge on a single electron is $1 \cdot 602 \times 10^{-19}$ coulomb. Hence, when a current of 1 ampere (or 1 coulomb/second) flows in a conductor, the number of electrons passing any given point must be such that:

$1 \cdot 602 \times 10^{-19} \times$ no. of electrons/sec $= 1$ coulomb/sec

$\therefore$ no. of electrons/sec $= 6 \cdot 24 \times 10^{18}$

i.e. when the current in a circuit is 1 ampere, electrons are passing any given point of the circuit at the rate of $6 \cdot 24 \times 10^{18}$ per second. This inconceivably large number may suggest that the electrons are travelling along the wire at an enormous speed. This, however, is not the case. Consider a conductor, Fig. 87, having a cross-sectional area of a square metres and suppose the electrons to be travelling at a speed of v metres/sec; then the electrons which passed plane A at the beginning of a second will have reached plane B, v metres away, by the end of that second. Consequently all the electrons which pass plane A during 1 second will occupy the volume va cubic metres between planes A and B. If

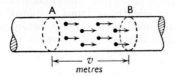

FIG. 87.—Speed of electrons along a conductor.

N_f is the number of free electrons per cubic metre of conductor,

$$\left.\begin{array}{l}\text{no. of electrons which have} \\ \text{passed across plane A in 1} \\ \text{sec}\end{array}\right\}=\left\{\begin{array}{l}\text{no. of electrons in space} \\ \text{between planes A and} \\ \text{B}\end{array}\right.$$
$$=N_f v a.$$

If the current in the conductor is 1 ampere, then:
$$N_f v a = 6{\cdot}24 \times 10^{18}.$$

For copper, it has been found that N_f is about 10^{29};

$$\therefore \qquad v = \frac{6{\cdot}24 \times 10^{18}}{a \times 10^{29}} = \frac{6{\cdot}24 \times 10^{-11}}{a} \text{ m/sec.}$$

For a current density of 1000 A/in^2,

$$\left.\begin{array}{l}\text{cross-sectional area of} \\ \text{conductor to carry 1 A}\end{array}\right\}=\frac{1}{1000}\times\frac{2{\cdot}54^2}{100^2}$$
$$=6{\cdot}45 \times 10^{-7} \text{ m}^2,$$

$$\therefore \qquad v = \frac{6{\cdot}24 \times 10^{-11} \times 10^7}{6{\cdot}45} = 9{\cdot}67 \times 10^{-5} \text{ m/sec}$$
$$=0{\cdot}58 \text{ cm/min.}$$

It will be seen that the electrons are moving along the conductor more slowly than at a snail's pace!

In an insulator, the electrons are tightly bound to their respective atoms so that there are very few free electrons available; consequently, such a material is a very poor conductor of electricity.

70. Electron-Volt. Since the charge on an electron is 1.6×10^{-19} coulomb or ampere-second, the work done in moving an electron between two points having a difference of potential of 1 volt is 1.6×10^{-19} watt-second or joule. This amount of energy is referred to as an electron-volt, a term that has acquired considerable importance in the field of electronics,

i.e. $\qquad$ 1 electron-volt $= 1.6 \times 10^{-19}$ joule $\quad$. (52)

71. Capacitor or Condenser. Two metal plates, separated by an insulator, constitute a *capacitor* * or *condenser,* namely an arrangement which has the capacity of storing electricity as an excess of electrons on one plate and a deficiency on the other.

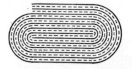

The most common type of capacitor used in practice consists of two strips of metal foil, represented by full lines in Fig.

FIG. 88.—Paper insulated capacitor.

88, separated by strips of waxed paper, shown dotted, these strips being wound spirally, forming—in effect— two very large surfaces near to each other. The whole assembly is thoroughly soaked in hot paraffin wax. In radio receivers, some of the capacitors consist of two sets of metal vanes, one of which is fixed and the other set is so arranged that the vanes can be moved into and out of the space between the fixed vanes without touching the latter.

A capacitor may be regarded as a reservoir of electricity and its action can be demonstrated by connecting a capacitor of, say, 20 microfarads (Art. 74) in series with

* Recommended by the British Standards Institution, but the term "condenser" is still widely used.

a high resistance R, a centre-zero microammeter A and
a two-way switch S, as in Fig. 89. An electrostatic
voltmeter (Art. 146) is connected across C. With R
equal to, say, 1 megohm, it is found that when S is
closed on *a*, the deflection on A rises immediately to its
maximum value and then falls off to zero, as indicated
by curve A in Fig. 90. At the same time, the p.d.
across C grows in the manner shown by curve M. When
S is moved over to *b*, the current again rises immediately
to the same maximum but in the reverse direction, and
then falls off as shown by curve B. Curve N shows the
corresponding variation of p.d. across C.

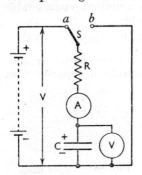

If the experiment is repeated
with R equal to, say, 2 megohms, it
is found that the initial current, both on charging and on
discharging, is halved, but it
takes about twice as long to fall
off, as shown by the dotted
curves D and E. Curves P and
Q represent the corresponding
variation of the p.d. across C
during charge and discharge respectively.

The shaded area between
curve A and the horizontal axis
in Fig. 90 represents the product
of the average charging current
(in amperes) and the time (in
seconds), namely the quantity of electricity (in coulombs)
required to charge the capacitor to a p.d. of *V* volts.
Similarly the shaded area enclosed by curve B represents
the same quantity of electricity obtainable during discharge.

FIG. 89. — Capacitor
charged and discharged
through high resistance.

72. Hydraulic Analogy. The operation of charging
and discharging a capacitor may be more easily understood if we consider the hydraulic analogy given in
Fig. 91, where P represents a piston operated by a rod R,
and D is a rubber diaphragm stretched across a cylindrical chamber C. The cylinders are connected by
pipes E, E and are filled with water.

When no pressure is being exerted on P, the diaphragm is flat, as shown dotted, and the piston is in position A. If P is pushed towards the left, water is withdrawn from G and forced into F and the diaphragm is in consequence distended, as shown by the full line. The greater the pressure applied to P, the greater is the amount of water displaced. But the rate at which this

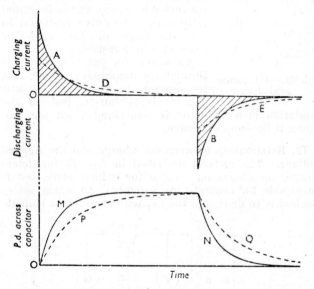

FIG. 90.—Charging and discharging currents and p.d.'s.

displacement takes place depends upon the resistance offered by pipes E, E; thus the smaller the cross-sectional area of the pipes, the longer is the time required for the steady state to be reached. The pressure applied to P is analogous to the e.m.f. of the battery, the quantity of water displaced corresponds to the charge, the rate at which the water passes any point in the pipes corresponds to the current, and the cylinder C with its elastic diaphragm is the analogue of the capacitor.

When the force exerted on P is removed, the distended diaphragm forces water out of F back into G; and if the frictional resistance of the water in the pipes exceeds a certain value, it is found that the piston is merely pushed back to its original position A. The strain energy stored in the diaphragm due to its distension is converted into heat by the frictional resistance. The effect is similar to the discharge of the capacitor through a high resistance.

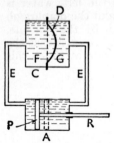

Fig. 91.—Hydraulic analogy.

No water can pass from F to G through the diaphragm so long as it remains intact; but if it is strained excessively it bursts, just as the insulation in a capacitor is punctured when the p.d. across it becomes excessive.

73. Relationship between the Charge and the Applied Voltage. The method described in Art. 71 for determining the charge on a capacitor is instructive, but is unsuitable for accurate measurement. A much better method is to discharge the capacitor through a ballistic

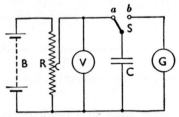

Fig. 92.—Measurement of charge by ballistic galvanometer.

galvanometer (Art. 57), since the deflection of the latter is proportional to the charge.

Let us charge a capacitor C (Fig. 92) to various voltages by means of a slider on a resistance R connected across a battery B, S being on a; and for each voltage note the deflection of G when C is discharged through it.

Thus, if θ is the first deflection or "throw" observed when the capacitor, charged to a p.d. of V volts, is discharged through G, and if k is the ballistic constant of G in coulombs per unit of first deflection, then:

$$\text{discharge through G} = Q = k\theta \text{ coulombs.}$$

It is found that for a given capacitor,

$$\frac{\text{charge on C (in coulombs)}}{\text{p.d. across C (in volts)}} = \text{a constant} \quad . \quad (53)$$

74. Capacitance. The property of a capacitor to store an electric charge when its plates are at different potentials is referred to as its *capacitance*.

The unit of capacitance is termed the *farad* (symbol F) —a curtailment of "Faraday"—and may be defined as *the capacitance of a capacitor which requires a p.d. of 1 volt to maintain a charge of 1 coulomb on that capacitor.*

It follows from expression (53) and from the definition of the farad that:

$$\frac{\text{charge (in coulombs)}}{\text{applied p.d. (in volts)}} = \text{capacitance (in farads)}$$

or in symbols, $$\frac{Q}{V} = C$$

and $$Q = CV \quad . \quad . \quad . \quad . \quad (54)$$

In practice, the farad is found to be inconveniently large and the capacitance is usually expressed in *microfarads* (μF) or in picofarads or micro-microfarads (pF or $\mu\mu F$),

where 1 farad = 1,000,000 microfarads

and 1 microfarad = 1,000,000 pF or $\mu\mu F$.

Example 41. *A capacitor having a capacitance of 80 microfarads is connected across a 500-V d.c. supply. Calculate the charge.*

From (54), charge $= \dfrac{80}{1,000,000}$ (farad) $\times 500$ (volts)

$$= 0 \cdot 04 \text{ coulomb.}$$

75. Capacitors in Parallel. Suppose two capacitors, having capacitances C_1 and C_2 farads respectively, to

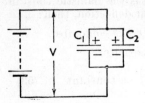

be connected in parallel (Fig. 93) across a p.d. of V volts. The charge on C_1 is Q_1 coulombs and that on C_2 is Q_2 coulombs, where:

$$Q_1 = C_1 V, \quad \text{and} \quad Q_2 = C_2 V.$$

If we were to replace C_1 and C_2 by a single capacitor of such capacitance C farads that the same total charge of $(Q_1 + Q_2)$

Fig. 93.—Capacitors in parallel.

coulombs would be produced by the same p.d., then $Q_1 + Q_2 = CV$.

Substituting for Q_1 and Q_2, we have:

$$C_1 V + C_2 V = CV$$

$$\therefore \qquad C = C_1 + C_2 \quad . \quad . \quad . \quad . \quad (55)$$

Hence *the resultant capacitance of capacitors in parallel is the arithmetic sum of their respective capacitances.*

76. Capacitors in Series. Suppose C_1 and C_2 in Fig. 94 to be two capacitors connected in series with suitable centre-zero ammeters A_1 and A_2, a high resistance R, and a two-way switch S. When S is put over to a, A_1 and A_2 are found to indicate exactly the same charging current, each reading decreasing simultaneously from a maximum to zero, as already shown in Fig. 90. Similarly, when S is put over to b, A_1 and A_2 indicate similar discharges. It follows that during charge the displacement of electrons from the positive plate of C_1 to the negative

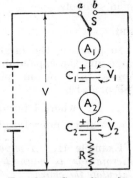

Fig. 94.—Capacitors in series.

plate of C_2 is exactly the same as that from the upper plate (Fig. 94) of C_2 to the lower plate of C_1. In other words, the displacement of Q coulombs of electricity is the same in every part of the circuit and the charge on each capacitor is therefore Q coulombs.

If V_1 and V_2 be the corresponding p.d.'s across C_1 and C_2 respectively, then from (54):

$$Q = C_1 V_1 = C_2 V_2 \quad . \quad . \quad . \quad . \quad (56)$$

so that $\qquad V_1 = \dfrac{Q}{C_1}, \quad$ and $\quad V_2 = \dfrac{Q}{C_2}.$

If we were to replace C_1 and C_2 by a single capacitor of capacitance C farads such that it would have the same charge Q coulombs with the same p.d. of V volts, then:

$$Q = CV, \quad \text{or} \quad V = Q/C$$

But it is evident from Fig. 94 that $V = V_1 + V_2$. Substituting for V, V_1 and V_2, we have:

$$\frac{Q}{C} = \frac{Q}{C_1} + \frac{Q}{C_2}$$

$$\therefore \qquad \frac{1}{C} = \frac{1}{C_1} + \frac{1}{C_2} \quad . \quad . \quad . \quad . \quad (57)$$

Hence *the reciprocal of the resultant capacitance of capacitors connected in series is the sum of the reciprocals of their respective capacitances.*

77. Distribution of Voltage across Capacitors in Series. From expression (56),

$$\frac{V_2}{V_1} = \frac{C_1}{C_2} \quad . \quad . \quad . \quad . \quad . \quad (58)$$

But $\qquad V_1 + V_2 = V$

$$\therefore \qquad V_2 = V - V_1.$$

Substituting for V_2 in (58), we have:

$$\frac{V - V_1}{V_1} = \frac{C_1}{C_2}$$

$$\therefore \qquad \frac{V}{V_1} = \frac{C_1}{C_2} + 1 = \frac{C_1 + {}_2}{C_2}$$

$$\therefore \qquad V_1 = V \times \frac{C_2}{C_1 + C_2} \quad . \quad . \quad . \quad (59)$$

and $\qquad V_2 = V \times \dfrac{C_1}{C_1 + C_2} \quad . \quad . \quad . \quad (60)$

Example 42. *Three capacitors have capacitances of 2,
4 and 8 microfarads respectively. Find the total
capacitance when they are connected* (a) *in parallel,*
(b) *in series.*

(a) From (55):

total capacitance $=2+4+8=14$ microfarads.

(b) If C be the resultant capacitance in microfarads
when the capacitors are in series, then from (57):

$$\frac{1}{C}=\frac{1}{2}+\frac{1}{4}+\frac{1}{8}=0\cdot5+0\cdot25+0\cdot125=0\cdot875$$

∴ $C=1\cdot143$ microfarads.

Example 43. *If two capacitors having capacitances of
6 and 10 microfarads respectively are connected in series
across a 200-V supply, find* (a) *the p.d. across each
capacitor,* (b) *the charge on each capacitor.*

(a) Let V_1 and V_2 be the p.d.'s across the 6- and
10-μF capacitors respectively; then, from expression
(59),

$$V_1=200\times\frac{10}{6+10}=125 \text{ volts}$$

and $V_2=200-125=75$ volts.

(b) Charge on each capacitor

$$=\text{charge on } C_1$$
$$=6\times10^{-6} \text{ (farad)}\times125 \text{ (volts)}$$
$$=0\cdot00075 \text{ coulomb.}$$

**78. Relationship between the Capacitance and the
Dimensions of a Capacitor.** It follows from expression (55) that if two similar capacitors are connected
in parallel the capacitance is double that of one capacitor.
But the effect of connecting two similar capacitors in
parallel is merely to double the area of each plate. In
just the same way the effect of connecting, say, five
similar capacitors in parallel is to increase the area of
the plates five times and to increase the capacitance
fivefold. In general, we may therefore say that the

capacitance of a capacitor is proportional to the area of the plates.

On the other hand if two similar capacitors are connected in series, it follows from expression (57) that the capacitance is halved. We have, however, doubled the thickness of the insulation between the plates that are connected to the supply. If, say, five similar capacitors are connected in series, the thickness of the insulation between the outermost plates is increased fivefold, but the capacitance is reduced to a fifth of that of one capacitor. Hence we may say in general that the capacitance of a capacitor is inversely proportional to the distance between the plates; and the above relationships may be summarised thus:

$$\left.\begin{array}{c}\text{capacitance of} \\ \text{a capacitor}\end{array}\right\} \propto \frac{\text{area of plates}}{\text{distance between plates}}.$$

79. Electric Force and Electric Flux Density.

Let us consider a capacitor consisting of metal plates, M and N, in a glass enclosure G, shown chain-dotted in Fig. 95, from which all the air has been removed. Let a be the area in square metres of one side of each plate and let d be the distance in metres between the plates. Let Q be the charge in coulombs due to a p.d. of V volts between the plates.

Suppose the dimensions of the plates to be so large compared with the distance between them that we may assume negligible fringing of the electric flux, i.e. all the electric lines may be assumed to pass straight across from M to N, as shown by the dotted lines in Fig. 95.

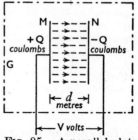

FIG. 95.—A parallel-plate capacitor.

The *electric force* or *electric field strength* in the region between the two plates M and N is the *potential drop per unit length* or *potential gradient*, namely V/d volts/metre; and the *direction* of the electric force at any point is the direction of the mechanical force on a positive charge situated at that point, namely from the positively-charged plate M towards the negatively-charged plate N in Fig. 95. The symbol for electric force is $\mathscr{E}$,

i.e. $$\mathscr{E} = V/d \text{ volts/metre} \quad . \quad . \quad . \quad . \quad (61)$$

In the rationalized M.K.S. system, *one* line of electric flux is assumed to emanate from a positive charge of 1 coulomb and to enter a negative charge of 1 coulomb. Hence the electric flux between M and N in Fig. 95 is Q lines (sometimes referred to as "tubes"). The *electric flux density*, D, namely the number of lines of electric flux per square metre, is given by:

$$D = Q/a \text{ coulombs per square metre} \quad . \quad (62)$$

From expressions (61) and (62),

$$\frac{\text{electric flux density}}{\text{electric force}} = \frac{Q}{a} \div \frac{V}{d} = \frac{Q}{V} \times \frac{d}{a} = \frac{Cd}{a}.$$

In electromagnetism, the ratio of the magnetic flux density in a vacuum to the magnetising force is termed the "permeability of free space" or "magnetic space constant" and represented by μ_0. Similarly, in electrostatics, the ratio of the electric flux density in a vacuum to the electric force is termed the *permittivity of free space* (vacuum) or *electric space constant* and is represented by ϵ_0 * (pronounced epsilon).

Hence, $$\epsilon_0 = \frac{Cd}{a}$$

or $$C = \frac{\epsilon_0 a}{d} \quad . \quad . \quad . \quad . \quad . \quad (63)$$

The effect of filling the space between M and N (Fig. 95) with air at atmospheric pressure is to increase the capacitance by 0·06 per cent compared with the value when the space is completely evacuated; hence for all practical purposes, expression (63) can be applied to capacitors having air dielectric.

80. Determination of the Value of ϵ_0. Suppose the capacitor in Fig. 95 to consist of metal plates of known

* The British Standards Institution is recommending the use of ϵ instead of κ (kappa) as the symbol for permittivity.

dimensions separated by an air space of known length. The capacitor is charged to a known p.d. of V volts and then discharged through a ballistic galvanometer G having a ballistic constant of k coulombs per unit deflection. If the galvanometer deflection is θ divisions, discharge through $G=Q=CV=k\theta$ coulombs.

$$\therefore \qquad C=\frac{k\theta}{V} \text{ farads.}$$

Hence, $$\epsilon_0=\frac{k\theta}{V} \cdot \frac{d}{a} \quad . \quad . \quad . \quad . \quad (64)$$

Since the values of a and d are assumed to be known for the capacitor tested, the value of ϵ_0 can be determined from expression (64). From carefully conducted tests, it has been found that:

$$\epsilon_0=8.85 \times 10^{-12} \text{ M.K.S. units} \quad . \quad (65)$$

Hence the capacitance of a parallel-plate capacitor with vacuum or air dielectric is given by:

$$C=\frac{8.85 \times 10^{-12} \times a \text{ (square metres)}}{d \text{ (metres)}} \text{ farads .} \quad (66)$$

It may be mentioned at this point that there is a definite relationship between μ_0, ϵ_0 and the velocity of light and other electromagnetic waves; thus,

$$\frac{1}{\mu_0\epsilon_0}=\frac{1}{4\pi \times 10^{-7} \times 8.85 \times 10^{-12}}=9 \times 10^{16}=(3 \times 10^8)^2$$

But the velocity of light $=3 \times 10^8$ metres/second

$$\therefore \quad \left.\begin{array}{l} \text{velocity of light} \\ \text{in metres/sec} \end{array}\right\}=\frac{1}{\sqrt{(\mu_0\epsilon_0)}} \quad . \quad . \quad . \quad . \quad (67)$$

This relationship was discovered by Prof. Clerk Maxwell in 1865 and enabled him to predict the existence of radio waves about twenty years before their effect was demonstrated experimentally by Prof. H. Hertz.

81. Relative Permittivity or Dielectric Constant. If the experiment described in Art. 80 is performed with a sheet of glass filling the space between plates A and B, it is found that the value of the capacitance is greatly increased; and the ratio of the capacitance of a capacitor

6

having a certain material as dielectric to the capacitance of that capacitor with vacuum (or air) dielectric is termed the *relative permittivity* or *dielectric constant* of that material and is represented by the symbol ϵ_r. Values of the relative permittivity of some of the most important insulating materials are given in the following table:

Material	Relative permittivity
Air	1·0006
Paper (dry)	2–2·5
Bakelite	4·5–5·5
Glass	5–10
Rubber	2–3·5
Mica	3–7
Porcelain	6–7

From expression (63), it follows that if the space between the metal plates of the capacitor in Fig. 95 is filled with a dielectric having a relative permittivity ϵ_r,

$$\text{capacitance} = C = \frac{\epsilon_0 \epsilon_r a}{d} \text{ farads} \quad \cdots \cdots \quad (68)$$

$$= \frac{8·85 \times 10^{-12} \epsilon_r a \text{ (square metres)}}{d \text{ (metres)}} \text{ farads}$$

and charge due to a p.d. of V volts $\left.\right\} = Q = CV$

$$= \frac{\epsilon_0 \epsilon_r a V}{d} \text{ coulombs.}$$

Hence, for a capacitor with a dielectric having a relative permittivity or dielectric constant ϵ_r,

$$\frac{\text{electric flux density}}{\text{electric force}} = \frac{D}{\mathscr{E}} = \frac{Q}{a} \div \frac{V}{d} = \frac{Qd}{Va} = \epsilon_0 \epsilon_r$$

$$= \text{absolute permittivity} \quad (69)$$

This expression is similar in form to expression (29) deduced for the magnetic circuit, namely:

$$\frac{\text{magnetic flux density}}{\text{magnetising force}} = \frac{B}{H} = \mu_0 \mu_r.$$

Suppose a capacitor to be made up of n parallel plates, alternate plates being connected together as in Fig. 96.

Let a=area of *one* side of each plate in square metres,

   d=thickness of dielectric in metres

and ϵ_r=relative permittivity of the dielectric.

Fig. 96 shows a capacitor with seven plates, four being connected to A and three to B.   It will be seen that each side of the three plates connected to B is in contact with the dielectric, whereas only one side of each of the outer plates is in contact with it.   Consequently, the useful surface area of each set of plates is $6a$ square metres. Hence, for n plates, the useful area of each set is $(n-1)a$ square metres.

FIG. 96.—Multi-plate capacitor.

$$\therefore \quad \text{capacitance}=\frac{\epsilon_0\epsilon_r(n-1)a}{d}\text{ farads}$$

$$=\frac{8\cdot85\times10^{-12}\epsilon_r(n-1)a}{d}\text{ farads} \quad (70)$$

Example 44.   *A capacitor is made with 7 metal plates connected as in Fig. 96 and separated by sheets of mica having a thickness of 0·3 mm and a relative permittivity of 6.   The area of one side of each plate is 500 cm². Calculate the capacitance in microfarads.*

Using expression (70), we have $n=7$, $a=0\cdot05$ m², $d=0\cdot0003$ m and $\epsilon_r=6$.

$$\therefore \quad C=\frac{8\cdot85\times10^{-12}\times6\times6\times0\cdot05}{0\cdot0003}=0\cdot0531\times10^{-6}\text{ F}$$

$$=0\cdot0531\ \mu\text{F}.$$

Example 45.   *A p.d. of 400 V is maintained across the terminals of the capacitor of Example 44.   Calculate (a) the charge, (b) the electric field strength or potential gradient and (c) the electric flux density in the dielectric.*

(a) Charge$=Q=CV=0\cdot0531\ (\mu\text{F})\times400\ (\text{V})$

$=21\cdot24$ microcoulombs.

(b) Electric field strength or potential gradient

$$= V/d = 400/0 \cdot 0003 = 1,333,000 \text{ V/m}$$
$$= 1333 \text{ kV/m.}$$

(c) Electric flux density

$$= Q/a = 21 \cdot 24/(0 \cdot 05 \times 6)$$
$$= 70 \cdot 8 \text{ microcoulombs/m}^2.$$

82. Charging and Discharging Currents of a Capacitor.
Suppose C in Fig. 97 to represent a capacitor of, say,

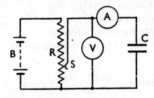

FIG. 97.—Charging and discharging of a capacitor.

30 μF connected in series with a centre-zero micro-ammeter A across a slider S and one end of a resistor R. A battery B is connected across R. If S is moved at a

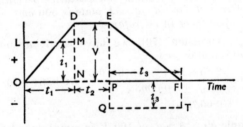

FIG. 98.—Voltage and current during charging and discharging of a capacitor.

uniform speed along R, the p.d. applied to C, indicated by voltmeter V, is increased uniformly from 0 to V volts, as shown by line OD in Fig. 98.

If C is the capacitance in farads and if the p.d. across C is increased from 0 to V volts in t_1 seconds,

$$\text{charging current} = i_1 = \frac{Q(\text{coulombs or ampere-seconds})}{t_1 \text{ (seconds)}}$$

$$= CV/t_1 \text{ amperes,}$$

i.e. charging current in amperes $\Big\} = \Big\{$ rate of increase of charge in coulombs/sec

$$= C \text{ (farads)} \times \text{rate of increase of p.d. in volts/sec.}$$

Since the p.d. in the above experiment was increased at a uniform rate, the charging current, i_1, remains constant and is represented by the dotted line LM in Fig. 98.

Suppose the p.d. across C to be maintained constant at V volts during the next t_2 seconds. Since the rate of change of p.d. is now zero, the current (apart from a slight leakage current) is zero and is represented by the dotted line NP. If the p.d. across C is then reduced to zero at a uniform rate by moving slider S backwards, the microammeter indicates a current i_3 flowing in the reverse direction, represented by the dotted line QT in Fig. 98. If t_3 is the time in seconds for the p.d. to be reduced from V volts to zero,

then $\qquad Q = -i_3 t_3$ coulombs

$\therefore \qquad i_3 = -Q/t_3 = -C \times V/t_3$ amperes

i.e. discharge current in amperes $\Big\} = \Big\{$ rate of decrease of charge in coulombs/sec

$$= C \text{ (farads)} \times \text{rate of decrease of p.d. in volts/sec.}$$

Since $Q = i_1 t_1 = -i_3 t_3$ (assuming negligible leakage current through C),

$\therefore \qquad$ areas of rectangles OLMN and PQTF are equal.

83. Derivation of Curves representing the Charging and Discharging Currents of a Capacitor in Series with a Resistor.

In Art. 71 we derived the curves of the charging and discharging currents from the readings on a microammeter connected in the circuit. We will now

consider how these curves can be derived from the values
of the capacitance, the resistance and the applied voltage.   At the instant when S is closed on a (Fig. 89),
there is no p.d. across C; consequently the whole of the
applied voltage is applied to R and the initial value of
the charging current is $I = V/R$.

The growth of the p.d. across C is represented by the
curve in Fig. 99.   Suppose v to be the p.d. across C

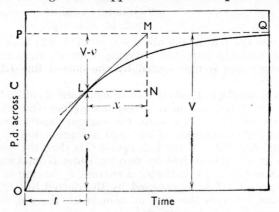

FIG. 99.—Growth of p.d. across a capacitor in series with
a resistor.

and i to be the charging current t seconds after S is put
over to a.   The corresponding p.d. across $R = V - v$,
where V is the terminal voltage of the battery.

Hence $iR = V - v$

and $i = \dfrac{V - v}{R}$ . . . . . (71)

If this current remained *constant* until the capacitor
was fully charged, and if the time taken was x seconds:

corresponding quantity
of electricity $\Big\}$ $= ix = \dfrac{V - v}{R} \times x$ coulombs.

Since the p.d. across a capacitor is proportional to the
charge, the p.d. would have increased uniformly up to

V volts, as represented by the tangent LM drawn to the curve at L.

But the charge added to the capacitor also

$$=\text{increase of p.d.} \times C$$
$$=(V-v) \times C$$

Hence

$$\frac{V-v}{R} \times x = C(V-v)$$

and

$$x = CR = \text{the time constant, } T, \text{ of the circuit} . \quad (72)$$

The construction of the curve representing the growth of the p.d. across a capacitor is therefore similar to that

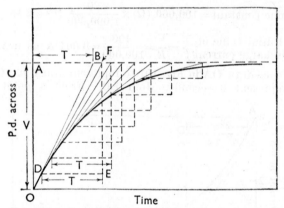

Fig. 100.—Growth of p.d. across a capacitor in series with a resistor.

described in Art. 65 for the growth of current in an inductive circuit. Thus, OA in Fig. 100 represents the battery voltage V, and AB the time constant T. Join OB, and from a point D fairly near the origin draw DE$=T$ seconds and draw EF perpendicularly. Join DF, etc. Draw a curve such that OB, DF, etc., are tangents to it.

From expression (71) it is evident that the instantaneous value of the charging current is proportional to

$(V-v)$, namely the vertical distance between the curve and the horizontal line PQ in Fig. 99. Hence the shape of the curve representing the charging current is the inverse of that of the p.d. across the capacitor and is the same for both charging and discharging currents (assuming the resistance to be the same), and its construction is illustrated by the following example.

Example 46. *A capacitor having a capacitance of 20 μF is charged to a p.d. of 400 V and then discharged through a resistance of* 100,000 Ω. *Derive a curve representing the discharge current.*

From (72):

$$\text{time constant} = 100,000 \ (\Omega) \times \frac{20}{1,000,000} \ (\text{F}) = 2 \text{ sec.}$$

$$\left.\begin{array}{l}\text{Initial value of} \\ \text{discharge current}\end{array}\right\} = \frac{V}{R} = \frac{400}{100,000} = 0\cdot004 \text{ A} = 4 \text{ mA.}$$

Hence draw OA in Fig. 101 to represent 4 mA and OB to represent 2 seconds. Join AB. From a point C

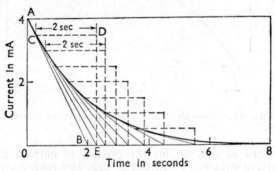

Fig. 101.—Discharge current, Example 46.

corresponding to, say, 3·5 mA, draw CD equal to 2 seconds and DE vertically. Join CE. Repeat the construction at intervals of, say, 0·5 mA and draw a curve to which AB, CE, etc., are tangents. This curve represents the variation of discharge current with time.

84. Energy Stored in a Capacitor. If a capacitor having capacitance C farads is charged at a constant rate of I amperes for t seconds, as in Fig. 102, the charge is It coulombs. If the final p.d. across the capacitor is V volts, the charge is also CV coulombs.

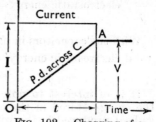

FIG. 102.—Charging of a capacitor.

$$\therefore \quad CV = It, \text{ and } V = \frac{It}{C}.$$

The p.d. across C is therefore proportional to the duration of the charge and is represented by the straight line OA. From Fig. 102 it follows that:

average p.d. across C during charging $= \tfrac{1}{2}V$ volts

and average power to C during charging $= I \times \tfrac{1}{2}V$ watts

$\therefore$ energy supplied to C during charging

$$= \text{average power} \times \text{time}$$
$$= \tfrac{1}{2}IVt \text{ joules}$$
$$= \tfrac{1}{2}V \times CV \text{ joules}$$

i.e. electrostatic energy stored in $C = \tfrac{1}{2}CV^2$ joules (73)

Example 47. *A 50-μF capacitor is charged from a 200-V supply. After being disconnected it is immediately connected in parallel with a 30-μF capacitor. Find: (a) the p.d. across the combination; (b) the electrostatic energies before and after the capacitors are connected in parallel.*

(a) From (54), charge $= 50 \times 10^{-6}$ (F) $\times 200$ (V)

$$= 0.01 \text{ coulomb.}$$

When the capacitors are connected in parallel, the total capacitance is 80 μF, and the charge of 0.01 coulomb is divided between the two capacitors:

$\therefore \qquad 0.01$ (coulomb) $= 80 \times 10^{-6}$ (F) $\times$ p.d. (volts)

$\therefore$ p.d. across capacitors $= 125$ V.

6*

(b) From (73) it follows that when the 50-μF capacitor is charged to a p.d. of 200 V :

$$\text{electrostatic energy} = \tfrac{1}{2} \times 50 \times 10^{-6} \text{ (F)} \times (200 \text{ V})^2$$
$$= 1 \text{ joule.}$$

With the capacitors in parallel :

$$\text{total electrostatic energy} = \tfrac{1}{2} \times 80 \times 10^{-6} \text{ (F)} \times (125 \text{ V})^2$$
$$= 0\cdot625 \text{ joule.}$$

It is of interest to note that there is a reduction in the energy stored in the capacitors. This loss appears as heat produced in the wires by the circulating current responsible for equalising the p.d.'s and in the spark that may occur when the capacitors are connected in parallel.

Summary of Important Formulae

$$1 \text{ electron-volt} = 1\cdot6 \times 10^{-19} \text{ joule} \quad . \quad . \quad (52)$$

$$Q \text{ (coulombs)} = C \text{ (farads)} \times V \text{ (volts)} \quad . \quad (54)$$

$$1 \text{ microfarad} = 10^{-6} \text{ farad}$$

$$\left.\begin{array}{c}\text{1 picofarad or}\\ \text{micro-microfarad}\end{array}\right\} = 10^{-12} \text{ farad.}$$

For capacitors in parallel, $C = C_1 + C_2 +$.   .   (55)

For capacitors in series, $\dfrac{1}{C} = \dfrac{1}{C_1} + \dfrac{1}{C_2} +$.   .   (57)

For C_1 and C_2 in series, $V_1 = V \cdot \dfrac{C_2}{C_1 + C_2}$.   .   (59)

and $\qquad\qquad\qquad V_2 = V \cdot \dfrac{C_1}{C_1 + C_2}$.   .   (60)

$$\left.\begin{array}{c}\text{Electric force or}\\ \text{potential gradient}\end{array}\right\} = \mathscr{E} = V/d \text{ volts/metre} \quad (61)$$

$$\left.\begin{array}{c}\text{Electric flux}\\ \text{density}\end{array}\right\} = D = Q/a \text{ coulombs/square metre} \quad (62)$$

$$\frac{\text{Electric flux density}}{\text{Electric force}} = \frac{D}{\mathscr{E}} = \epsilon_0 \epsilon_r \quad . \quad . \quad . \quad . \quad (69)$$

$$= \text{absolute permittivity}$$

where ϵ_0 =permittivity of free space or electric space constant

$$=8\cdot85 \times 10^{-12} \text{ M.K.S. units} \quad . \quad . \quad . \quad (65)$$

$$\frac{1}{\sqrt{\mu_0 \epsilon_0}} =3 \times 10^8 \text{ m/sec}$$

$$=\text{velocity of electromagnetic waves} . \quad . \quad (67)$$

Relative permittivity or dielectric constant of a material

$$=\frac{\text{capacitance of capacitor with that material as dielectric}}{\text{capacitance of same capacitor with vacuum dielectric}}$$

Capacitance of parallel-plate capacitor with n plates $\left.\right\} =\dfrac{\epsilon_0 \epsilon_r (n-1)a}{d}$ farads $\quad (70)$

Charging current of capacitor in amperes $\left.\right\} = \left\{\begin{array}{l} \text{rate of increase of charge in} \\ \text{coulombs/sec} \end{array}\right.$

$$=C \text{ (farads)} \times \text{rate of increase of p.d. in volts/sec.}$$

For R and C in series,

time constant in seconds $\left.\right\} =T=R \text{ (ohms)} \times C \text{ (farads)} \quad (72)$

energy stored in capacitor $=\frac{1}{2}CV^2$ joules $\quad . \quad . \quad (73)$

EXAMPLES IX

1. A capacitor is formed of two metallised paper sheets, each side of which has an area of 2000 cm². The two sheets are separated by paper 0·05 mm thick having a relative permittivity of 2·5. Calculate the capacitance.

2. A 1-microfarad capacitor is constructed of two strips of metal foil separated by paper dielectric 0·02 mm thick, wound spirally. The waxed paper has a dielectric constant of 3·0. The width of each metal strip is 8 cm. Find the length, in metres, of metal foil required.

3. Two capacitors, having capacitances of 10 and 15 μF respectively, are connected in series across a 200-V d.c. supply. Calculate (a) the charge on each capacitor, (b) the p.d. across each capacitor. Also find the capacitance of a single capacitor that would be equivalent to these two capacitors in series.

4. A 20-μF capacitor is charged off a 60-V d.c. supply. After being disconnected from the supply, it is immediately connected across an uncharged 5-μF capacitor. Calculate (a) the p.d. across the parallel capacitors, (b) the charge on each capacitor.

5. A variable capacitor having a capacitance of 800 $\mu\mu$F is charged to a p.d. of 100 V. The plates of the capacitor are then separated until the capacitance is reduced to 200 $\mu\mu$F. What is the change of p.d. across the capacitor? Also, what is the energy stored in the capacitor when its capacitance is (a) 800, (b) 200 $\mu\mu$F?

6. A capacitor consists of two flat plates, each 20 cm $\times$ 20 cm, separated by an air space 2 mm wide. The capacitor is charged off a 400-V d.c. supply, and a sheet of glass 30 cm $\times$ 30 cm is placed between the plates immediately they are disconnected from the supply. Find: (a) the capacitance with air dielectric, (b) the capacitance with glass dielectric, assuming the relative permittivity of glass to be 6, (c) the p.d. across the capacitor after the glass plate is inserted, (d) the charge on the capacitor and (e) the energy stored in the capacitor before and after inserting the glass plate.

7. A capacitor having a capacitance of 10 μF connected in series with a resistance of 50,000 Ω is switched across a 50-V d.c. supply. Derive curves showing how the charging current and the p.d. across the capacitor vary with time.

8. A capacitor of 0·005 microfarad receives a charge of 10 microcoulombs. Find the energy stored in the capacitor. If the capacitor is made of parallel plates 1 mm apart in air, calculate the number of plates, assuming that each side of a plate is roughly 900 cm^2 in area.

Draw a curve showing how the p.d. across the capacitor decreases with time if the insulation resistance of the capacitor is 400 megohms.

9. A 20-μF capacitor is charged and discharged thus:

Steady charging current of 0·02 A from 0 to 0·5 second.
,, ,, ,, 0·01 A from 0·5 to 1·0 second.
Zero current from 1·0 to 1·5 second.
Steady discharging current of 0·01 A from 1·5 to 2·0 second.
,, ,, ,, 0·005 A from 2·0 to 4·0 ,,

Draw graphs to scale showing how the current and the capacitor voltage vary with time.

10. Three capacitors of 2, 3 and 6 μF respectively are connected in series across a 500-V, d.c. supply. Calculate (a) the charge on each capacitor, (b) the p.d. across each capacitor and (c) the energy stored in the 6-μF capacitor.

11. Two capacitors having capacitances of 10 and 15 μF respectively are connected in parallel and a capacitor of 8 μF is connected in series. Find the capacitance of a single capacitor that is equivalent to the above combination.

12. The energy stored in a certain capacitor when connected across a 400-V, d.c. supply is 0·3 joule. Calculate (a) the capacitance and (b) the charge on the capacitor.

13. A parallel-plate capacitor has a capacitance of 300 $\mu\mu$F. It has 9 plates, each 4 cm $\times$ 3 cm, separated by mica having a dielectric constant of 5. Find the thickness of the mica.

14. Three capacitors of identical dimensions have dielectrics of relative permittivity 1, 3 and 5 respectively. They are connected in series across a 400-V d.c. supply. Calculate the p.d. across each capacitor.

15. A capacitor is charged to a p.d. of 20 V and then discharged through a ballistic galvanometer having a ballistic constant of 0·1 microcoulomb per scale division. If the first deflection or "throw" of the galvanometer is 83 divisions, what is the value of the capacitance in μF?

16. A capacitor consists of two metal plates, each 20 cm × 20 cm, spaced 1 mm apart, the dielectric being air. The capacitor is charged to a p.d. of 100 V and then discharged through a ballistic galvanometer having a ballistic constant of 0·0011 microcoulomb per scale division. The amplitude of the first deflection is 32 divisions. Calculate the value of ϵ_0.

Also, calculate the electric force and the electric flux density in the air dielectric when the terminal p.d. is 100 V.

17. When the capacitor of Question 16 is immersed in oil, charged to a p.d. of 30 V and then discharged through the same galvanometer, the first deflection is 27 divisions. Calculate the dielectric constant of the oil.

Also calculate the electric force and the electric flux density in the oil when the terminal p.d. is 30 V. What is the value of the energy stored in the capacitor?

18. A capacitor consists of two metal plates, each having an area of 600 cm², spaced 2 mm apart. The whole of the space between the plates is filled with a dielectric having a relative permittivity of 5. A p.d. of 400 V is maintained between the two plates. Calculate (a) the capacitance, (b) the charge, (c) the electric force and (d) the electric flux density.

19. A condenser consists of two metal plates, each 10 cm square, placed parallel and 3 mm apart. The space between the plates is occupied by a plate of insulating material 3 mm thick. The condenser is charged to 300 V.

(a) The metal plates are isolated from the 300-V supply and the insulating plate is removed. What is expected to happen to the voltage between the metal plates?

(b) If the metal plates are moved to a distance of 6 mm apart, what is the further effect on the voltage between them?

Assume throughout that the insulation is perfect.

(Joint Section A)

20. A slab of insulating material, 4 mm thick, is inserted between the plates of a parallel-plate capacitor. To restore the capacitance to its original value, it is necessary to increase the spacing between the plates by 2 mm. Calculate the dielectric constant of the slab.

21. What are the different values of capacitance which could be obtained if you were supplied with two capacitors of 0·1 μF and 0·2 μF capacitance?

If both capacitors have negligible leakance and the 0·1-μF capacitor is charged to 200 V while the 0·2-μF capacitor is charged to 150 V, calculate the charge on each capacitor.

The two charged capacitors are joined in parallel, positive to positive; what will be the resulting voltage across each? What would have been the voltage if the connections had been reversed?

(C & G, Telecom. Prin. I)

22. Deduce an expression for the energy stored in a condenser of capacitance C farads charged to a p.d. of V volts.

The voltage applied across a condenser having a capacitance of 10 μF is varied thus: The p.d. is increased uniformly from 0 to 600 V in 2 seconds. It is then maintained constant at 600 V for 1 second and subsequently decreased uniformly to zero in 5 seconds. Plot a graph showing the variation of current during these 8 seconds and calculate (a) the charge and (b) the energy stored in the condenser when the terminal voltage is 600 V. (I.Mech.E., Prin. of Elect.)

23. Derive an expression for the equivalent capacitance of two condensers of capacitance C_1 and C_2 respectively, connected in series.

If two condensers having capacitances of 2 and 3 μF respectively are connected in series across a 100-V d.c. supply, find (a) the equivalent capacitance, (b) the charge on each condenser and (c) the p.d. across the 2-μF condenser.   (I.Mech.E., Prin. of Elect.)

24. What do you understand by the term "electric field strength"?

A capacitor consists of two similar square aluminium plates, each 10 cm by 10 cm, mounted parallel and opposite each other. What is their capacitance in $\mu\mu$F, when the distance between them is 1 cm and the dielectric air? If the capacitor is given a charge of 500 micro-microcoulombs, what will be the difference of potential between the plates? How will this be affected if the space between the plates is filled with wax which has a dielectric constant of 4·0?

                                        (C. & G., Telecom. Prin. I)

25. A capacitor of 0·1 μF capacitance, charged to a p.d. between plates of 100 V, is discharged through a resistor of 1 megohm. Calculate:

    (i) the initial value of the discharge current,
    (ii) its value 0·1 second later,
    (iii) the initial rate of decay of the capacitor voltage,
    (iv) the energy dissipated in the resistor.

Using the above data, sketch the variation of discharge current with time.   (C. & G., Telecom. Prin. II)

26. Describe a typical form of construction for a 10-μF 500-V paper-insulated condenser. State the type of defect which may develop in such a condenser, and simple tests that can be applied to reveal them.

A 10-μF condenser charged to 500 V is connected across a 4-μF condenser. Calculate (a) the common voltage across the two condensers and (b) the stored energy before and after they are connected together. Account for any difference.   (Joint Section A)

27. A 0·1-μF capacitor is charged to a p.d. of 5 V. Calculate (a) the charge in microcoulombs and (b) the number of electrons displaced.

28. When the current in a wire is 600 A, what is the number of electrons per second passing a given point of the wire?

29. If the number of electrons passing per second through an ammeter is 7×10^{16}, what is the ammeter reading?

30. If there are 3×10^{15} electrons passing per second between two metal surfaces and if the p.d. between the surfaces is 200 V, calculate the energy absorbed in 20 minutes (a) in joules and (b) in electron-volts.

31. In a radio valve, the current between the filament and the anode is 3 mA and the p.d. is 120 V. Calculate (a) the number of electrons per second passing from the filament to the anode and (b) the energy absorbed in 5 minutes in (i) electron-volts and (ii) joules.

CHAPTER X

ALTERNATING VOLTAGE AND CURRENT

85. A Sine Wave. Since alternating voltages and currents are often represented by sine waves, it is very desirable that students should plot sine waves to scale so as to become familiar with their exact shape. This may be done either by reference to the sine tables * on p. 354 or graphically, as in Fig. 103. Thus, with any convenient radius OA, draw a circle and insert radii

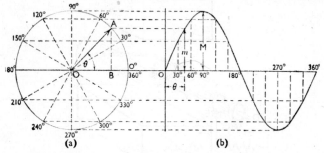

Fig. 103.—Construction of a sine wave.

every, say, 30°. On the right, mark off a horizontal scale in degrees and draw the dotted vertical lines to meet the horizontal projections from the corresponding points on the circle. A curve drawn through the various intersections is a sine wave; thus for any angle θ in Fig. 103:

$$\sin \theta = \frac{\text{perpendicular}}{\text{hypotenuse}} = \frac{AB}{OA}$$

$$\therefore \qquad AB = OA \times \sin \theta.$$

* A good sine wave can be drawn with the aid of ordinates spaced 30° apart on the horizontal axis; thus, $\sin 0° = 0$, $\sin 30° = 0.5$, $\sin 60° = 0.866$, $\sin 90° = 1.0$, $\sin 120° = 0.866$, $\sin 150° = 0.5$, etc.

In Fig. 103 (b), M is the maximum value of the alternating quantity and is also referred to as the *peak* or the *crest* value.   If m is the instantaneous value of the alternating quantity, $m = M \sin \theta$.

86. Generation of an Alternating E.M.F.   Fig. 104 shows a loop AB carried by a spindle DD rotated at a constant speed in an anti-clockwise direction in a uniform magnetic field due to poles NS.   The ends of the loop are brought out to two slip-rings C_1 and C_2 attached to but insulated from DD.   Bearing on these rings are carbon brushes E_1 and E_2 which are connected to an

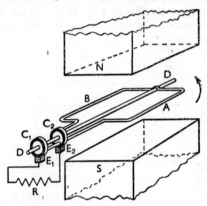

Fig. 104.—Generation of an alternating e.m.f.

external resistance R.   When the plane of the loop is horizontal, the two sides A and B are moving parallel to the lines of magnetic flux; therefore, no lines of flux are being cut and no e.m.f. is being generated in the loop.

In Fig. 105 (a), the vertical dotted lines represent the lines of magnetic flux and loop AB is shown after it has rotated through an angle θ from the horizontal position, namely the position of zero e.m.f.   Suppose the peripheral velocity of each side of the loop to be v metres per second; then at the instant shown in Fig. 105, this peripheral velocity can be represented by the length of a line AL drawn at right angles to the plane of the loop. We can resolve AL into two components AM and AN, perpendicular and parallel respectively to the direction of the magnetic flux, as shown in Fig. 105 (b)

Since $\qquad \widehat{\text{MLA}} = 90° - \widehat{\text{MAL}} = \widehat{\text{MAO}} = \theta,$

∴ $\qquad\qquad$ AM = AL sin θ = v sin θ.

The e.m.f. generated in A is due entirely to the component of the velocity perpendicular to the magnetic field. Hence, if B is the flux density in webers per

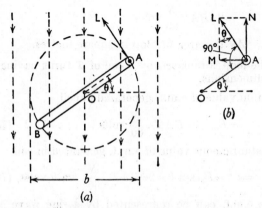

FIG. 105.—Instantaneous value of generated e.m.f.

square metre and if l is the length in metres of each of the parallel sides A and B of the loop, it follows from expression (25) that:

e.m.f. generated in $\left.\right\}$ = Blv sin θ volts
one side of loop

and

total e.m.f. generated $\left.\right\}$ = $2Blv$ sin θ volts $\quad$. $\quad$ (74)
in loop

i.e. the generated e.m.f. is proportional to sin θ. When $\theta = 90°$, the plane of the loop is vertical and both sides of the loop are cutting the magnetic flux at the maximum rate, so that the generated e.m.f. is then at its maximum value E_m. From expression (74), it follows that when $\theta = 90°$, $E_m = 2Blv$ volts.

If $b =$ breadth of the loop in metres

and $N =$ speed of rotation in revolutions per minute,

then $v = \dfrac{\pi bN}{60}$ metres/sec

and $E_m = 2Bl \times \dfrac{\pi bN}{60}$ volts

$$= 2\pi BA \cdot \frac{N}{60} \text{ volts}$$

where $A = lb =$ area of loop in square metres.

If the loop is replaced by a coil of T turns having the same dimensions,

maximum value of e.m.f. generated in coil

$$= E_m = 2\pi BAT \cdot \frac{N}{60} \text{ volts} \quad . \quad . \quad . \quad . \quad (75)$$

and instantaneous value of e.m.f. generated in coil

$$= e * = E_m \sin \theta = 2\pi BAT \cdot \frac{N}{60} \cdot \sin \theta \text{ volts} \quad (76)$$

This e.m.f. can be represented by a sine wave as in Fig. 106, where E_m represents the maximum value of the e.m.f. and e is the value after the loop has rotated through an angle θ from the position of zero e.m.f. When the loop has rotated through 180° or π radians, the e.m.f. is again zero. When θ is varying between 180° and 360° (π and 2π radians), side A of the loop is moving towards the right in Fig. 104 and is therefore cutting the magnetic flux in the opposite direction to that during the first half-revolution. Hence, if we regard the e.m.f. as positive while θ is varying between 0 and 180°, it is

* Small letters are used to represent instantaneous values and capital letters represent definite values such as maximum, average or r.m.s. values. Capital I and V without any suffix represent r.m.s. values.

negative while θ is varying between 180° and 360°; i.e. when θ varies between 180° and 270°, the value of the e.m.f. increases from zero to $-E_m$ and then decreases to zero as θ varies between 270° and 360°. Subsequent revolutions of the loop merely produce a repetition of the e.m.f. wave.

Each repetition of a variable quantity, recurring at equal intervals, is termed a *cycle*, and the duration of one cycle is termed its *period* (or *periodic time*). The

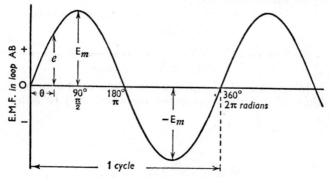

FIG. 106.—Sine wave of e.m.f.

number of such cycles that occur in one second is termed the *frequency* of that quantity. The frequency which has been adopted for power purposes in this country is 50 cycles/second (or c/s), the period being 0·02 second; but in radio work the frequency may be millions of cycles per second.

Example 48. *A coil of 100 turns is rotated at 150 r.p.m. in a magnetic field having a uniform density of 0·05 Wb/m², the axis of rotation being at right angles to the direction of the flux. The mean area per turn is 40 cm². Calculate (a) the frequency, (b) the period, (c) the maximum value of the generated e.m.f. and (d) the value of the generated e.m.f. when the coil has rotated through 30° from the position of zero e.m.f.*

(a) Since the e.m.f. generated in the coil undergoes

one cycle of variation when the coil rotates through one revolution,

∴   frequency = no. of cycles/second

                = no. of revolutions/second

                = 1500/60 = 25 c/s.

(b)   Period = time of 1 cycle

                = 1/25 = 0·04 sec.

(c) From expression (75),

$$E_m = 2\pi \times 0{\cdot}05 \times 0{\cdot}004 \times 100 \times 1500/60$$

$$= 3{\cdot}14 \text{ volts.}$$

(d) For $\theta = 30°$, sin $30° = 0{\cdot}5$,

∴ $e = 3{\cdot}14 \times 0{\cdot}5 = 1{\cdot}57$ volts.

In practice, the e.m.f. generated in a conductor of an alternating-current generator (or alternator) is seldom

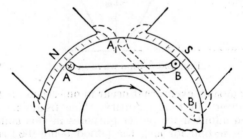

Fig. 107.—Generation of an alternating e.m.f.

sinusoidal. For instance, let us consider a 4-pole machine, a portion of which is shown in Fig. 107, and suppose AB to represent a full-pitched coil, i.e. a coil of such width that when side A is opposite the centre of a N pole, the other side B is opposite the centre of an adjacent S pole. The gaps under the poles are assumed to be of uniform length, so that the flux is uniformly distributed over the pole faces—as indicated by the short dotted lines. Beyond the pole-tips, however, the density of the fringing flux decreases rapidly owing to the greater length of the paths of the magnetic flux between the poles and the armature.

Since the value of the e.m.f. generated in AB is proportional to the rate at which these conductors cut the magnetic field, it follows that while A and B are moving under the pole-faces, the rate of cutting the magnetic flux remains constant and the e.m.f. is represented by the straight line CD in Fig. 108. After the coil has passed beyond the pole-faces, the e.m.f. decreases rapidly, as indicated by DE, until when the conductors are midway between the poles—as shown by A_1B_1—the e.m.f. is zero. As the conductors move into the fields of the succeeding poles, the e.m.f. generated in the coil grows in the reverse direction, as indicated by EF

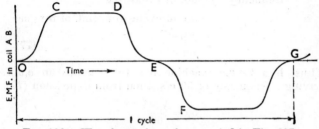

FIG. 108.—Waveform of e.m.f. generated in Fig. 107.

in Fig. 108. Hence the e.m.f. generated in the coil varies in the manner shown in that figure; and the variation which takes place during interval OG is repeated indefinitely, so long as the speed is kept constant.

The sharpness of the corners at C and D in Fig. 108 can be reduced by rounding off the pole-tips in Fig. 107, thereby giving a more gradual variation of the flux density in those regions. Also, in an actual machine, the conductors are distributed in slots around the periphery of the armature, and it is found that the effect of this distribution is to make the waveform of the resultant e.m.f. nearly sinusoidal. In most a.c. calculations, the waveforms of both the voltage and the current are assumed to be sinusoidal.

87. Relationship between Frequency, Speed and Number of Poles Pairs. Let us consider the 4-pole machine of Fig. 107. When conductor A is moving across the flux entering the armature from pole N, the direction of the e.m.f. is, by the Right-Hand Rule (Art. 47), towards the paper. When A is moving across the flux entering pole S from the armature, the direction of the e.m.f. is outwards from the paper; i.e. when the conductor passes a pair of poles, the e.m.f. varies through one cycle. Hence for a 4-pole machine, the number of cycles of e.m.f. generated during one revolution is 2, namely the number of pairs of poles. It follows that if a machine has p pairs of poles and if the speed of rotation is N r.p.m.,

$$\text{frequency} = f = \text{no. of cycles/sec}$$
$$= \text{no. of cycles/rev} \times \text{no. of revs/sec}$$
$$= \frac{Np}{60} \quad \cdot \quad \cdot \quad \cdot \quad \cdot \quad \cdot \quad \cdot \quad (77)$$

Thus, if a 2-pole machine has to generate an e.m.f. having a frequency of 50 c/s, then from expression (77),

$$50 = \frac{N \times 1}{60}$$

$$\therefore \qquad\qquad N = 3000 \text{ r.p.m.}$$

Since it is not possible to have fewer than two poles, the highest speed at which a 50-c/s alternator can be operated is 3000 r.p.m.

88. Average or Mean Value of an Alternating Current or Voltage. Let us first consider the case of a wave which is not sinusoidal. For instance, the wave in Fig. 109 (a) is typical of the current taken by a transformer on no load. The base line for the first half-cycle is divided into, say, 6 equal parts and the mid-ordinates i_1, i_2, etc, are drawn and measured. Then:

$$\text{average value of current} = I_{av} = \frac{i_1 + i_2 + i_3 + i_4 + i_5 + i_6}{6}.$$

In general, if n equally-spaced mid-ordinates i_1, i_2,

. . . i_n are taken over either the positive or the negative half-cycle:

$$\text{average value of current} = I_{av} = \frac{i_1 + i_2 + \ldots + i_n}{n} \quad (78)$$

The larger the number of ordinates used, the more accurate is the result. With symmetrical waves it would be useless to add together the mid-ordinates over a whole cycle because the result would be zero.

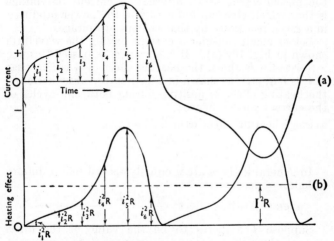

FIG. 109.—Average and r.m.s. values.

If the above calculation is repeated with a sine wave, it is found that:

$$\text{average value} = 0.637 * \times \text{maximum value} \quad . \quad (79)$$

It is sometimes necessary to determine the average value of an alternating current or voltage; but in general the effective value, referred to in the next article, is far more important.

* By the aid of integral calculus, it can be shown that this value is $\frac{2}{\pi} = 0.637$.

89. Effective or R.M.S. Value of an Alternating Current or Voltage.   In Art. 18 it was shown that when a current I amperes flows through a resistance R ohms with a difference of potential of V volts across it:

$$\text{power} = \frac{V^2}{R} = I^2R \text{ watts.}$$

In other words, for a given resistance the power is proportional to the square of the voltage and the square of the current; consequently the important quantity in the measurement of an alternating current or voltage is that which gives an indication of the power produced in a given resistance by that current or voltage.

Let us again consider a current having the waveform shown in Fig. 109 (a).   If this current is passed through a resistance R ohms, the heating effect of i_1 is i_1^2R, that of i_2 is i_2^2R, etc., as shown in Fig. 109 (b).   Furthermore, the heating effect is positive during both half-cycles of the current wave; hence:

average heating effect over half a cycle

$$= \frac{i_1^2R + i_2^2R + \ldots + i_6^2R}{6}.$$

In general if there are n equally spaced mid-ordinates in half a cycle, then:

$$\text{average heating effect} = \frac{i_1^2R + i_2^2R + \ldots + i_n^2R}{n}.$$

Suppose I amperes to be the value of the *direct current* through the *same* resistance R to produce a steady heating effect equal to the average heating effect of the alternating current, and thus to produce the same quantity of heat in half a cycle:

then $I^2R = \dfrac{i_1^2R + i_2^2R + \ldots + i_n^2R}{n}$

$$\therefore \quad I = \sqrt{\left(\frac{i_1^2 + i_2^2 + \ldots + i_n^2}{n} \right)} \quad \ldots \quad (80)$$

=square *root* of the *mean* of the *squares* of the current

= root-mean-square (or r.m.s.) value of the current.

This quantity is also termed the *effective* or *virtual* *
value of the current. It will therefore be noted that the
r.m.s. or *effective value of an alternating current is
measured in terms of the direct current that produces the
same heating effect in the same resistance.*

If the construction described above be applied to a
sine wave of current it is found that the variation of the
heating effect follows a curve which is symmetrical †
about the dotted horizontal line in Fig. 110. In virtue
of this symmetry the shaded areas above the dotted line

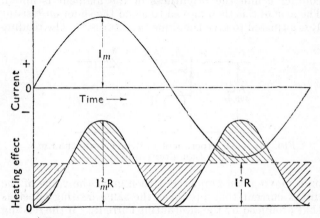

FIG. 110.—R.m.s. value of sinusoidal current.

are equal to those below the dotted line. Hence if I_m
be the maximum or peak value of the alternating
current, the average heating effect over a cycle (or half
a cycle) is half the maximum heating effect, namely

* This term is not recommended by the British Standards
Institution.

† The symmetry can also be proved by trigonometry: thus,
$\sin^2 \theta = \frac{1}{2} - \frac{1}{2} \cos 2\theta$. In words, this means that the square of a
sine wave may be regarded as being made up of two compo-
nents: (a) a constant quantity equal to half the maximum
value of the $\sin^2 \theta$ curve; and (b) a cosine curve having twice
the frequency of the $\sin \theta$ curve. From Fig. 110 it is seen that
the curve of the heating effect undergoes two cycles of change
during one cycle of current.

$\frac{1}{2}I_m^2 R$ watts. If I amperes be the value of the *direct* current to give the same heating effect in the same resistance, then:

$$I^2 R = \tfrac{1}{2}I_m^2 R$$

$$\therefore \qquad\qquad I = 0.707\ I_m \quad . \quad . \quad . \quad . \quad (81)$$

The following simple experiment may be found useful in illustrating the significance of the r.m.s. value of an alternating current. A metal-filament lamp L (Fig. 111) is connected to an a.c. supply by closing switch S on contact a and the brightness of the filament is noted. The arm of S is then moved to b and the slider on resistor R is adjusted to give the same brightness.* The reading

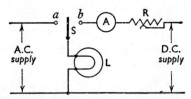

FIG. 111.—An experiment to demonstrate the r.m.s. value of an alternating current.

on a moving-coil ammeter A then gives the value of the direct current that produces the same heating effect as that produced by the alternating current. If the reading on ammeter A is, say, 0·3 ampere when equality of brightness has been attained, the r.m.s. value of the alternating current is 0·3 ampere.

90. Form Factor and Peak or Crest Factor of a Wave. The *form factor* is the ratio of the r.m.s. value to the average value of the wave; thus for a sine wave:

$$\text{form factor} = \frac{0.707 \times \text{maximum value}}{0.637 \times \text{maximum value}}$$

$$= 1.11 \qquad . \quad . \quad . \quad . \quad (82)$$

* For more precise adjustment, an illumination meter can be placed at a convenient distance from the lamp and R adjusted to give the same reading when S is moved over from a to b.

The *peak* or *crest factor* is the ratio of the peak (or maximum) value to the r.m.s. value of the wave; thus for a sine wave:

$$\text{peak or crest factor} = \frac{\text{maximum value}}{0.707 \times \text{maximum value}}$$

$$= 1.414 \quad . \quad . \quad . \quad . \quad . \quad (83)$$

91. Measurement of the R.M.S. Values of Alternating Currents and Voltages. If an ammeter or a voltmeter is to read the r.m.s. value, its action must depend upon some effect which is proportional to the square of the quantity to be measured; and the instruments principally used for this purpose can be grouped thus:

(a) Moving-iron ammeters and voltmeters (Art. 142)
(b) Thermal ammeters and voltmeters (Art 144)
(c) Dynamometer ammeters and voltmeters (Art. 145)
(d) Electrostatic voltmeters (Art. 146).

Summary of Important Formulae

Instantaneous value of e.m.f. generated in a coil rotating in a uniform magnetic field

$$= e = E_m \sin \theta$$

$$= 2\pi BAT \cdot \frac{N}{60} \cdot \sin \theta \text{ volts} \quad . \quad . \quad (76)$$

$$f = \frac{Np}{60} \quad . \quad . \quad . \quad . \quad . \quad . \quad . \quad . \quad (77)$$

For *n* equidistant mid-ordinates over half a cycle,

$$\text{average value} = \frac{i_1 + i_2 + \ldots + i_n}{n} \quad . \quad . \quad . \quad (78)$$

$$\left.\begin{array}{l}\text{and r.m.s. or}\\ \text{effective value}\end{array}\right\} = \sqrt{\left(\frac{i_1^2 + i_2^2 + \ldots + i_n^2}{n}\right)} \quad . \quad . \quad (80)$$

For sinusoidal waves,

$$\text{average value} = 0.637 \times \text{maximum value} \quad . \quad . \quad (79)$$

$$\left.\begin{array}{l}\text{and r.m.s. or}\\ \text{effective value}\end{array}\right\} = 0.707 \times \text{maximum value} \quad . \quad . \quad (81)$$

$$\text{Form factor} = \frac{\text{r.m.s. value}}{\text{average value}} \quad \cdots \quad (82)$$

$$= 1 \cdot 11 \text{ for a sine wave.}$$

$$\left.\begin{array}{c}\text{Peak or crest} \\ \text{factor}\end{array}\right\} = \frac{\text{peak or maximum value}}{\text{r.m.s. value}} \quad (83)$$

$$= 1 \cdot 414 \text{ for a sine wave.}$$

EXAMPLES X

1. Calculate the speed at which an 8-pole alternator must be driven in order that it may generate an e.m.f. having a frequency of 60 c/s.

2. An alternator driven by an internal-combustion engine at 375 r.p.m. is required to generate an alternating e.m.f. having a frequency of 50 c/s. Calculate the number of poles for which the alternator must be wound.

3. If a 4-pole alternator is driven at a speed of 1800 r.p.m., calculate the frequency of the generated e.m.f.

4. A coil of 200 turns is rotated at 600 r.p.m. in a magnetic field having a uniform density of 5000 μWb/m^2, the axis of rotation being at right angles to the direction of the field. The mean area per turn is 30 cm^2. Calculate (a) the frequency and the period, (b) the r.m.s. and the maximum values of the generated e.m.f.

5. A circular coil of 60 turns, carried by a spindle placed at right angles to a magnetic field of uniform density, is rotated at a uniform speed. The mean diameter of the coil is 30 cm. Calculate the speed in order that the frequency of the generated e.m.f. may be 40 c/s and find the density of the magnetic field if the r.m.s. value of the generated e.m.f. is 36 V. What are the average and the maximum values of the e.m.f.?

What should be the direction of the spindle relative to that of the magnetic field if no e.m.f. is to be generated when the coil is rotated?

6. Draw to an adequate scale the sine wave representing a current having an amplitude of 20 A. By means of the mid-ordinate method, find (a) the average value and (b) the r.m.s. value of the current.

7. Draw sine waves to represent a voltage having a peak value of 200 V and a current having a peak value of 50 A, the current being assumed to lag 30° behind the voltage.

8. A sinusoidal current has an r.m.s. value of 10 A at a frequency of 50 c/s. Find the duration of 1 cycle in milliseconds. Plot the current wave over one cycle, using a vertical scale of 1 inch to represent 5 A and a horizontal scale of 1 inch to represent 5 milliseconds. From this graph, find (a) the value of the current 3 milliseconds after it has passed through its zero value and (b) the time taken for the current to grow from zero to 6 A. Check these values mathematically from the expression: $i = I_m \sin \theta$.

9. What is meant by the r.m.s. value of an alternating current and why is this value used?

A sinusoidal alternating current has a maximum value of 2 A. Draw to scale the curve of current over half a cycle and obtain graphically the r.m.s. value of the current.   (N.C.T.E.C., S2)

10. The time between the positive peak of an alternating voltage wave and the first succeeding negative peak is 0·02 sec. What is the frequency? Plot this voltage wave and obtain the r.m.s. value from your graph, assuming the wave is sinusoidal and 200-V peak value. If this voltage is applied to a resistance of 57·6 ohms, calculate the power in watts.   (U.E.I., S2)

11. An alternating current had the following values for half-cycle:

Angle in radians .	0	$\pi/9$	$\pi/6$	$\pi/3$	$\pi/2$	$2\pi/3$	$5\pi/6$	$8\pi/9$	π
Current in amp .	0	5	20	35	40	35	20	5	0

These current values are joined by straight lines. Obtain the r.m.s. value of this current from your graph. If the time of one complete cycle is 0·015 sec, what is the frequency?   (U.E.I., S2)

12. Define the r.m.s. value of an alternating current and explain why the r.m.s. value is usually much more important than either the peak or the average value of an alternating current.

An alternating current has the following values (in amperes) at equal intervals of time: 0, 2, 3, 3·5, 4, 4·4, 4·5, 3, 0, −2, −3, etc. Draw to scale the waveform over one cycle and determine the average and the r.m.s. values of the current.   (I.Mech.E., Prin. of Elect.)

13. The half-wave of an alternating current has the following values:

Time (sec) .	0	0·001	0·002	0·003	0·004	0·005
Amperes . .	0	1·9	4·5	8·0	10·8	12·5
Time (sec) .		0·006	0·007	0·008	0·009	0·010
Amperes . .		10·8	9·0	6·0	2·4	0

Find graphically or otherwise the r.m.s. value of the current. What is the power dissipated if the resistance of the circuit is 20 Ω?
(C. & G., El. Eng. Pract., Prelim.)

14. What is meant by the "root mean square" value of an alternating current? Explain why this value is used. An alternating current has the following values over one-half of a cycle:

Time in millisec .	0	1	2	3	4	5	6	7	8	9	10
Current in amp .	0	2·5	3·4	3·1	3·3	3·6	3·3	3·1	3·4	2·5	0

Determine the r.m.s. value and the frequency of the current wave.
(N.C.T.E.C., S2)

15. Define the r.m.s. and the average values of an alternating current and explain why the r.m.s. value is usually of greater importance than the average value.

An alternating current varies in the following manner during one half-cycle: During the first quarter-cycle, it increases uniformly from 0 to 10 A; during the next eighth of a cycle, it decreases uniformly from 10 to 8 A; and during the remainder of the half-cycle, it decreases uniformly to zero. Plot a graph of the current wave over half a cycle and determine the r.m.s. and the average values of the current.
(I.Mech.E., Prin. of Elect.)

16. If the waveform of a voltage has a form factor of 1·15 and a peak factor of 1·5, and if the peak value is 4·5 kV, calculate the average and the r.m.s. values of the voltage.

17. If the waveform of an alternating current is an isosceles triangle having a peak value of 10 A, find the average and the effective values of the current and the form and peak factors of the wave.

18. An alternating current was measured by a d.c. milliammeter in conjunction with a full-wave rectifier. The reading on the milli-ammeter was 7 mA. Assuming the waveform of the alternating current to be sinusoidal, calculate (a) the r.m.s. value and (b) the maximum value of the alternating current.

CHAPTER XI

RESISTANCE AND INDUCTANCE IN A.C. CIRCUITS

92. Alternating Current in a Circuit possessing Resistance only. Consider a circuit having a resistance R ohms connected across the terminals of an alternator A, as in Fig. 112, and suppose the alternating voltage to be represented by the sine wave of Fig. 113. If the value of the voltage at any instant B is v volts, the value of the current * at that instant is given by:

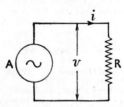

FIG. 112.—Circuit with resistance only.

$$i = \frac{v}{R} \text{ amperes.}$$

When the voltage is zero the current is also zero; and since the current is proportional to the voltage, the waveform of the current is exactly the same as that of the voltage. Also the two quantities are *in phase* with each other; that is, they pass through their zero values at the same instant and attain their maximum values in a given direction at the same instant. Hence the current wave is as shown dotted in Fig. 113.

If V_m and I_m be the maximum values of the voltage and current respectively, it follows that:

$$I_m = \frac{V_m}{R} \quad . \quad . \quad . \quad . \quad (84)$$

* An arrow or arrowhead is used to indicate the direction in which the current flows when it is regarded positive. It is immaterial which direction is chosen as positive; but once it has been decided upon for a given circuit or network, the same direction must be adhered to for all the currents and voltages involved in that circuit or network.

But the r.m.s. value of a sine wave is 0·707 times the maximum value, so that:

$$\text{r.m.s. value of voltage} = V = 0.707 V_m$$

and   r.m.s. value of current $= I = 0.707 I_m$.

Substituting for I_m and V_m in (84) we have:

$$\frac{I}{0.707} = \frac{V}{0.707 R}$$

∴ $$I = \frac{V}{R} \quad . \quad . \quad . \quad . \quad . \quad (85)$$

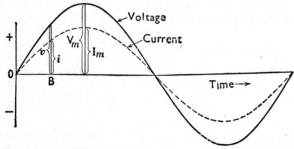

FIG. 113.—Voltage and current curves for non-inductive circuit.

Hence Ohm's Law can be applied without any modification to an a.c. circuit consisting of resistance only.

If the instantaneous value of the applied voltage is represented by:

$$v = V_m \sin \theta,$$

then instantaneous value of current in a resistive circuit $\Big\} = i = \dfrac{V_m}{R} \sin \theta$.   (86)

93. Alternating Current in a Circuit possessing Inductance only. Let us consider the effect of a sinusoidal current flowing through a coil having an inductance of L henrys and a negligible resistance, as in Fig. 114. For instance, let us consider what is happening during the first quarter-cycle of Fig. 115. This quarter-cycle has been divided into three equal intervals, OA, AC and

CF seconds. During interval OA, the current increases from O to AB; hence the average rate of increase of current is AB/OA amperes/second, and is represented by ordinate JK drawn midway between O and A. From expression (40), the e.m.f., in volts, induced in a coil= $-L\times$rate of increase of current in amperes per second; consequently, the average value of the induced e.m.f. during interval OA is $-L\times$AB/OA, namely $-L\times$JK volts, and is represented by ordinate JQ in Fig. 115. The negative sign denotes that the induced e.m.f. tends to oppose the growth of the current in the positive direction.

Similarly, during interval AC, the current increases from AB to CE, so that the average rate of increase of

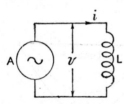

FIG. 114.—Circuit with inductance only.

current is DE/AC amperes/second, which is represented by ordinate LM in Fig. 115; and the corresponding induced e.m.f. is $-L\times$LM volts and is represented by LR. During the third interval CF, the average rate of increase of current is GH/CF, namely NP amperes/second; and the corresponding induced e.m.f. is $-L\times$NP volts and is repre-

sented by NS. At instant F, the current has ceased growing but has not yet begun to decrease; consequently the rate of change of current is then zero. The induced e.m.f. will therefore have decreased from a maximum at O to zero at F. Curves can now be drawn through the derived points, as shown in Fig. 115.

During the second quarter-cycle, the current decreases, so that the rate of increase of current is negative and the induced e.m.f. becomes positive, tending to prevent the current decreasing. Since the sine wave of current is symmetrical about ordinate FH, the curves representing the rate of increase of current and the e.m.f. induced in the coil will be symmetrical with those derived for the first quarter-cycle. It will now be evident that the rate of change of current at any instant is proportional to the slope of the current wave at that instant; consequently the value of the induced e.m.f. increases from zero at F to a maximum at T and then decreases to zero at U in Fig. 115.

By using shorter intervals, for example by taking ordinates at intervals of 10° and noting the corresponding values of the ordinates from the sine tables on p. 354, it is possible to derive fairly accurately the shapes of the curves representing the rate of change of current and the

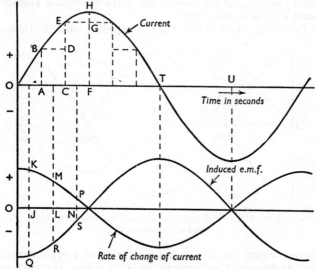

Fig. 115.—Curves of current, rate of change of current and induced e.m.f.

induced e.m.f. It is found that both curves are sinusoidal * in shape.

From Fig. 115, it will be seen that the induced e.m.f. attains its maximum positive value a quarter of a cycle *after* the current has done the same thing—in fact, it goes through all its variations a quarter of a cycle after

* It can be proved with the aid of differential calculus that the waveforms are sinusoidal.

7

the current has gone through similar variations. Hence the induced e.m.f. is said to *lag* a quarter of a cycle behind the current or the current is said to *lead* a quarter of a cycle in front of the induced e.m.f.

Since the resistance of the coil is assumed negligible, we may regard the whole of the applied voltage as being absorbed in neutralising the induced e.m.f. Hence the curve of applied voltage in Fig. 116 can be drawn exactly equal and opposite to that of the induced e.m.f.; and since the latter is sinusoidal, the wave of applied voltage must also be a sine curve.

From Fig. 116 it is seen that the applied voltage attains

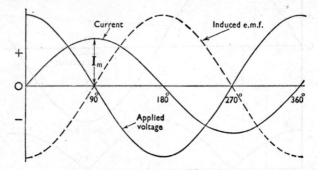

FIG. 116.—Voltage and current curves for purely inductive circuit.

its maximum positive value a quarter of a cycle earlier than is done by the current; in other words, the voltage applied to a purely inductive circuit leads a quarter of a cycle or 90° in front of the current, or the current lags a quarter of a cycle or 90° behind the applied voltage.

The student may quite reasonably ask: If the applied voltage is neutralised by the induced e.m.f., how can there be any current? The answer is that if there were no current there would be no flux, and therefore no induced e.m.f. The current has to vary at such a rate that the e.m.f. induced by the corresponding variation of flux is equal and opposite to the applied voltage. Actually there is a slight difference between the applied voltage and the induced e.m.f., this difference being the voltage required to send the current through the low resistance of the coil.

94. Mechanical Analogy of an Inductive Circuit. One of the most puzzling things to a student commencing the study of alternating currents is the behaviour of a current in an inductive circuit. For instance, why should the current in Fig. 116 be at its maximum value when there is no applied voltage? Why should there be no current when the applied voltage is at its maximum? Why should it be possible to have a voltage applied in one direction and a current flowing in the reverse

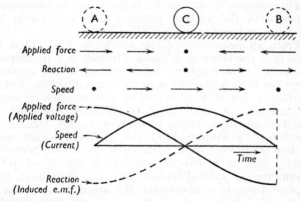

FIG. 117.—Mechanical analogy of a purely inductive circuit.

direction as is the case during the second and fourth quarter-cycles in Fig. 116?

It may therefore be found helpful to consider a simple mechanical analogy—the simpler the better. In Mechanics, it is found that the *inertia* of a body opposes any change in the *speed* of that body. The effect of inertia is therefore analogous to that of *inductance* in opposing any change in the *current*.

Suppose we take a heavy metal cylinder C (Fig. 117), such as a pulley or an armature, and roll it backwards and forwards on a horizontal surface between two

extreme positions A and B.   Let us consider the forces
and the speed while C is being rolled from A to B.
At first the speed is zero, but the force applied to the
body is at its maximum causing C to accelerate towards
the right.   This applied force is reduced—as indicated
by the length of the arrows in Fig. 117—until it is zero
when C is midway between A and B.   C ceases to
accelerate and will therefore have attained its maximum
speed from left to right.

Immediately after C has passed the mid-point, the
direction of the applied force is reversed and increased
until the body is brought to rest at B and then begins
its return movement.

The reaction of C, on the other hand, is equal and
opposite to the applied pressure and corresponds to
the e.m.f. induced in the inductive circuit.

From an inspection of the arrows in Fig. 117 it is
seen that the speed in a given direction is a maximum
a quarter of a complete oscillation after the applied
force has been a maximum in the same direction, but a
quarter of an oscillation before the reaction reaches
its maximum in that direction.   This is analogous to
the current in a purely inductive circuit lagging a
quarter of a cycle behind the applied voltage and
leading a quarter of a cycle in front of the induced
e.m.f.   Also it is evident that when the speed is a
maximum the applied force is zero, and that when the
applied force is a maximum the speed is zero; and
during the second half of the movement indicated in
Fig. 117, the direction of motion is opposite to that of
the applied pressure.   These relationships correspond
exactly to those found for an inductive circuit.

**95. Numerical Relationship between Current and Volt-
age in a Purely Inductive Circuit.**   From Fig. 116 it is
seen that the current increases from zero to its maximum
value I_m in a quarter of a cycle.   If the frequency is
f cycles/second, the duration of one cycle is $\frac{1}{f}$ second and
that of a quarter-cycle is $\frac{1}{4f}$ second.

Hence, average rate of increase of current during quarter of a cycle

$$= I_m \div \frac{1}{4f} = 4fI_m \text{ amperes/second.}$$

From expression (40) it follows that:

average e.m.f. induced in coil $= -L \times 4fI_m$ volts

∴ average value of applied voltage $= +4fLI_m$ volts.

But in Art. 88 it was shown that for a sinusoidal wave: average value of voltage $= 0 \cdot 637 \times$ max. value of voltage

$$= \frac{2}{\pi} \times V_m.$$

Hence $\qquad \frac{2}{\pi} V_m = 4fLI_m$

and $\qquad \frac{V_m}{I_m} = 2\pi fL.$

If V and I are the r.m.s. values of the applied voltage and current respectively:

$$\frac{V}{I} = \frac{0 \cdot 707 V_m}{0 \cdot 707 I_m} = 2\pi fL$$

$$= \textit{inductive reactance} \text{ of the circuit.}$$

Since the reactance is the ratio of the voltage to the current, it is expressed in ohms. It is represented by the symbol X_L.

The above relationship can also be expressed thus:

$$I = \frac{V}{2\pi fL} = \frac{V}{X_L} \quad . \quad . \quad . \quad (87)$$

It is evident that the inductive reactance is proportional to the frequency and that for a given voltage, the current is inversely proportional to the frequency. These relationships are represented graphically by the straight line and hyperbola respectively in Fig. 118.

If instantaneous value of applied voltage $\Big\} = v = V_m \sin \theta$

then instantaneous value of current in a purely inductive circuit $\Big\} = i = \frac{V_m}{2\pi fL} \sin (\theta - \pi/2)$ (88)

96. Alternating Current in a Circuit possessing Resistance and Inductance in Series. Suppose the circuit to consist of a resistance R ohms in series with an inductance L henrys (Fig. 119), and suppose the current to be

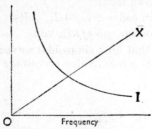

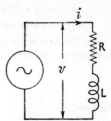

FIG. 118.—Effect of frequency on inductive reactance and current.

FIG. 119.—Resistance and inductance in series.

sinusoidal, as shown in Fig. 120. From Art. 92 it follows that the p.d. across R is in phase with the current; and in Art. 93 it was shown that the voltage applied to

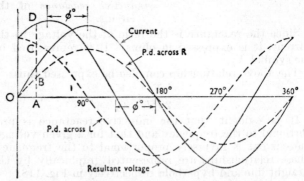

FIG. 120.—Voltage and current curves for Fig. 119.

an inductance leads 90° in front of the current. The curves for these p.d.'s are shown dotted in Fig. 120. At any instant the resultant voltage is the sum of the p.d.'s across R and L; thus at instant A, the p.d. across R is AB and that across L is AC, so that the total applied voltage=AB+AC=AD. By adding together the two dotted curves in this way, we can derive the curve representing the resultant voltage across R and L.

It is seen that the resultant voltage attains its maximum positive value ϕ * degrees before the current does so; similarly the resultant voltage passes through zero ϕ degrees before the current passes through zero in the *same* direction.

It will now be evident that the representation of alternating currents and voltages by curves such as those of Fig. 120 becomes involved when the circuit is anything but a simple resistance or reactance. Also the calculations become very cumbersome. Both the representation and the calculations can be simplified considerably by the use of vector diagrams.

97. Representation of an Alternating Quantity by a Rotating Vector. In Fig. 121 (a), OA represents to scale the maximum value of the alternating quantity, say, current; i.e. $OA=I_m$. Suppose OA to rotate counter-clockwise about O at a uniform angular velocity. This is purely a conventional direction which has been universally adopted. Also an arrowhead is always placed at the outer end of the vector, partly to indicate which end is assumed to move and partly to indicate the precise length of the vector when two or more vectors happen to coincide.

Let us assume that Fig. 121 (a) shows OA when it has rotated through an angle θ from the position occupied when the current was passing through its zero value. If AB and AC be drawn perpendicular to the horizontal and vertical axes respectively:

$OC=AB=OA \sin \theta$

$=I_m \sin \theta$

$=i$, namely the value of the current at that instant.

This relationship follows from the method used in Fig. 103 to construct a sine wave. Hence the projection of

* Small ϕ is used for angles and capital Φ for flux.

OA on the vertical axis represents to scale the instantaneous value of the current. Thus when $\theta = 90°$, the projection is OA itself; when $\theta = 180°$, the projection is zero and corresponds to the current passing through zero from a positive to a negative value; when $\theta = 210°$, the vector is in position OA_1, and the projection $= OD = \frac{1}{2}OA_1 = -\frac{1}{2}I_m$; and when $\theta = 360°$, the projection is again zero and corresponds to the current passing through zero from a negative to a positive value. It follows that OA rotates through one revolution or 2π radians in one cycle of the current wave.

If f is the frequency in cycles/second, then OA rotates through f revolutions or $2\pi f$ radians in 1 second. Hence

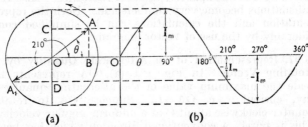

FIG. 121.—Vector representation of an alternating quantity.

the angular velocity of OA is $2\pi f$ radians/second and is denoted by the symbol ω (omega):

i.e. $\omega = 2\pi f$ radians/second.

If the time taken by OA in Fig. 121 to rotate through an angle θ radians be t seconds, then:

$$\theta = \text{angular velocity} \times \text{time}$$
$$= \omega t = 2\pi f t \text{ radians.}$$

We can therefore express the instantaneous value of the current thus:

$$i = I_m \sin \theta = I_m \sin \omega t = I_m \sin 2\pi f t.$$

Let us next consider how two quantities such as voltage and current can be represented by rotating vectors. Fig. 122 (b) shows the voltage leading in front of the current by an angle ϕ. In Fig. 122 (a), OA represents the maximum value of the current and OB that of the voltage. The angle between OA and OB must be the same angle ϕ as in Fig. 122 (b), OB leading in front

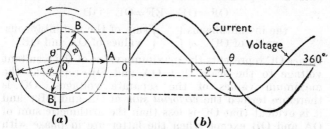

FIG. 122.—Vector representation of quantities differing in phase.

of OA. Consequently when OA is along the horizontal axis, the current at that instant is zero and the value of the voltage is represented by the projection of OB on the vertical axis. These values correspond to instant O in Fig. 122 (b).

After the vectors have rotated through an angle θ, they occupy positions OA_1 and OB_1 respectively; and the instantaneous values of the current and voltage are again given by the projections of OA_1 and OB_1 on the vertical axis, as shown by the horizontal dotted lines.

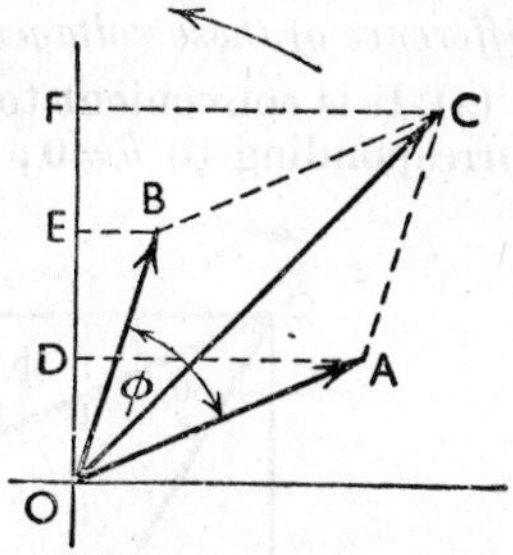

FIG. 123.—Addition of vectors.

98. Addition of Alternating Voltages or Currents by means of Vectors. Suppose OA and OB in Fig. 123 to be rotating vectors representing to scale the maximum values of two alternating voltages differing in phase by some angle ϕ. Complete the parallelogram OACB and draw the diagonal OC. Project OA, OB and OC on to the vertical axis. Then for the positions shown in Fig. 123:

7*

instantaneous value of OA=OD

instantaneous value of OB=OE

and   instantaneous value of OC=OF.

Since BC is parallel and equal to OA, EF=OD

∴   OF=OE+EF=OE+OD

i.e. the instantaneous } = { sum of the instantaneous
value of OC } { values of OA and OB.

Hence OC represents the maximum value of the resultant voltage to the scale that OA and OB represent the maximum values of the separate voltages. OC is therefore termed the *vectorial sum* of OA and OB; and it is evident that OC is less than the arithmetic sum of OA and OB except when the latter are in phase with each other. This is the reason why it is seldom correct in a.c. work to add voltages or currents together arithmetically.

Example 49. *The instantaneous values of two alternating voltages are represented respectively by $v_1 = 60 \sin \theta$ and $v_2 = 40 \sin (\theta - \pi/3)$. Derive an expression for the instantaneous value of* (a) *the sum and* (b) *the difference of these voltages.*

(a) It is convenient to draw the vectors in the position corresponding to $\theta = 0$; i.e. OA in Fig. 124 is drawn to

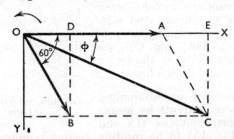

FIG. 124.—Addition of vectors in Example 49.

scale along the X axis to represent 60 volts, and OB is drawn $\pi/3$ radians or 60° behind OA to represent 40 volts. The diagonal OC of the parallelogram drawn on

OA and OB represents the vectorial sum of OA and OB. By measurement, OC=87 volts and angle ϕ between OC and the X axis is 23·5° or 0·41 radian; hence:

$$\left.\begin{array}{c}\text{instantaneous sum of the}\\ \text{two voltages}\end{array}\right\} = 87 \sin (\theta - 0\cdot 41).$$

Alternatively, this expression can be found thus:

Horizontal component of OA=60 V

„   „   OB=OD=40 cos 60° = 20 V

$\therefore\quad\left.\begin{array}{c}\text{resultant horizontal}\\ \text{component}\end{array}\right\} = \text{OA}+\text{OD}=60+20$

$=80$ V=OE in Fig. 124.

Vertical component of OA=0

„   „   OB=BD=$-40 \sin 60°$

$=-34\cdot 64$ V

$\therefore\quad\left.\begin{array}{c}\text{resultant vertical}\\ \text{component}\end{array}\right\} = -34\cdot 64 \text{ V}=\left\{\begin{array}{c}\text{CE in Fig.}\\ 124.\end{array}\right.$

The minus sign merely signifies that the resultant vertical component is *below* the horizontal axis and that the resultant voltage must therefore lag behind OA.

$$\left.\begin{array}{c}\text{Hence maximum value}\\ \text{of resultant voltage}\end{array}\right\} = \text{OC}=\sqrt{[(80)^2+(-34\cdot 64)^2]}$$

$$=87\cdot 2 \text{ V}.$$

If ϕ is the angle of lag of OC behind OA,

$$\tan \phi=\frac{\text{EC}}{\text{OE}}=\frac{-34\cdot 64}{80}=-0\cdot 433$$

$\therefore\qquad\qquad \phi=23\cdot 4°=0\cdot 41$ radian,

$$\left.\begin{array}{c}\text{and instantaneous value}\\ \text{of resultant voltage}\end{array}\right\} = 87\cdot 2 \sin (\theta - 0\cdot 41).$$

(b) The construction for subtracting OB from OA is obvious from Fig. 125.

By measurement, OC=53 volts

and $\qquad\qquad\qquad \phi=41°=0\cdot 71$ radian,

$\therefore\quad\left.\begin{array}{c}\text{instantaneous dif-}\\ \text{ference of the}\\ \text{two voltages}\end{array}\right\} = 53 \sin (\theta + 0\cdot 71).$

Alternatively, resultant horizontal component $\Big\} = OA - OE = 60 - 20$

$$= 40 \text{ V} = OD \text{ in Fig. 125,}$$

and resultant vertical component $\Big\} = B_1E = 34 \cdot 64 \text{ V}$

$$= DC \text{ in Fig. 125.}$$

∴ maximum value of resultant voltage $\Big\} = OC = \sqrt{[(40)^2 + (34 \cdot 64)^2]}$

$$= 52 \cdot 9 \text{ V}$$

and $\tan \phi = \dfrac{DC}{OD} = \dfrac{34 \cdot 64}{40} = 0 \cdot 866$

∴ $\phi = 40 \cdot 9° = 0 \cdot 71$ radian

and instantaneous value of resultant voltage $\Big\} = 52 \cdot 9 \sin (\theta + 0 \cdot 71).$

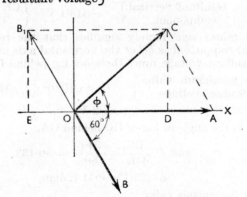

FIG. 125.—Subtraction of vectors in Example 49.

99. Application of Vectors to a Circuit consisting of Resistance and Inductance in Series. It is evident from Fig. 119 that the quantity which is common to the resistance and the inductance is the current. Hence we commence the vector diagram by drawing a vector OA (Fig. 126) in any convenient direction to represent the maximum current, I_m, to scale. From Fig. 120 it is seen that the p.d. across R is in phase with the current; hence draw OB in phase with OA to represent RI_m to some convenient scale. It is often helpful—especially to a beginner—to draw OA and OB slightly apart so that the identity of each may be easily recognised.

The voltage applied to the inductance L leads 90° in front of the current; and in Art. 95, its peak value was shown to be $2\pi fLI_m$. Hence draw OC 90° in front of OA to represent the maximum value of the p.d. across L. A vector OD, drawn equal and opposite to OC, represents the peak value of the e.m.f. induced in L.

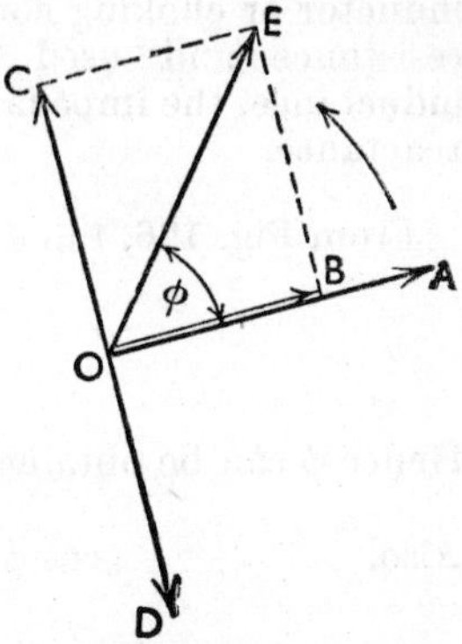

FIG. 126.—Vector diagram for Fig. 119.

The maximum value, V_m, of the resultant applied voltage is represented to scale by the diagonal OE of the parallelogram OBEC; and angle ϕ between OA and OE represents the phase difference between the current and the applied voltage.

Since the angle between OB and BE is a right angle:

$$OE^2 = OB^2 + BE^2 = OB^2 + OC^2$$

$$\therefore \quad V_m^2 = (RI_m)^2 + (2\pi fLI_m)^2$$

and $\quad V_m = I_m\sqrt{[R^2 + (2\pi fL)^2]} = I_m\sqrt{(R^2 + X_L^2)}.$

If V and I are the effective values of the voltage and current respectively, then:

$$\frac{V}{I} = \frac{0\cdot707V_m}{0\cdot707I_m}$$

$$= \sqrt{(R^2 + X_L^2)} = \text{impedance (in ohms) (89)}$$

or $\qquad I = \frac{V}{\sqrt{(R^2 + X_L^2)}} = \frac{V}{Z} \quad \cdot \quad \cdot \quad \cdot \quad \cdot \quad \cdot \quad (90)$

The impedance of any a.c. circuit is always given by the ratio of the voltage to the current, irrespective of the nature of the circuit, and is represented by the symbol Z.

When a circuit is non-inductive its impedance is the same as the resistance. When the circuit consists of a inductor or choking coil, namely a coil having a very low resistance and used primarily because it possesses inductance, the impedance is practically the same as the reactance.

From Fig. 126, $\tan \phi = \dfrac{EB}{OB} = \dfrac{OC}{OB} = \dfrac{2\pi f L I_m}{R I_m}$

$$= \frac{2\pi f L}{R} = \frac{\text{reactance}}{\text{resistance}} \quad . \quad . \quad (91)$$

Hence ϕ can be obtained from the table on p. 354.

Also, $\cos \phi = \dfrac{OB}{OE} = \dfrac{R I_m}{Z I_m}$

$$= \frac{\text{resistance}}{\text{impedance}} \quad . \quad . \quad . \quad (92)$$

Similarly, $\sin \phi = \dfrac{\text{reactance}}{\text{impedance}} \quad . \quad . \quad . \quad (93)$

100. Vector Diagrams drawn with R.M.S. Values instead of Maximum Values. In practice, ammeters and voltmeters usually measure the r.m.s. value of the current and voltage. It is therefore much more convenient to make the vectors represent the r.m.s. rather than the maximum values. Since the r.m.s. value of a sine wave is 0·707 times the peak value, it follows that if the vectors in Fig. 126, for instance, are drawn to represent to scale the r.m.s. values of the current and voltages, the angles and therefore the phase relationships of the various quantities remain unaffected.

Vector diagrams are extremely helpful in a.c. calculations, and students should cultivate the habit of introducing a vector diagram wherever possible.

Example 50. *A coil having a resistance of 12 Ω and an inductance of 0·1 H is connected across a 100-V, 50-c/s supply. Calculate:* (a) *the reactance and the impedance* *of the coil,* (b) *the current and* (c) *the phase difference between the current and the applied voltage.*

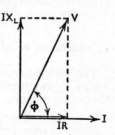

When solving problems of this kind, students should first of all draw a circuit diagram (Fig. 119) and insert all the known quantities. They should then proceed with the vector diagram, Fig. 127. It is not essential to draw the vector diagram to exact scale, but it is helpful to draw it approximately correctly since it is then easy to make a rough check of the calculated values.

FIG. 127. — Vector diagram for Example 50.

(a) Reactance $= X_L = 2\pi f L$

$$= 2\pi \times 50 \times 0 \cdot 1 = 31 \cdot 4 \ \Omega.$$

Impedance $= Z = \sqrt{(R^2 + X_L^2)}$

$$= \sqrt{(12^2 + 31 \cdot 4^2)} = 33 \cdot 6 \ \Omega.$$

(b) Current $= I = \dfrac{V}{Z} = \dfrac{100}{33 \cdot 6} = 2 \cdot 975$ A.

(c) Tan $\phi = \dfrac{X}{R} = \dfrac{31 \cdot 4}{12} = 2 \cdot 617.$

From table, p. 354, $\phi = 69°$.

Example 51. *A metal-filament lamp, rated at* 1·5 *kW,* 100 *V, is to be operated in series with a choking coil across a* 230-*V,* 50-*c/s supply. Calculate:* (a) *the p.d. across the coil,* (b) *the inductance of the coil and* (c) *the phase difference between the current and the supply voltage. Neglect the resistance of the coil.*

(a) The metal filament of the lamp can be regarded as a non-inductive resistance R in Fig. 128, where L represents the inductance of the coil to be connected in series.

$$\text{Rated current of lamp} = \frac{\text{rated power in watts}}{\text{rated voltage}}$$

$$= \frac{1500 \text{ W}}{100 \text{ V}} = 15 \text{ A}$$

$$\therefore \text{ resistance of filament} = R = \frac{100 \text{ V}}{15 \text{ A}} = 6 \cdot 67 \ \Omega.$$

The vector diagram for this circuit is given in Fig. 129, where V_L represents the voltage across the inductance. From this diagram it follows that:

$$230^2 = 100^2 + V_L^2$$

$$\therefore \qquad V_L^2 = 42,900$$

and $\qquad V_L = 207 \text{ volts} = \text{p.d. across coil.}$

(b) Since $V_L = 2\pi f L I$

$$\therefore \qquad 207 = 2 \times 3 \cdot 14 \times 50 \times L \times 15$$

and $\qquad L = 0 \cdot 044 \text{ henry.}$

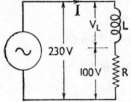

FIG. 128.—Circuit diagram for Example 51.

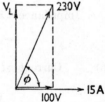

FIG. 129.—Vector diagram for Example 51.

(c) From Fig. 129 it is seen that:

$$\tan \phi = \frac{\text{voltage across coil}}{\text{voltage across lamp}}$$

$$= \frac{207}{100} = 2 \cdot 07.$$

From tables, p. 354, $\phi = 64 \cdot 2° =$ angle of lag of current behind the supply voltage.

Example 52. A non-inductive resistance of 40 Ω and a coil having an inductance of 0·15 H and a negligible resistance are connected in parallel across a 115-V, 60-c/s *supply. Calculate* (a) *the current in each circuit,* (b) *the resultant current and* (c) *the phase difference between the resultant current and the supply voltage.*

(a) The circuit is shown in Fig. 130, from which it is seen that:

$$\text{current through } R = I_R = \frac{115}{40} = 2 \cdot 875 \text{ A}$$

and current through $L = I_L = \dfrac{115}{2 \times 3 \cdot 14 \times 60 \times 0 \cdot 15} = 2 \cdot 035 \text{A}.$

When drawing a vector diagram (Fig. 131) for parallel circuits it is best to start with the voltage, since this is

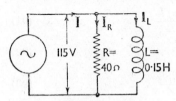

FIG. 130.—Circuit diagram   FIG. 131.—Vector diagram
for Example 52.   for Example 52.

common to the two circuits. Then I_R is drawn in phase with the supply voltage V and I_L is drawn 90° behind V.

(b) The resultant current I is the vectorial sum of I_R and I_L; and from Fig. 131 it is seen that:

$$I^2 = I_R^2 + I_L^2 = (2 \cdot 875)^2 + (2 \cdot 035)^2 = 12 \cdot 4$$

∴ $I = 3 \cdot 52$ A.

(From Fig. 131, $\tan \phi = \dfrac{I_L}{I_R} = \dfrac{2 \cdot 035}{2 \cdot 875} = 0 \cdot 708$

∴ $\phi = 35 \cdot 3°.$

Summary of Important Formulae

For purely resistive circuit,

$$i = \frac{V_m}{R} \sin \theta \quad . \quad . \quad . \quad . \quad (86)$$

and $$I = \frac{V}{R} \quad . \quad . \quad . \quad . \quad . \quad (85)$$

For purely inductive circuit,

$$i = \frac{V_m}{2\pi f L} \sin (\theta - \pi/2) \quad . \quad . \quad (88)$$

and

$$I = \frac{V}{2\pi f L} \quad . \quad . \quad . \quad . \quad (87)$$

Inductive reactance $= X_L = 2\pi f L$ ohms.

For R and L in series,

$$\text{Impedance} = Z = \sqrt{[R^2 + (2\pi f L)^2]} \text{ ohms} \quad (89)$$

$$I = \frac{V}{\sqrt{[R^2 + (2\pi f L)^2]}} \quad . \quad . \quad . \quad (90)$$

$$\tan \phi = \frac{2\pi f L}{R} \quad . \quad . \quad . \quad . \quad . \quad (91)$$

$$\cos \phi = \frac{R}{Z} \quad . \quad . \quad . \quad . \quad . \quad (92)$$

and

$$\sin \phi = \frac{2\pi f L}{Z} \quad . \quad . \quad . \quad . \quad (93)$$

EXAMPLES XI

1. Draw sine waves to represent two currents, one having an amplitude of 10 A and the other of 7 A, assuming the smaller current to lag 60° behind the larger current. Derive a curve representing the sum of the two currents, and from this curve determine the maximum value of the resultant current.

Check this result by drawing a vector diagram to scale or by calculating the vectorial sum of the two currents.

2. A sinusoidal alternating current having a peak value of 10 A flows through a coil having an inductance of 0·01 H. The period is 0·02 second. Draw to scale a curve representing the current and, by taking ordinates every 15°, derive curves representing (a) the rate of change of current and (b) the induced e.m.f.

3. Explain the meaning of the following terms used in a.c. work: wave shape, peak value, cycle, frequency, phase, r.m.s. and mean values.

Two sinusoidal e.m.f.'s of peak values 100 V and 50 V respectively but differing in phase by 60 electrical degrees are induced in the same circuit. Find *either* by means of a diagram *or* by calculation the peak value of the resultant e.m.f. What is its r.m.s. value?

(U.L.C.I., S2)

4. What is the justification for the representation of sinusoidally varying quantities by means of vectors?

The currents taken by two parallel circuits are 12 amps in phase with the applied voltage and 20 amps lagging 30° behind the applied voltage, respectively. Determine the current taken by the combined circuits and its phase with respect to the applied voltage.

(N.C.T.E.C., S2)

5. Two coils connected in series are fixed together with their planes inclined at an angle of 60° to each other and rotated at a steady speed at right angles to a uniform magnetic field. An e.m.f. having a maximum value of 50 V is induced in each coil. Draw the vector diagram and the corresponding sine waves, approximately to scale, of the voltage in each coil and the resultant voltage when (a) the windings of the coils are similarly connected and (b) the connections of one of the coils are reversed. (C. & G., El. Eng. Pract., Prelim.)

6. What is meant by the mean value, the r.m.s. value and the peak value of an alternating current? What relationships exist between them when the current is sinusoidal?

Two sinusoidal currents of r.m.s. values 10 A and 20 A and differing in phase by 30° flow in the same conductor. Find either diagrammatically or by calculation the peak value of the resultant current.
(U.L.C.I., S2)

7. In what circumstances can alternating currents and voltages be represented as vectors on the same diagram?

Three circuits in parallel take currents which can be represented by $i_1 = 10 \sin 314t$; $i_2 = 7 \sin (314t - \pi/3)$; $i_3 = 12 \sin (314t + \pi/4)$. Sketch a vector diagram to represent the three currents and their resultant. Calculate the resultant, and express it in the same form as the individual currents. Give the r.m.s. value and the frequency of the resultant current. (Joint Section A)

8. The following e.m.f.'s are being generated in three coils, A, B and C:

$$e_A = 100 \sin \omega t$$
$$e_B = 70 \sin (\omega t - \pi/3)$$
and $$e_C = 120 \cos \omega t.$$

If the three coils are connected in series, calculate (a) the maximum value of the resultant e.m.f. and (b) the phase of the resultant e.m.f. relatively to the e.m.f. in coil A. Check your result by means of a vector diagram drawn to scale. (I.Mech.E., Prin. of Elect.)

9. A coil of wire when connected to a d.c. supply of 100 V takes a current of 10 A. When connected to an a.c. supply of 100 V at a frequency of 50 c/s, the current taken is 5 A. Explain the difference and calculate the coefficient of self-inductance of the coil.
(N.C.T.E.C., S2)

10. A coil with an inductance of 0·07 H and a resistance of 22 Ω is connected to 100-V 50-c/s mains. Draw approximately to scale the vector diagram for this circuit and the corresponding sine waves of current and voltage in their phase relationship. Calculate the current and the cosine of the angle of phase difference.
(C. & G., El. Eng. Pract., Prelim.)

11. A coil having a resistance of 10 Ω and an inductance of 0·2 H is connected to a 100-V, 50-c/s supply. Calculate (a) the impedance of the coil, (b) the reactance of the coil, (c) the current taken, (d) the phase difference between the current and the applied voltage.
(N.C.T.E.C., S2)

12. A coil has an inductance of 0·07 H and a negligible resistance. Find the current taken from 200-V, 50-c/s mains when a resistance of 22 Ω is connected (a) in parallel, (b) in series with the coil. Draw the vector diagram for each case.
(C. & G., El. Eng. Pract., Prelim.)

13. A coil having an inductance of 0·2 H and a negligible resistance is connected across a 100-V a.c. supply. Calculate the current if the frequency is (a) 30 and (b) 500 c/s.

14. A coil having a resistance of 20 Ω takes a current of 4 A when connected to a 230-V, 50-c/s supply. Calculate (a) the inductance of the coil and (b) the phase difference between the current and the applied voltage. Sketch the vector diagram.

15. A resistance of 50 Ω and a coil having an inductance of 0·1 H and negligible resistance are connected in parallel across a 200-V, 60-c/s supply. Calculate (a) the current in each circuit, (b) the resultant current and (c) the phase angle between the resultant current and the applied voltage. Sketch the vector diagram.

16. If a current is represented by the expression $i = 10 \sin 628t$, calculate (a) the frequency and (b) the value of the current 2 milli-seconds after it has passed through its zero value.

CHAPTER XII

POWER IN AN A.C. CIRCUIT

101. Power in a Non-inductive Circuit. In Art. 89 it was explained that when an alternating current flows through a resistance R ohms, the average heating effect over a complete cycle is I^2R watts, where I is the r.m.s. value of the current in amperes.

If V volts be the r.m.s. value of the applied voltage, then for a non-inductive circuit, $V=IR$, so that:

$$\text{average value of the power} = I^2R = I \times IR$$
$$= IV \text{ watts.}$$

Hence the power in a non-inductive circuit is given by the product of the ammeter and voltmeter readings, exactly as in a d.c. circuit.

102. Power in a Purely Inductive Circuit. Consider a coil wound with such thick wire that the resistance is negligible in comparison with the inductive reactance X_L ohms. If such a coil be connected across a supply voltage V, the current is given by $I=V/X_L$ amperes. Since the resistance is very small, the heating effect and therefore the power are also very small, even though the voltage and the current be large. Such a curious conclusion—so different from anything we have experienced in d.c. circuits—requires fuller explanation if its significance is to be properly understood. Let us therefore consider Fig. 132, which shows the applied voltage and the current for a purely inductive circuit, the current lagging a quarter of a cycle behind the voltage.

The power at any instant is given by the product of the voltage and the current at that instant; thus at instant L, the p.d. is LN volts and the current is LM amperes, so that the power at that instant is LN × LM watts and is represented to scale by LP.

213

By repeating this calculation at various instants we can deduce the curve representing the variation of power over one cycle. It is seen that during interval OA the applied voltage is positive, but the current is negative, so that the power is negative; and that during interval AB, both the current and the voltage are positive, so that the power is positive.

The power curve is found to be symmetrical about the horizontal axis OD. Consequently the shaded areas marked " − " are exactly equal to those marked " +," so that the mean value of the power over the complete cycle OD is zero.

It is necessary, however, to consider the significance of the positive and negative areas if we are to under-

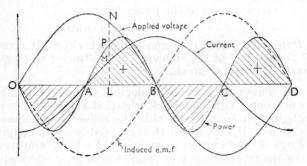

FIG. 132.—Power curve for purely inductive circuit.

stand what is really taking place. So let us consider an alternator P (Fig. 133) connected to a coil Q whose resistance is negligible, and let us assume that the voltage and current are as represented in Fig. 132. At instant A, there is no current and therefore no magnetic field through and around Q. During interval AB, the growth of the current is accompanied by a growth of flux as shown by the dotted lines in Fig. 133. But the existence of a magnetic field involves some kind of a strain in the space occupied by the field and the storing up of energy in that field, as already dealt with in Art. 66. The current and therefore the magnetic energy associated

with it reach their maximum values at instant B; and
since the loss in the coil is assumed negligible, it follows
that at that instant the whole of the energy supplied
to the coil during interval AB, and represented by the
shaded area marked " +," is stored up in the magnetic
field.

During interval BC the current and its magnetic
field are decreasing; and the e.m.f. induced by the
collapse of the magnetic flux is in the same direction as
the current.   But any circuit in which the current and
the induced or generated
e.m.f. are in the same
direction acts as a gene-
rator of electrical energy.
Consequently the coil is
now acting as a generator
transforming the energy
of its magnetic field into
electrical   energy,   the
latter being sent to alternator P to drive it as a

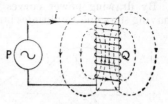

FIG. 133.—Magnetic field of an
inductive circuit.

motor.   The energy thus returned is represented by the
shaded area marked " —" in Fig. 132; and since the
positive and negative areas are equal, it follows that
during alternate quarter-cycles electrical energy is being
sent from the alternator to the coil, and during the other
quarter-cycles the same amount of energy is sent back
from the coil to the alternator.   Consequently the net
energy absorbed by the coil during a complete cycle is
zero; in other words the average power over a complete
cycle is zero.

103. Power in a Circuit having Resistance and Induct-ance in Series.

It has been shown in Art. 99 that in a
circuit having a resistance R ohms in series with an
inductance L henrys, the current lags behind the applied
voltage by an angle ϕ such that $\tan \phi = \dfrac{2\pi fL}{R}$.   In Fig.
134 the current and voltage are shown with a phase
difference of 60°.   The power wave is again derived
from the product of the instantaneous values of current

and voltage. It is seen that the positive area representing the energy absorbed by the circuit during interval AB is greater than the negative area representing the energy returned from the circuit to the alternator during interval BC. Also it is found that the power curve is symmetrical about a dotted line MN drawn midway between the positive and negative peaks of the power curve. Hence the height of this dotted line above the zero axis OABC represents the average value of the power over one cycle.

By drawing power curves for voltages and currents having the same amplitudes but various phase differences,

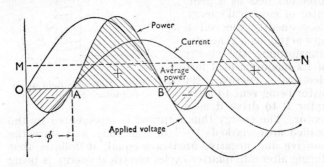

FIG. 134.—Power curve for circuit with R and L in series.

it can be seen that the larger the phase difference the smaller is the difference between the areas representing the positive and negative energies, and the smaller, therefore, is the mean value of the power.

In Art. 89 it was explained that in any circuit having a resistance R ohms the average heating effect due to a current having an effective value of I amperes is I^2R watts. On the other hand, the product of the effective values of the current and applied voltage is IV *voltamperes*, the latter term being used to distinguish this quantity from the power, expressed in watts.

Since the number of watts is very often less than the number of voltamperes, the latter has to be multiplied by some factor, equal to or less than unity, to give the power in watts.   This factor is therefore termed the *power factor*, i.e.:

power in watts=number of voltamperes ×power factor

or power factor$=\dfrac{\text{power in watts}}{\text{number of voltamperes}}$.   .   (94)

$$=\frac{I^2R\ (\text{watts})}{IV\ (\text{voltamperes})}=\frac{IR}{V}.$$

The vector diagram for a circuit having resistance and inductance in series has already been given in Fig. 127, from which it is seen that $\dfrac{IR}{V}=\cos\phi$, where ϕ is the phase difference between the current and the applied voltage.

Hence   power factor$=\cos\phi$.   .   .   .   (95)

It should be pointed out that expression (94) for power factor is always correct, whereas expression (95) is correct only when both the current and the voltage are sinusoidal, since it has been derived from a vector diagram, and vectors are based upon sine waves (see Art. 97).

If Z be the impedance of the circuit in ohms, then $V=IZ$,

∴   power factor$=\dfrac{IR}{IZ}=\dfrac{R}{Z}$.   .   .   (96)

Example 53.   *A coil having a resistance of 6 Ω and an inductance of 0·03 H is connected across a 50-V, 60-c/s supply.   Calculate* (a) *the current,* (b) *the phase angle between the current and the applied voltage,* (c) *the power factor,* (d) *the voltamperes and* (e) *the power.*

(a) The vector diagram for such a circuit is given in Fig. 127.

Reactance of circuit$=2\pi fL=2\times3\cdot14\times60\times0\cdot03$.

$$=11\cdot31\ \varOmega.$$

From (89), impedance$=\sqrt{[6^2+(11\cdot31)^2]}=12\cdot8\ \varOmega$

and   current$=\dfrac{50}{12\cdot8}=3\cdot91$ A.

(b) From (91), $\tan \phi = \dfrac{X}{R} = \dfrac{11 \cdot 31}{6} = 1 \cdot 885.$

From tables, p. 354, $\phi = 62° \ 3'.$

(c) From (95), power factor $= \cos 62° \ 3' = 0 \cdot 469$

or, from (96),   ,,   ,, $= \dfrac{6}{12 \cdot 8} = 0 \cdot 469.$

(d) Voltamperes $= 50 \times 3 \cdot 91 = 195 \cdot 5$ VA.

(e) Power $=$ voltamperes $\times$ power factor

$$= 195 \cdot 5 \times 0 \cdot 469 = 91 \cdot 7 \text{ W.}$$

Or, alternatively:

$$\text{power} = I^2 R = (3 \cdot 91)^2 \times 6 = 91 \cdot 7 \text{ W.}$$

104. Active and Reactive (or Wattless) Components of the Current. Let us again consider a circuit consisting

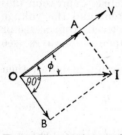

FIG. 135.—Active and reactive components of current.

of a resistance and an inductance in series, and suppose the applied voltage and the current to be represented by the vectors OV and OI respectively in Fig. 135.

Let us resolve the current I into two components, one component being in phase with the voltage V and the other lagging 90° (or quarter cycle) behind V; for instance, in Fig. 135, draw IA perpendicular to OV, and IB perpendicular to OB, which is at right-angles to OV. Consequently OAIB is a rectangle and the diagonal OI represents the vectorial sum of two currents represented by OA and OB; i.e. a current OI may be replaced by two currents represented in magnitude and phase by OA and OB respectively.

Since OI represents the actual current, I amperes, and since OA $=$ OI $\cos \phi$:

∴   power $= IV \cos \phi = V \times$ OI $\cos \phi$

$$= V \times \text{OA watts.}$$

Hence component OA of the current is such that the product of OA and the voltage gives the power. Therefore OA is termed the *active* or *power component* of the current, i.e.:

active or power component of current $=I \cos \phi$. (97)

Since OB lags 90° behind the voltage:

power due to a current OB $=$ OB $\times V \times \cos 90° = 0$.

Hence OB is referred to as the *reactive* or *wattless component* of the current. From Fig. 135 it is seen that:

reactive or wattless component of current

$$=\text{OB}=\text{IA}$$

$$=I \sin \phi \quad . \quad . \quad . \quad . \quad (98)$$

and reactive voltamperes (or VAr) $=IV \sin \phi$. (99)

Example 54. *A single-phase motor is taking a current of 45 A from a 400-V supply at a power factor of 0·8. Calculate* (a) *the active and reactive components of the current,* (b) *the kilovoltamperes,* (c) *the power taken from the supply,* (d) *the reactive kilovoltamperes and* (e) *the b.h.p. Assume the efficiency to be 86 per cent.*

(a) From (97), active component of current

$$=45 \times 0·8 = 36 \text{ A}.$$

Since $\cos \phi =$ power factor $=0·8$

∴ $\sin \phi = \sqrt{(1 - \cos^2 \phi)} = \sqrt{[1 - (0·8)^2]} = 0·6$.

From (98), reactive component of current

$$=45 \times 0·6 = 27 \text{ A}.$$

(b) Number of kilovoltamperes

$$= \frac{\text{number of voltamperes}}{1000}$$

$$= \frac{400 \times 45}{1000} = 18 \text{ kVA}.$$

(c) Number of kilowatts

$$= \text{number of kilovoltamperes} \times \text{power factor}$$

$$= 18 \times 0·8 = 14·4 \text{ kW}.$$

(d) Reactive kilovoltamperes

$$=kVA \times \sin \phi = 18 \times 0.6 = 10.8 \text{ kVAr.}$$

(e) Output power

$$=\text{input power} \times \text{efficiency}$$
$$=14.4 \times 0.86 \text{ kW}$$
$$=\frac{14.4 \times 0.86}{0.746} = 16.6 \text{ h.p.}$$

Example 55. *An alternator is supplying a load of 300 kW at a power factor of 0.6. If the power factor is raised to unity, how many more kilowatts can the alternator supply for the same kVA loading?*

Since the power in kW

$$=\text{number of kilovoltamperes} \times \text{power factor.}$$

∴ number of kilovoltamperes

$$=\frac{300}{0.6} = 500 \text{ kVA.}$$

When the power factor is raised to unity:

number of kilowatts

$$=\text{number of kilovoltamperes}$$
$$=500 \text{ kW.}$$

Hence increased power supplied by alternator

$$=500 - 300 = 200 \text{ kW.}$$

105. The Practical Importance of Power Factor. If an alternator is rated to give, say, 2000 A at a voltage of 400 V, it means that these are the highest current and voltage values the machine can give without the temperature exceeding a safe value. Consequently the rating of the alternator is given as $\frac{400 \times 2000}{1000} = 800$ kVA. The phase difference between the voltage and the current depends upon the nature of the load and not upon the generator. Thus if the power factor of the load is unity, the 800 kVA are also 800 kW; and the engine driving the generator has to be capable of developing this power together with the losses in the generator. But if the power factor of the load is, say, 0·5, the power is only 400 kW; so that the engine is only developing about one-half of the power of which it is capable, though the alternator is supplying its rated output of 800 kVA.

Similarly the conductors connecting the alternator to the load have to be capable of carrying 2000 A without excessive temperature rise. Consequently they can transmit 800 kW if the power factor is unity, but only 400 kW at 0·5 power factor, for the same rise of temperature.

It is therefore evident that the higher the power factor of the load, the greater is the *power* that can be generated by a given alternator and transmitted by a given conductor.

The matter may be put another way by saying that, for a *given power*, the lower the power factor the larger must be the size of the alternator to generate that power and the greater must be the cross-sectional area of the conductor to transmit it; in other words, the greater is the cost of generation and transmission of the electrical energy. This is the reason why supply authorities do all they can to improve the power factor of their loads either by the installation of capacitors (Chapter XIII) or special machines or by the use of tariffs which encourage consumers to do so.

Summary of Important Formulae

$$\text{Power factor} = \frac{\text{power in watts}}{\text{r.m.s. volts} \times \text{r.m.s. amperes}} \quad (94)$$

or, power in watts $= I V \times$ power factor.

For sinusoidal waves of voltage and current having phase difference ϕ,

$$\text{power factor} = \cos \phi \quad . \quad . \quad . \quad . \quad . \quad (95)$$

For circuit having resistance R and impedance Z,

$$\text{power factor} = R/Z \quad . \quad . \quad . \quad . \quad . \quad (96)$$

Active or power component of current

$$= I \cos \phi \quad . \quad . \quad . \quad . \quad (97)$$

Reactive or wattless component of current

$$= I \sin \phi \quad . \quad . \quad . \quad . \quad (98)$$

Reactive voltamperes (or VAr)

$$= I V \sin \phi \quad . \quad . \quad . \quad . \quad (99)$$

EXAMPLES XII

1. Define r.m.s. and mean values for an alternating voltage and give an example of the use of each value.

A circuit having a power factor of 0·866 lagging takes a current of 10 A from a 240-V 50-c/s supply. Write down an expression for the instantaneous values of voltage and current, and find the value of the current when the voltage is (a) passing through its maximum value, (b) 0·005 second later and (c) after a further 0·005 second.

What is the significance of a negative current?

(Joint Section A)

2. An alternating e.m.f. of 100 V, r.m.s. value, at 50 c/s, is applied to a 20-Ω non-inductive resistance. Plot to scale the voltage and current over one complete cycle and deduce the curve of power and state its mean value. What energy is used per cycle in watt-seconds?

(N.C.T.E.C., S2)

3. A coil having a resistance of 12 Ω and an inductance of 0·0159 H is connected to a 260-V, 50-c/s supply. Calculate the energy in joules expended in the coil in 5 min. Draw a vector diagram showing the voltage and current in their correct relative phase positions, to scales of 1 in =50 V, 1 in =5 A. (U.L.C.I., S2)

4. Define power factor and show that with sinusoidal waveforms, the power factor is the cosine of the angle of phase difference between current and voltage.

The power factor of a lagging load is 0·866. The voltage is 200 V and the current is 5 A. Find the equivalent series reactance and resistance of the load. (C. & G., El. Eng. Pract., Prelim.)

5. Explain what is meant by the self-inductance of a circuit.

A coil having a resistance of 10 Ω and an inductance of 0·05 H is connected across a 200-V, 50-c/s supply. Calculate (a) the current, (b) the phase difference between the current and the applied voltage and (c) the power absorbed. Sketch a vector diagram representing the current, the applied voltage and the voltage drops due to the resistance and the inductance of the coil.

(I.Mech.E., Prin. of Elect.)

6. Explain why the current in a purely inductive circuit lags a quarter of a cycle behind the applied voltage.

Three 100-watt, 115-V lamps, connected in parallel, are to be supplied at their rated voltage from 230-V, 50-c/s mains by the use of a suitable choking coil of negligible resistance in series with the bank of lamps. Calculate (a) the voltage across the coil, (b) the inductance of the coil and (c) the power factor of the whole circuit. Sketch the vector diagram. (I.Mech.E., Prin. of Elect.)

7. When a d.c. supply of 5 V is applied across a certain circuit, the current flowing is 0·1 A. When the d.c. supply is replaced by a

sinusoidal a.c. supply at a frequency of 80 c/s, it is found that a voltage of 10 V is required to cause a current of 0·1 A to flow in the same circuit. Give reasons for the difference and calculate (i) the d.c. resistance of the circuit, (ii) the power absorbed under the d.c. conditions and (iii) the impedance of the circuit at 80 c/s.

If the power absorbed by the circuit in the a.c. case is 0·6 watt, calculate:

(iv) the power factor of the circuit and (v) its resistance to a.c. of the value stated. How do you account for the fact that (v) is greater than (i)?   (C. & G., Telecom. Prin. II)

8. Two air-core coils are connected in series. With a direct-current of 1 A, the voltages across the coils are 60 V and 80 V respectively. With 1 A alternating current, the voltages are 70 V and 100 V respectively. Find the power factor of each coil and that of the whole circuit.   (C. & G., El. Eng. Pract., Prelim.)

9. An a.c. electromagnet has a wire resistance of 8 Ω. When connected to 250-V, 50-c/s mains, the current taken is 10 A and the power dissipated is 1 kW. Calculate (a) the inductance of the circuit at this value of the current and (b) the iron losses.
                                        (C. & G., El. Eng. Pract., Prelim.)

10. Why is it more economical to use a reactor instead of a resistor for dimming a bank of lamps?

If the lamp-bank takes 5 kW at 250 V, find the impedance of the reactor of negligible resistance required to reduce the voltage to 150 V assuming that the resistance of the lamps does not change.
                                        (C. & G., El. Eng. Pract., Prelim.)

11. A coil having a resistance of 20 Ω is found to take 950 W from a 230-V, 50-c/s supply. Calculate (a) the inductance and the power factor of the coil, (b) the active and reactive components of the current and (c) the reactive voltamperes taken by the coil. Sketch the vector diagram.

12. A resistance of 100 Ω and a coil having an inductance of 0·3 H and a negligible resistance are connected in parallel across a 400-V, 60-c/s supply. Calculate (a) the current in each circuit, (b) the resultant current, (c) the phase angle between the resultant current and the supply voltage, (d) the power and (e) the power factor of the combined circuits.

13. Describe clearly the difference between *resistance*, *reactance* and *impedance* and illustrate your answer by means of simple vector diagrams.

A resistive inductor having an inductance of 0·319 H and an impedance of 200 Ω at 50 c/s is connected in parallel with a pure resistance of 200 Ω. This parallel circuit is then connected across a 100-V, 50-c/s supply. Determine the total power dissipated.
                                         (C. & G., Telecom. Prin. II)

14. Deduce an expression for the mean power in a circuit if the applied voltage is $V \sin \omega t$ and the current is $I \sin (\omega t - \phi)$.

A single-phase load takes 100 A at a power of 0·7 (lagging) from a 230-V, 50-c/s supply. A second load takes 44 A at a power factor of 0·9 (leading). Calculate the kW, the kVA and the overall power factor of the total load taken from the supply.   (Joint Section A)

15. A coil A takes 6 A and dissipates 200 W when connected to a 100-V, 50-c/s supply, while another coil B takes 8 A and dissipates 600 W when connected to a similar supply. Calculate (a) the current taken, (b) the power dissipated and (c) the circuit power factor when the coils are joined in series and connected to a 200-V, 50-c/s supply.
                                                (Joint Section A)

16. A single-phase induction motor runs off a 400-V supply with an efficiency of 85 per cent and a power factor of 0·8 when the output power is 5 h.p.   Calculate (a) the current, (b) the active and reactive components of the current and (c) the kVAr taken by the motor.

17. A motor developing 2 b.h.p. is taking 12 A at power factor 0·75 from a 200-V supply.   Calculate its efficiency.

18. (a) Define the following terms applied to an alternating current waveform: Average value, maximum value and r.m.s. value.   If the maximum value of a sine wave is 200, give the average and r.m.s. values.

(b) Calculate the power input of a single-phase motor which takes 15 A, r.m.s., at 240 V.   The current lags behind the voltage by 30 degrees (electrical).   (C. & G., El. Inst. Work)

19. A single-phase 250-V motor with a full load output of 30 b.h.p. at 85 per cent efficiency and 0·75 power factor is supplied by a twin cable, each core of which has a cross-section of 0·02 sq. in.   Calculate the maximum length of the cable so that the voltage drop in the cable shall not be greater than 28 V.   Resistivity of copper is 0·7 microhm per inch cube.   (C. & G., El. Inst. Work)

(*Note.*   It is assumed that the *IR* drop in the cable is 28 V; the arithmetic difference between the voltages at the two ends of the cable is then less than 28 V.)

CHAPTER XIII

CAPACITANCE IN AN A.C. CIRCUIT

106. Alternating Current in a Circuit possessing Capacitance only. Fig. 136 shows a capacitor C connected in series with an ammeter A across the terminals of an alternator; and the alternating voltage applied to C is represented in Fig. 137. Suppose this voltage to be positive when it makes D positive relative to E.

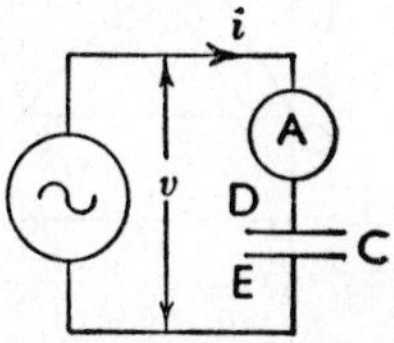

If the p.d. across the capacitor increases by v volts in t seconds and if i amperes is the average charging current, the increase of charge is $i \times t$ coulombs. If the capacitance is C farads, the increase of charge is also Cv coulombs,

$$\therefore \qquad it = Cv$$

and

$$i = C \times \frac{v}{t} = C \times \text{rate of increase of p.d.}$$

FIG. 136.—Circuit with capacitance only.

In Fig. 137, the p.d. is increasing at the maximum rate at instant O; consequently the charging current is also at its maximum value I_m at that instant.

At instant L, the applied voltage has reached its maximum value V_m; and for a very brief interval of time the p.d. is neither increasing nor decreasing, so that there is no current. During interval LM the applied voltage is decreasing. Consequently the capacitor discharges, the discharge current being in the negative direction.

At instant M, the slope of the voltage curve is at its maximum, i.e. the p.d. is varying at the maximum rate; consequently the current is also a maximum at that instant.

It is common practice to speak of the current *through* a capacitor; but it will be seen from the above explanation that the current does not really pass through a capacitor, and that the ammeter in Fig. 136 is operated by the to and fro movement of the electrons in the circuit between plates D and E of the capacitor.

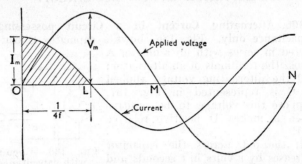

FIG. 137.—Voltage and current curves for capacitive circuit.

From a comparison of the voltage and current curves in Fig. 137 it is seen that the current is leading in front of the voltage by a quarter of a cycle. A simple mechanical analogy may again assist in understanding this relationship.

107. Analogies of a Capacitance in an A.C. Circuit. If the piston P in Fig. 91 be moved backwards and forwards, the to and fro movement of the water causes the diaphragm to be distended in alternate directions. This hydraulic analogy, when applied to capacitance in an a.c. circuit, becomes rather complicated owing to the inertia of the water and of the piston; and as we do not want to take the effect of inertia into account at this stage, it is more convenient to consider a very light flexible strip L (Fig. 138), such as a metre rule, having one end rigidly clamped. Let us apply an alternating pressure comparatively slowly by hand so as to oscillate L between position A and B.

When L is in position A, the applied pressure is at its maximum towards the *left*. As the pressure is relaxed,

L moves towards the *right*. Immediately L has passed the centre position the applied force has to be increased towards the right, while the speed in this direction is decreasing. These variations are indicated by the lengths of the arrows in Fig. 138. From the latter it is seen that the speed towards the right is a maximum a quarter of a cycle before the applied pressure is a maximum in the same direction. The speed is therefore the analogue of the alternating current, and the applied pressure is that of the applied voltage.

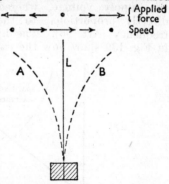

FIG. 138.—Mechanical analogy

108. Numerical Relationship between Current and Voltage in a Capacitive Circuit. At instant L in Fig. 137 the p.d. across C is V_m, so that the charge on C is CV_m coulombs. But the charge is also equal to the product of the average current during interval OL and the duration of that interval; hence if I_m is the maximum value of the current, the average current is $\frac{2}{\pi}I_m$ (Art. 88)

and $\qquad CV_m = \frac{2}{\pi} \times I_m \times \frac{1}{4f}$

where $\quad f$ = frequency in cycles/second

$\therefore \qquad \frac{V_m}{I_m} = \frac{1}{2\pi fC} = X_C =$ capacitive reactance . (100)

Hence,

$$\frac{\text{r.m.s. value of p.d.}}{\text{r.m.s. value of current}} = \frac{V}{I} = \frac{0 \cdot 707 V_m}{0 \cdot 707 I_m} = \frac{1}{2\pi fC}$$

and $\qquad I = 2\pi fCV = \frac{V}{X_C}$ . . . . (101)

It is seen that capacitive reactance is inversely proportional to the capacitance and to the frequency of the supply voltage, whereas inductive reactance is directly proportional to the inductance and to the frequency (Art. 95). The hyperbola and straight line in Fig. 139 show how the capacitive reactance and the

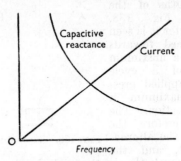

FIG. 139.—Effect of frequency on capacitive reactance and current.

current due to a given applied voltage vary with the frequency.

Example 56. *A 30-μF capacitor is connected across a 400-V, 50-c/s supply. Calculate* (a) *the reactance of the capacitor and* (b) *the current.*

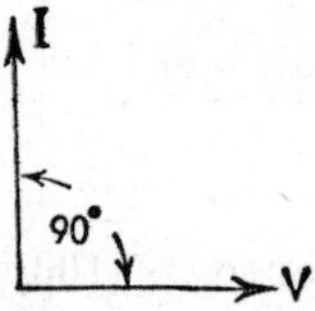

FIG. 140. — Vector diagram for capacitive circuit.

From (100):

$$\text{reactance} = \frac{1}{2 \times 3 \cdot 14 \times 50 \times 30 \times 10^{-6}}$$
$$= 106 \cdot 2 \ \Omega.$$

From (101):

$$\text{current} = \frac{400}{106 \cdot 2} = 3 \cdot 77 \ \text{A}.$$

Fig. 140 represents the voltage and current vectors for this circuit.

Example 57. *A metal-filament lamp, rated at 750 W, 100 V, is to be connected in series with a capacitor across* *a* 230-*V*, 60-*c/s supply.   Calculate* (a) *the capacitance required and* (b) *the power factor of the combination.*

(a) The circuit is given in Fig. 141, where R represents the resistance of the lamp.   In the vector diagram of Fig. 142, the voltage V_R across R is in phase with the

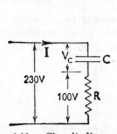

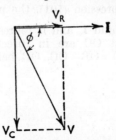

FIG. 141.—Circuit diagram for Example 57.

FIG. 142.—Vector diagram for Example 57.

current *I*, while the voltage V_C across C lags 90° behind *I*. The resultant voltage *V* is the vectorial sum of V_R and V_C, and from the diagram :

$$V^2 = V_R^2 + V_C^2$$

$$\therefore \quad (230)^2 = (100)^2 + V_C^2$$

$$\therefore \quad V_C = 207 \text{ volts} = \text{voltage across C.}$$

$$\text{Rated current of lamp} = \frac{750 \text{ watts}}{100 \text{ volts}} = 7 \cdot 5 \text{ A.}$$

From (101) $7 \cdot 5 = 2 \times 3 \cdot 14 \times 60 \times C \times 207$

$$\therefore \quad C = 96 \times 10^{-6} \text{ farad}$$

$$= 96 \text{ microfarads.}$$

(b) Power factor $= \cos \phi = \dfrac{V_R}{V}$ (from Fig. 142)

$$= \frac{100}{230} = 0 \cdot 435 \text{ leading.}$$

109. Alternating Current in a Circuit consisting of Resistance, Inductance and Capacitance in Series (Fig. 143).   Let *V* and *I* be the r.m.s. values of the supply voltage and current respectively. The p.d. across R is RI volts in phase with the current and is represented by OA in Fig. 144. From expression (87), the p.d. across L is $2\pi fLI$, leading 90° in front of the current, and is represented by vector OB. From expression (101), the p.d. across C is $\dfrac{I}{2\pi fC}$, lagging 90° behind I, and is represented by vector OC. Since OB and OC are in direct opposition, their resultant is OD=OB−OC, OB being assumed greater than OC in

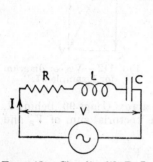

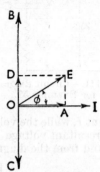

Fig. 143.—Circuit with R, L and C in series.

Fig. 144.—Vector diagram for Fig. 143.

Fig. 144; and the supply voltage is the vectorial sum of OA and OD, namely OE. From the vector diagram:

$$OE^2 = OA^2 + OD^2 = OA^2 + (OB - OC)^2$$

$$\therefore \qquad V^2 = (RI)^2 + \left(2\pi fLI - \frac{I}{2\pi fC}\right)^2$$

so that

$$V = I\sqrt{\left[R^2 + \left(2\pi fL - \frac{1}{2\pi fC}\right)^2\right]}$$

and

$$I = \frac{V}{\sqrt{\left[R^2 + \left(2\pi fL - \frac{1}{2\pi fC}\right)^2\right]}} = \frac{V}{Z} \quad (102)$$

where Z=impedance of circuit in ohms.

From (102) it is seen that:

resultant reactance

$$=2\pi fL-\frac{1}{2\pi fC}$$

=inductive reactance −capacitive reactance.

If ϕ=phase difference between the current and the supply voltage,

$$\tan \phi=\frac{AE}{OA}=\frac{OD}{OA}=\frac{OB-OC}{OA}=\frac{2\pi fLI-\dfrac{I}{2\pi fC}}{RI}$$

$$=\frac{\text{inductive reactance −capacitive reactance}}{\text{resistance}} \quad (103)$$

$$\cos \phi=\frac{OA}{OE}=\frac{RI}{ZI}=\frac{\text{resistance}}{\text{impedance}} \quad \cdot \quad \cdot \quad \cdot \quad \cdot \quad \cdot \quad (104)$$

$$\sin \phi=\frac{AE}{OE}=\frac{\text{resultant reactance}}{\text{impedance}} \quad \cdot \quad \cdot \quad \cdot \quad \cdot \quad (105)$$

If the inductive reactance is greater than the capacitive reactance, $\tan \phi$ is positive and the current lags behind the applied voltage; if less, $\tan \phi$ is negative, signifying that the current leads in front of the applied voltage.

Example 58. *A resistance of 12 Ω, an inductance of 0·15 H and a capacitance of 100 μF are connected in series across a 100-V, 50-c/s supply. Calculate* (a) *the impedance,* (b) *the current,* (c) *the voltages across resistance, inductance and capacitance respectively,* (d) *the power factor, and* (e) *the power.*

The circuit diagram is the same as that of Fig. 143.

(a) From (102):

$$Z=\sqrt{\left[12^2+\left(2\times3\cdot14\times50\times0\cdot15-\frac{10^6}{2\times3\cdot14\times50\times100}\right)^2\right]}$$

$$=\sqrt{[144+(47\cdot1-31\cdot85)^2]}=19\cdot4\ \Omega.$$

(b) Current$=\dfrac{V}{Z}=\dfrac{100}{19\cdot4}=5\cdot15$ A.

(c) Voltage across $R = V_R$

$$= 12 \times 5 \cdot 15 = 61 \cdot 8 \text{ V}.$$

Voltage across $L = V_L$

$$= 47 \cdot 1 \times 5 \cdot 15 = 242 \cdot 5 \text{ V}.$$

Voltage across $C = V_C$

$$= 31 \cdot 85 \times 5 \cdot 15 = 164 \text{ V}.$$

These voltages and the current are represented vectorially in Fig. 145, and the significance of the voltages across the inductance and the capacitance being greater than the applied voltage is explained in Art. 110.

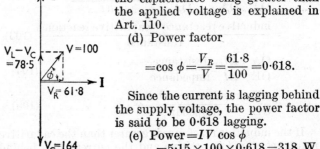

(d) Power factor

$$= \cos \phi = \frac{V_R}{V} = \frac{61 \cdot 8}{100} = 0 \cdot 618.$$

Since the current is lagging behind the supply voltage, the power factor is said to be 0·618 lagging.

(e) Power $= IV \cos \phi$

$$= 5 \cdot 15 \times 100 \times 0 \cdot 618 = 318 \text{ W}.$$

FIG. 145. — Vector diagram for Example 58.

Or, alternatively:

$$\text{power} = I^2 R = (5 \cdot 15)^2 \times 12 = 318 \text{ W}.$$

Example 59. *A resistance of* 50 Ω, *an inductance of* 0·15 *H, and a capacitance of* 100 μF *are connected in parallel across a* 100-*V,* 50-*c/s supply. Calculate* (a) *the current in each circuit,* (b) *the resultant current,* (c) *the power factor and* (d) *the power.*

(a) The circuit diagram is given in Fig. 146, where I_R, I_L and I_C represent the currents through the resistance, inductance and capacitance respectively.

$$I_R = \frac{100}{50} = 2 \text{ A}$$

$$I_L = \frac{100}{2 \times 3 \cdot 14 \times 50 \times 0 \cdot 15} = 2 \cdot 125 \text{ A}$$

and $I_C = 2 \times 3 \cdot 14 \times 50 \times 100 \times 10^{-6} \times 100 = 3 \cdot 14 \text{ A}.$

In the case of parallel circuits, the first vector (Fig. 147) to be drawn is that representing the quantity that is common to those circuits, namely the voltage. I_R is

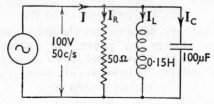

FIG. 146.—Circuit diagram for Example 59.

then drawn in phase with V, I_L lagging 90° and I_C leading 90°.

(b) The resultant of I_C and I_L.

$$= I_C - I_L = 3 \cdot 14 - 2 \cdot 125$$
$$= 1 \cdot 015 \text{ A, leading } 90° \text{ in front of } V$$

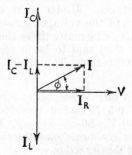

FIG. 147.—Vector diagram for Example 59.

The current I taken from the alternator is the resultant of I_R and $(I_C - I_L)$, and from Fig. 147:

$$I^2 = I_R^2 + (I_C - I_L)^2 = 2^2 + (1 \cdot 015)^2 = 5 \cdot 03$$
$$\therefore \qquad I = 2 \cdot 24 \text{ A.}$$

(c) Power factor of the combined circuits

$$= \cos \phi = \frac{I_R}{I} = \frac{2}{2 \cdot 24} = 0 \cdot 893.$$

8*

Since the current is leading in front of the supply voltage, the power factor is said to be 0·893 leading.

(d) Power $= IV \cos \phi$

$= 2·24 \times 100 \times 0·893 = 200$ W.

Or alternatively, since neither the inductance nor the capacitance absorbs any power, the resistance is responsible for all the power; and since I_R is in phase with the supply voltage, the power is $I_R V$, namely

$$2 \text{ A} \times 100 \text{ V} = 200 \text{ W.}$$

110. Electrical Resonance. In the preceding article it was shown that for a circuit consisting of resistance, inductance and capacitance in series, the resultant reactance is $\left(2\pi fL - \dfrac{1}{2\pi fC}\right)$. Consequently, if we arrange the values of f, L and C so that the inductive reactance and the capacitive reactance neutralise each other, the resultant reactance is zero and the impedance is the same as the resistance. Under these circumstances it is possible for each of the voltages across the inductance and the capacitance to be many times the supply voltage, and the circuit is then said to be in *resonance*, i.e. in a state of electrical vibration. This effect is best illustrated by an example.

Example 60. *A circuit consists of a resistance of 4 Ω, an inductance of 0·5 H and a variable capacitance in series across a 100-V, 50-c/s supply. Calculate (a) the capacitance to give resonance and (b) the voltages across the inductance and the capacitance.*

(a) For resonance:

inductive reactance = capacitive reactance

i.e.　　　　　　　$2\pi fL = \dfrac{1}{2\pi fC}$

∴　　　　　　　$C = \dfrac{1}{4 \times (3·14)^2 \times (50)^2 \times 0·5}$

　　　　　　　　$= 20·3 \times 10^{-6}$ farad

　　　　　　　　$= 20·3$ microfarads.

(b) At resonance:

$$\text{impedance} = \text{resistance} = 4 \ \Omega$$

$$\therefore \qquad I = \frac{100}{4} = 25 \text{ A.}$$

From (87):

$$\text{p.d. across inductance} = V_L = 2 \times 3 \cdot 14 \times 50 \times 0 \cdot 5 \times 25$$

$$= 3925 \text{ V,}$$

p.d. across capacitance $= V_C = $ p.d. across inductance.

Or, alternatively, from (101):

$$V_C = \frac{25 \times 10^6}{2 \times 3 \cdot 14 \times 50 \times 20 \cdot 3} = 3925 \text{ V.}$$

The voltages and current are represented vectorially, but not to scale, in Fig. 148. In this example the voltages across the inductance and the capacitance are each nearly forty times the supply voltage. A fuller explanation, however, is necessary to understand the significance of such a result.

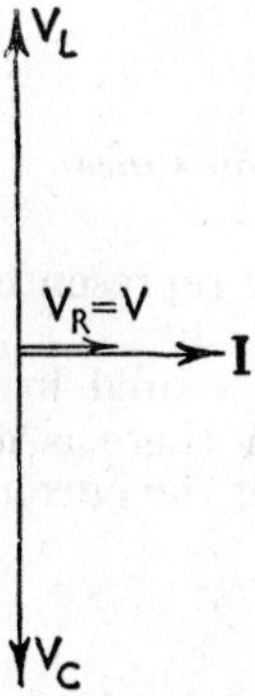

FIG. 148.—Vector diagram for resonant circuit.

111. Natural Frequency of Oscillation of a Circuit possessing Inductance and Capacitance. Suppose C in Fig. 149 to be a capacitor whose capacitance can be varied from, say, 1 to 20 microfarads, and suppose L to be an inductor whose inductance is variable between, say, 0·1 and 0·01 henry. A loudspeaker P is connected across a variable low resistance R. A two-way switch S enables C to be charged from a battery B and discharged through L, and R is adjusted to give a convenient volume of sound in P. It is found that each time C is discharged through L, a pizzicato note is emitted by P, similar to the sound produced by plucking the string of a violin or 'cello. Further, the pitch of the note can be varied by varying either C or L—the larger the capacitance and the inductance, the lower the pitch. But it is well known that a musical sound

requires the vibration of some medium for its production
and that the pitch is dependent upon the number of
vibrations per second. Hence it follows that the discharge current through P is an alternating current of
diminishing amplitude as shown by the full line in

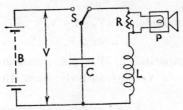

FIG. 149.—Capacitor discharged through inductance.

Fig. 150, the p.d. across the condenser being represented
by the dotted line.

From Art. 84 it follows that the energy stored in C
at instant O is $\frac{1}{2}CV^2$ joules. At instant A there is no
p.d. across and therefore no energy in C; but the current

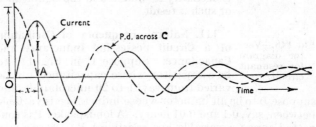

FIG. 150.—Voltage and current curves for Fig. 149.

is I amperes, so that the energy stored in L is $\frac{1}{2}LI^2$ joules
(Art. 66). If we neglect the energy wasted in the
resistance of the circuit during interval OA, then:

$$\frac{1}{2}LI^2 = \frac{1}{2}CV^2$$

and
$$I = V\sqrt{\left(\frac{C}{L}\right)} \quad . \quad . \quad . \quad (106)$$

If x seconds be the duration of the quarter-cycle OA: average e.m.f. induced in L during OA

$$= -L \times \text{average rate of increase of current}$$

$$= -L \times \frac{I}{x} \text{ volts.}$$

If the small voltage drop due to the resistance of the circuit be neglected, the average p.d. applied to L is the same as the average p.d. across C. Hence—assuming a sine wave—we have $\dfrac{LI}{x} = \dfrac{2}{\pi} V$ (see footnote, p. 183).

Substituting for I the value given in (106):

$$\frac{LV}{x} \times \sqrt{\left(\frac{C}{L}\right)} = \frac{2}{\pi} V,$$

$$\therefore \qquad x = \frac{\pi}{2}\sqrt{(\mathrm{LC})} \text{ seconds,}$$

so that the duration of one cycle $= 4x = 2\pi\sqrt{(\mathrm{LC})}$ seconds, and frequency = number of cycles/second

$$= \frac{1}{2\pi\sqrt{(\mathrm{LC})}} \quad \cdots \cdots \quad (107)$$

This quantity is termed the *natural frequency* of the circuit and represents the frequency with which energy is oscillating backwards and forwards between the capacitor and the inductor, the energy being at one moment stored as electrostatic energy in the capacitor, and a quarter of a cycle later as magnetic energy in the inductor. Owing to loss in the resistance of the circuit, the net amount of energy available to be passed backwards and forwards between L and C gradually decreases.

112. Oscillation of Energy at Resonance. In Art. 110 it was explained that resonance occurs in an a.c. circuit when

$$2\pi f L - \frac{1}{2\pi f C} = 0,$$

i.e. when $\qquad f = \dfrac{1}{2\pi\sqrt{(\mathrm{LC})}} \quad \cdots \quad (108)$

A comparison of expressions (107) and (108) shows that the condition for resonance is that the frequency of the applied alternating voltage must be equal to the natural frequency of oscillation of the circuit. This condition enables a large amount of energy to be maintained in oscillation between L and C; thus, if the current and the p.d. across the capacitor in a resonant circuit be represented by the curves of Fig. 151, the magnetic energy

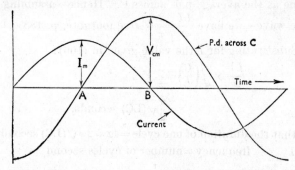

Fig. 151.—Curves of current and p.d. for Fig. 143.

stored in L at instant A is $\frac{1}{2}LI_m^2$ joules, and the electrostatic energy in C at instant B is $\frac{1}{2}CV_{cm}^2$ joules.

Since $I_m = 2\pi f C V_{cm}$, and from (108), $L = \dfrac{1}{(2\pi f)^2 C}$,

$$\therefore \quad \frac{1}{2}LI_m^2 = \frac{1}{2} \times \frac{1}{(2\pi f)^2 C} \times (2\pi f C V_{cm})^2$$

$$= \frac{1}{2}CV_{cm}^2,$$

i.e. the magnetic energy in L at instant A is exactly equal to the electrostatic energy in C at instant B, and the power taken from the supply is simply that required to move this energy backwards and forwards between L and C through the resistance of the circuit.

If the frequency of the voltage applied to a circuit consisting of resistance, inductance and capacitance in series be varied through resonance, the value of the voltage being kept constant, the current increases to a maximum at the resonant frequency and then decreases; thus Fig. 152 represents the variation for the circuit of Example 60, the voltage being kept constant at 100 V.

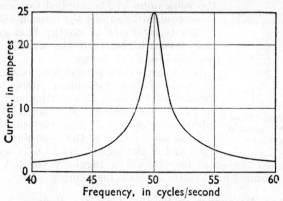

FIG. 152.—Resonance curve for an acceptor.

A resonant circuit of this type is frequently termed an *acceptor* and is much used in wireless work.

113. Mechanical Analogy of a Resonant Circuit. It was pointed out in Art. 94 that inertia in mechanics is analogous to inductance in the electric circuit, and in Art. 72 that elasticity is analogous to capacitance. A very simple mechanical analogy of an electrical circuit possessing inductance, capacitance and a very small resistance can therefore be obtained by attaching a weight W (Fig. 153) to the lower end of a spiral spring S, the upper end of which is rigidly supported. If W is pulled down a short distance and then released, it will oscillate up and down with gradually decreasing amplitude. By varying the value of W and the length of S it can be shown that the greater the weight and the more flexible the spring, the lower is the natural frequency of oscillation of the system.

If we set W into a slight oscillation and then give it a small downward tap each time it is moving downwards, the oscillations may be made to grow to a large amplitude. In other words, when the frequency of the applied force is the same as the natural frequency of oscillation, a small force can build up large oscillations, the work done by the applied force being that required to supply the losses involved in the transference of energy backwards and forwards between the kinetic and potential forms of energy.

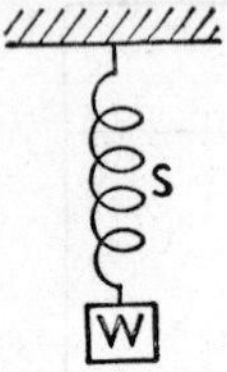

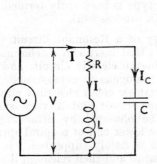

FIG. 153.—
Mechanical
analogy.

Examples of resonance are very common; for instance, the rattling of some loose member of a vehicle at a particular speed or of a loudspeaker diaphragm when reproducing a sound of a certain pitch, and the oscillations of the pendulum of a clock and of the balance wheel of a watch due to the small impulse given regularly through the escapement mechanism from the mainspring.

114. Resonance in Parallel Circuits. Suppose a coil having an inductance L henrys and a very low resistance

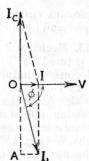

FIG. 154.—Parallel
circuits.

FIG. 155.—Vector diagram
for Fig. 154.

R to be connected in parallel with a capacitor of capacitance C farads, as in Fig. 154.

Current through coil $= I_1 = \dfrac{V}{\sqrt{[R^2 + (2\pi fL)^2]}}$; and from (91), the phase angle ϕ between I_1 and the applied voltage is such that $\tan \phi = \dfrac{2\pi f L}{R}$. Since R is very small compared with $2\pi f L$, $\tan \phi$ is very large, so that ϕ is nearly $90°$. as shown in Fig. 155.

Current taken by capacitor $= I_C = 2\pi f C V$, leading $90°$ in front of V.

If I_1 and I_C are such that the resultant current I is in phase with the supply voltage, as shown in Fig. 155, the circuit is said to be in resonance.

From Fig. 155. $I_C = OA = I_1 \sin \phi$ . . .   (109)

But $\sin \phi = \dfrac{\text{reactance of coil}}{\text{impedance of coil}} = \dfrac{2\pi f L}{\sqrt{[R^2 + (2\pi f L)^2]}}$.

Substituting for I_C, I_1 and $\sin \phi$ in (109), we have:

$$2\pi f C V = \frac{2\pi f L V}{R^2 + (2\pi f L)^2}$$

$\therefore$ $$f = \frac{1}{2\pi} \sqrt{\left[\frac{1}{LC} - \left(\frac{R}{L}\right)^2\right]}.$$

If R is very small compared with $2\pi f L$, as in radio circuits,

$$C = \frac{1}{(2\pi f)^2 L},$$

so that $$f = \frac{1}{2\pi \sqrt{(LC)}},$$

which is the same as the resonant frequency of a series circuit (Art. 110).

Since the resultant current in a resonant parallel circuit is in phase with the supply voltage,

$$\left.\begin{array}{r}\text{impedance of such} \\ \text{a circuit}\end{array}\right\} = \frac{V}{I} = \frac{V}{OA \cot \phi}$$

$$= \frac{V}{I_C} \tan \phi = \frac{1}{2\pi f C} \cdot \frac{2\pi f L}{R}$$

$$= \frac{L}{CR} \quad \text{. . . . . . .}   (110)$$

This means that a resonant parallel circuit is equivalent to a non-inductive resistance of $L/(CR)$ ohms. This quantity is often termed the *dynamic impedance* of the circuit; and it is obvious that the lower the resistance of the coil, the higher is the dynamic impedance of the parallel circuit. This type of circuit when used in radio work is referred to as a *rejector* since its impedance is a maximum and the resultant current a minimum at resonance.

If the alternator voltage in Fig. 154 is kept constant but its frequency varied, the current decreases to a minimum at the resonant frequency; thus Fig. 156

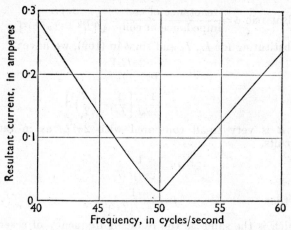

FIG. 156.—Resonance curve for a rejector.

represents the variation of the resultant current for an inductor having a resistance of 4 Ω and an inductance of 0·5 H connected in parallel with a capacitance of 20·3 μF across a constant voltage of 100 V, the values being the same as those of the series circuit of Example 60. Since Fig. 152 and 156 refer to circuits having the same constants, it is of interest to note that a change of 10 per cent in the frequency from the resonant value reduces the current to about an eighth in the series circuit and increases the resultant current about eight times when the circuits are in parallel.

Summary of Important Formulae

Capacitive reactance $= X_C = 1/(2\pi fC)$ . . .   (100)

For circuit with R, L and C in series,

$$\text{Impedance} = Z = \sqrt{\left[R^2 + \left(2\pi fL - \frac{1}{2\pi fC}\right)^2\right]} . \quad (102)$$

$$\tan \phi = \frac{2\pi fL - 1/(2\pi fC)}{R} \quad \cdots \quad (103)$$

$$\cos \phi = R/Z \quad \cdots \cdots \cdots \quad (104)$$

$$\sin \phi = \frac{2\pi fL - 1/(2\pi fC)}{Z} \quad \cdots \cdots \quad (105)$$

When a capacitor, charged to a p.d. of V volts, is dis-charged through an inductor of low resistance,

$$\text{peak value of initial current} = V \sqrt{\left(\frac{C}{L}\right)} \quad \cdots \quad (106)$$

and   frequency of oscillations $= \dfrac{1}{2\pi\sqrt{(LC)}}$.   (107)

For resonance in a series circuit,

$$f = \frac{1}{2\pi\sqrt{(LC)}} \quad \cdots \cdots \quad (108)$$

For resonance in a parallel circuit,

$$f = \frac{1}{2\pi}\sqrt{\left[\frac{1}{LC} - \left(\frac{R}{L}\right)^2\right]}$$

$$= \frac{1}{2\pi\sqrt{(LC)}} \quad \text{when} \quad R \ll 2\pi fL.$$

$$\left.\begin{array}{l}\text{Dynamic impedance of}\\ \text{parallel resonant circuit}\end{array}\right\} = \frac{L}{CR} \quad \cdots \cdots \quad (110)$$

EXAMPLES XIII

1. A capacitor having a capacitance of 50 μF is connected across a 110-V, 30-c/s supply. Calculate (a) the reactance and (b) the current.

2. A resistance of 20 Ω and a capacitance of 100 μF are connected in series across a 200-V, 50-c/s supply. Calculate (a) the current, (b) the p.d.'s across the resistance and the capacitance, (c) the phase difference between the current and the applied voltage, (d) the power and (e) the power factor. Sketch the vector diagram.

3. A resistance of 130 Ω and a capacitance of 30 μF are connected in parallel across a 200-V, 50-c/s supply. Calculate (a) the current in each circuit, (b) the resultant current, (c) the phase difference between the resultant current and the applied voltage, (d) the power and (e) the power factor. Sketch the vector diagram.

4. Explain what is meant by the reactance of a condenser.

A current of 4·8 A is taken when a 30-Ω resistor and a condenser are joined in series and connected to a 240-V 50-c/s supply. Find the impedance of the circuit, the capacitance of the condenser, the power dissipated and the circuit power factor.   (Joint Section A)

5. A capacitor is shunted by a non-reactive resistor of 200 Ω and the combination takes a current of 2 A when connected to 250-V, 50-c/s supply mains. Calculate the capacitance and the power factor of the combination.   (C. & G., El. Eng. Pract., Prelim.)

6. Explain why the current taken by a capacitor (or condenser) leads a quarter of a cycle in front of the applied voltage.

A resistance of 120 Ω is connected in parallel with a capacitance of 30 μF across a 200-V, 50-c/s supply. Calculate (a) the current in each circuit, (b) the resultant current and (c) the power factor of the combined circuit. Sketch the vector diagram.
        (I.Mech.E., Prin. of Elect.)

7. It is desired to operate a 100-W, 120-V electric lamp at its correct rating from a 240-V, 50-c/s supply. Give details of the simplest manner in which this could be done using (a) a resistor, (b) a capacitor, (c) an inductor having a resistance of 10 Ω. What power factor would be presented to the supply in each case and which method is the most economical of power?   (C. & G., Telecom. Prin. II)

8. A circuit consists of a resistance of 10 Ω, an inductance of 0·1 H and a capacitance of 50 μF connected in series across a 100-V, 50-c/s supply. Calculate (a) the current, (b) the p.d.'s across R, L and C respectively, (c) the phase angle between the current and the applied voltage, (d) the power factor and (e) the power.

9. A coil is connected in series with a capacitor of 60 μF across a 200-V, 50-c/s supply. The current is 3 A and the power absorbed is 144 W. Calculate (a) the p.d. across the capacitor, (b) the resistance and inductance of the coil, (c) the power factor of the coil and (d) the power factor of the whole circuit. Sketch the complete vector diagram.

10. A coil having a resistance of 10 Ω and an inductance of 0·05 H is connected in series with a capacitor of 150 μF to 100-V, 50-c/s mains. Find (a) the voltage across the coil and (b) the power factor of the whole circuit, stating whether it is lagging or leading.
        (C. & G., El. Eng. Pract., Prelim.)

11. Explain what is meant by "series resonance" in an a.c. circuit and deduce the condition for such resonance.

A coil having a resistance of 5 Ω and an inductance of 0·2 H is connected in series with a variable condenser across a 30-V, 50-c/s supply. Calculate the capacitance of the condenser required to produce resonance and find the corresponding values of (a) the current, (b) the voltages across the coil and the condenser and (c) the power factor. Sketch the complete vector diagram.
        (I.Mech.E., Prin. of Elect.)

12. Derive an expression for the resonant frequency of a circuit which consists of an inductance, L henrys, having a resistance of R ohms, connected in series with a capacitance of C farads.

If $L = 0·1$ H, $R = 20$ Ω and $C = 0·1$ μF, at what frequency will the circuit take the maximum current from a sinusoidal a.c. supply of 1 volt? What is the value of the current and the power absorbed?
        (C. & G., Telecom. Prin. II)

13. A network consisting of a resistor of 300 Ω, capacitor of 2 μF and inductor of 0·02 H in series is connected across a sinusoidal a.c. supply which has a constant output of 9 V, r.m.s., at all frequencies. Calculate (a) the resonant frequency, (b) the current in the circuit at resonance, (c) the power absorbed by the circuit at resonance and (d) the voltage across the condenser at resonance.

What would be the power absorbed by the circuit if the applied frequency were twice the resonant frequency?
(C. & G., Telecom. Prin. II)

14. A resistance of 10 Ω, an inductance of 0·06 H and a capacitance of 300 μF are connected in parallel across a 100-V, 25-c/s supply. Calculate (a) the current in each circuit, (b) the resultant current, (c) the power factor of the combination and (d) the power.

15. Draw and explain the vector diagram for a circuit consisting of a capacitance in parallel with an inductive resistance.

If the resistance and inductance of such a circuit are 20 Ω and 0·07 H respectively, find the capacitance required to produce resonance when connected in parallel on a 50-c/s supply.
(C. & G., El. Eng. Pract., Prelim.)

16. Explain the meaning of the term "resonance" as applied to a parallel-connected inductor and capacitor, and show the effect of resistance in the circuit.

An inductor of 5 mH and resistance 0·1 Ω resonates at 200 kc/s when connected in parallel with a certain capacitor. Find the value of the capacitance. Using a vector diagram calculate the magnitude and phase relation of the current in the two components relative to the impressed voltage.
(C. & G., Telecom. Prin. II)

17. An inductive circuit takes 10 A and dissipates 1920 watts when connected to a 240-V, 50-c/s supply. When a loss-free condenser is connected across the circuit, the magnitude of the supply current is unaltered. Draw and explain the vector diagram and calculate the size of the condenser.
(Joint Section A)

18. A coil having a resistance of 20 Ω and an inductance of 0·1 H is connected in parallel with a condenser having a capacitance of 50 μF across a 100-V, 50-c/s supply. Calculate (a) the current in each circuit, (b) the resultant current and (c) the power factor of the whole circuit. Sketch the vector diagram.
(I.Mech.E., Prin. of Elect.)

19. A capacitor having a capacitance of 2 μF is charged to a p.d. of 200 V and then connected across a coil having an inductance of 0·05 H and a negligible resistance. Calculate (a) the maximum current that can flow in the coil and (b) the frequency of the oscillations.

20. Define power factor and explain why it should be kept as high as possible in power-supply systems.

A single-phase motor takes 50 A at a power factor of 0·6 (lagging) from a 250-V, 50-c/s supply. What value must a shunting condenser have to raise the overall power factor to 0·9 (lagging)? How does the installation of the condenser affect the line and motor currents?
(Joint Section A)

21. A single-phase motor takes 15 A from a 230-V, 50-c/s supply at a power factor of 0·7 lagging. A capacitor of 80 μF is connected in parallel with the motor. With the aid of a vector diagram, find (a) the resultant current and (b) the power factor of the combination.

22. A single-phase motor takes 20 A from a 400-V, 50-c/s supply, the power factor being 0·8 lagging. Calculate (a) the capacitance to be connected in parallel with the motor to raise the power factor to 0·9 lagging and (b) the additional capacitance required to raise the power factor to unity.

CHAPTER XIV

ARMATURE WINDINGS OF D.C. MACHINES

115. Introductory. The fundamental phenomena of electromagnetic induction have been described in Chapter VI, and it was shown in Art. 48 that the value of the e.m.f., in volts, generated in a conductor is equal to the magnetic flux, in webers, cut per second. In Example 26 the value of the e.m.f. generated in one armature conductor of a typical 4-pole dynamo was found to be only 0·72 volt. Consequently, if the machine is required to generate, say, 500 V, it is necessary to use a large number of conductors and to connect them in such a way that their e.m.f.'s help one another, and at the same time to arrange for the magnetic field to be as intense and the speed as high as is practicable.

In the case of a dynamo, the speed is determined by that of the engine to which it is coupled, while for a motor the speed is determined by the machine which has to be driven. In all electrical machines the magnetic field is intensified by using an iron armature core so that the magnetic flux has to cross only a relatively short airgap.

In Fig. 107 we considered a conductor A situated on a revolving armature and passing successively under N and S poles. The alternating e.m.f. generated in the conductor varied through one cycle every time the conductor passed a pair of poles. A d.c. generator, however, has to give a voltage that remains constant in direction and as constant as possible in magnitude. It is therefore necessary to use a *commutator* to enable a steady or direct voltage to be obtained from the alternating e.m.f. generated in the rotating conductors.

Fig. 157 shows a longitudinal or axial section and an end elevation of half of a relatively small commutator. It consists of a large number of wedge-shaped copper segments or bars C, assembled side by side to form a ring, the segments being insulated from one another by thin mica sheets P. The segments are shaped as shown so that they can be clamped securely between a V-ring B, which is a part of the cast-iron bush or sleeve, and another V-ring R which is tightened and kept in place by a nut N. The C.I. bush is keyed to the shaft S.

The copper segments are insulated from the V-rings by collars of micanite M, namely thin mica flakes cemented together with shellac varnish and moulded to the exact shape of the rings. These collars project well beyond the segments so as to reduce surface leakage of current from the commutator to the shaft. At the end adjacent

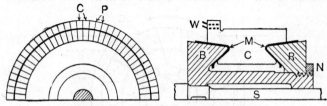

FIG. 157.—Commutator construction.

to the winding, each segment is arranged so that two of the armature wires W can be connected to it.

116. Ring-wound Armature.

The action of the commutator is most easily understood if we consider the earliest form of armature winding, namely the ring-wound armature shown in Fig. 158. In this diagram, C represents a core built of sheet-iron rings or laminations, insulated from one another. The core is wound with eight coils, each consisting of two turns; and the two ends of any one coil are connected to adjacent segments of the commutator. P and Q represent two carbon brushes, namely two blocks of specially treated carbon, bearing on the commutator. Actually these brushes are pressed by springs against the outer surface of the segments, but to avoid confusion in Fig. 158 they are shown on the inside. The term "brush" is a relic of the time when current was collected by a bundle of copper wires arranged somewhat like a brush.

The dotted lines in Fig. 158 represent the distribution of the magnetic flux; and it will be seen that this magnetic flux is cut only by that part of the winding that lies on the external surface of the core. It is also evident from Fig. 158 that between brushes Q and P, there are two paths in parallel through the armature winding and that all the conductors are divided equally between these two paths. Furthermore, as the armature rotates, this state of affairs remains unaltered.

Suppose the armature to be driven clockwise. Then, by applying the Right-hand Rule of Art. 47, we find that the direction of the e.m.f.'s generated in conductors under

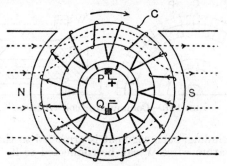

FIG. 158.—Ring-wound armature.

the N pole is towards the paper, and that of the e.m.f.'s in the conductors under the S pole is outwards from the paper, as indicated by the arrowheads. The result is that in each of the two *parallel* paths, the same number of conductors is generating e.m.f. acting from Q towards P. The effect is similar to that obtained if equal numbers of cells (in series) were connected in two parallel circuits, as shown in Fig. 159. In this case it is clear that P is the positive and Q the negative terminal, and that the total e.m.f. is equal to the sum of the e.m.f.'s of the cells connected in series between Q and P. Also, the current in each path is a half of the total current flowing outwards at P and returning at Q. Similarly, in the armature winding, the total e.m.f. between brushes P and Q depends upon the e.m.f. per conductor, and the number of conductors in series per path between Q and P; and the current in each conductor is half the total current at each brush.

It follows from Fig. 158 that the conductors generating e.m.f. are those which are moving opposite a pole, and that in each path the number of conductors simultaneously generating e.m.f. remains constant from instant to instant and is unaffected by the rotation of the armature. Hence, the p.d. between P and Q must also remain constant from instant to instant—a result made possible by the commutator.

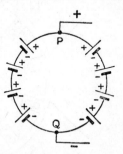

FIG. 159.—Equivalent circuit of an armature winding.

The ring winding of Fig. 158 has the disadvantages: (1) it is very expensive to wind, since each turn has to be taken round the core by hand; (2) only a small portion of each turn is effective in cutting magnetic flux. Hence, modern armatures are "drum" wound, the coils being placed in slots on the outer surface of the core, as shown in Fig. 160. This arrangement has the advantage of greater mechanical security for the winding and of shorter air-gap for the magnetic flux to cross between the poles and the armature "teeth," namely the portions of the core that project between the slots.

117. Double-layer Drum Windings.

Let us consider a 4-pole armature with, say, 11 slots, as shown in Fig. 160. In order that all the coils may be similar in shape and therefore may be wound to the correct shape before being assembled on the core, they have to be made such that one side 1 of a coil occupies the outer half of one slot while the other side 1' occupies the inner half of another slot. This necessitates a kink in the end-connections in order that the coils may overlap one another as they are being assembled. Fig. 161 shows the shape of the end-connections of a single coil consisting of a number of turns, while Fig. 162 (b) shows how three coils, 1–1′, 2–2′ and 3–3′ are arranged in the slots so that their end-connections overlap one another, the end elevation of the end-connections of coils 1–1′ and 3–3′ being as

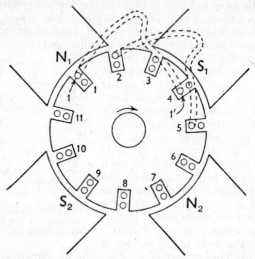

FIG. 160.—Arrangement of a double-layer winding.

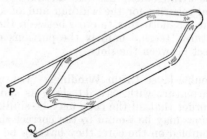

FIG. 161.—An armature coil.

shown in Fig. 162 (a). The end-connection of coil 2–2′ has been omitted from Fig. 162 (a) to enable the shape of the other end-connections to be shown more clearly. In Fig. 161, the two ends of the coil are brought out to

P and Q; and as far as the connections to the commutator segments are concerned, the number of turns
on each coil is of no consequence. Hence, in winding
diagrams it is customary to show only one turn between
any pair of segments.

From Fig. 160 it is evident that if the e.m.f.'s generated
in conductors 1 and 1' are to assist each other, 1' must
be moving under a S pole when 1 is moving under a
N pole; thus, by applying the Right-hand Rule (Art. 47)

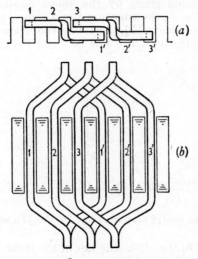

FIG. 162.—Arrangement of overlap of end-connections.

to Fig. 160 and assuming the armature to be rotated
clockwise, we find that the direction of the e.m.f.
generated in conductor 1 is towards the paper whereas
that generated in conductor 1' is outwards from the
paper. Hence, the distance between coil-sides 1 and
1' must be approximately the same as that between the
centres of adjacent poles—a distance that is termed a
pole-pitch. With 11 slots it is impossible to make the
distance between 1 and 1' exactly a pole-pitch, and in
Fig. 160, one side of coil 1–1' is shown in slot 1 and the

other side is in slot 4. The coil is then said to have a *coil span* of 4−1, namely 3. In practice, the coil span must be a whole number and is approximately equal to $\dfrac{\text{total number of slots}}{\text{total number of poles}}$.

In the example shown in Fig. 160 a very small number of slots has for simplicity been chosen. In actual machines the number of slots per pole usually lies between 10 and 15 and the coil span is slightly less than the value given by the above expression. For instance, if a 4-pole armature has 47 slots, the number of slots per pole=11¾, and the coil span would be 11; consequently, if one side of a coil lies in the outer

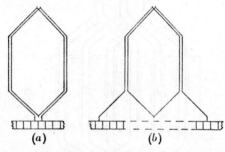

(a)   (b)

FIG. 163.—(a) Coil of a lap winding; (b) Coil of a wave winding.

half of slot 6, the other side lies in the inner half of slot (6+11), namely slot 17.

Let us now return to the consideration of the 11-slot armature. The 11 coils are assembled in the slots with a coil span of 3, and we are now faced with the problem of connecting to the commutator segments the 22 ends that are projecting from the winding.

Apart from a few special windings, armature windings can be divided into two groups, depending upon the manner in which the wires are joined to the commutator, namely :

    (a) lap windings,
    (b) wave windings.

In lap windings the two ends of any one coil are taken
to adjacent segments as in Fig. 163 (a), where a coil of
two turns is shown; whereas in wave windings the two
ends of each coil are bent in opposite directions and
taken to segments some distance apart, as in Fig. 163 (b).

118. Lap Winding.   Let us consider the 4-pole armature of Fig. 160 and assume for simplicity that there are
only 2 conductors per slot in each of the 11 slots.*   The
easiest way of indicating the connections of the wires
to the commutator segments is to use a developed
diagram, namely a diagram representing the winding

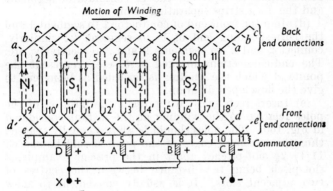

FIG. 164.—Developed diagram of a lap winding.

cut radially at one point and then laid flat as shown in
Fig. 164.   The full lines 1, 2, 3, etc., represent the
conductors (and their end-connections) occupying the
outer halves of the slots, while the dotted lines 1′, 2′,

* For teaching purposes, considerable economy of time is
effected by giving each student a duplicated sheet on which
the poles and parallel lines representing the conductors in
the slots have been drawn.   The back and front end connections, the commutator segments and the brushes are then
inserted by the student.   It is for this reason that an 11-slot
armature has been used for both lap and wave windings,
whereas with lap windings the number of slots is usually a
multiple of the number of pairs of poles.

3', etc., represent the conductors occupying the inner halves; thus 1 and 9' represent conductors occupying the outer and inner halves respectively of one slot, 2 and 10' occupy the next slot, etc. The procedure in drawing the complete developed winding is as follows:

(a) Draw parallel full and dotted lines to represent the conductors in the 11 slots and label the full lines 1, 2, etc.

(b) Adopting the coil span of 3 referred to in the preceding article, insert the back end-connections * by joining 1 in slot 1 to 1' in slot 4, 2 to 2', etc.

(c) Draw two parallel horizontal lines and vertical intersections to represent the 11 commutator segments and the mica strips separating them.

(d) Join the front end of conductor 1 to segment 1 and the corresponding end of 1' to segment 2; similarly, connect 2 and 2' to segments 2 and 3 respectively, etc. The end-connections marked a, b, etc., represent the points at which the winding is regarded as being cut to give the developed diagram.

(e) Insert rectangles to represent the position of the poles relative to the winding at the instant considered in Fig. 160. The poles should be shown equally spaced; thus the left-hand edges of the poles should be spaced $11/4 = 2\frac{3}{4}$ slot-pitches apart in the present example, a slot-pitch being the distance between the centres of two adjacent slots. It is usually convenient to show the width of each pole about two-thirds of the pole pitch.

(f) Assume the winding in Fig. 164 to be moving towards, say, the right and the poles to be *in front* of the winding; consequently from the Right-hand Rule it is found that the directions of the e.m.f.'s generated in conductors moving in the magnetic fields are as indicated by the arrowheads. These directions can also be deduced from Fig. 160; thus, the direction of the e.m.f.

* It is always assumed that we look at the armature from the commutator end, so that the wires on the commutator side of the armature core are referred to as the front end-connections and those on the far side of the core as the back end-connections.

generated in conductor 1 is towards the paper and therefore away from the commutator end of the armature.

(g) Indicate the position of the brushes. With a lap winding there must be as many brushes as there are poles, and they must be equally spaced around the commutator and connected through the latter to conductors in which practically no e.m.f.'s are being generated. With the small number of slots used in the present example, it is impossible to satisfy this requirement to the extent that is possible with a normal armature. Let us start with, say, conductor 5, which is moving in the interpolar space and therefore generating no e.m.f., and let us follow the path from this conductor to the nearest segment, namely 5, and place a *narrow* brush A opposite the centre of that segment. Since there are 11 segments, the distance between the centres of adjacent brushes must be $11/4 = 2\frac{3}{4}$ segment pitches. Hence, insert the other three brushes B, C and D as shown in Fig. 164.

(h) The polarities of the brushes can now be determined by taking any conductor, such as 1, which is definitely moving in a magnetic field and following the direction of the arrowhead on that conductor until we come to a segment on which a brush is bearing, namely D in this instance. Since the e.m.f. generated in the winding is acting towards D, the latter must be a positive brush. It is shown below that brushes A, B and C are negative, positive, and negative respectively. The positive brushes B and D are then connected together to the positive terminal X, and A and C to the negative terminal Y.

(i) Trace the circuits between the negative and positive terminals. Starting from Y, we may branch to either A or C. At A, we can branch to either 5 or 4'; and at C we can branch to 10, 9', 11 or 10'. If we follow 10, we come back via 10' to the same brush; in other words, coil 10–10' is short-circuited by brush C when the armature is in position shown. Consequently we need only consider branches 9' and 11 as far as brush C is concerned.

We may now tabulate the parallel paths thus:

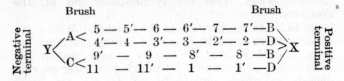

It is seen that in the four parallel paths between Y and X there are 20 conductors; and these, along with the 2 conductors short-circuited by brush C, account for all the 22 conductors on the armature. The inequality in the number of conductors per circuit is due to the fact that the number of slots is not a multiple of the number of poles and is of no real importance. The number of slots was chosen deliberately as 11 to enable the same number of conductors to be used for both lap and wave windings and to show that a lap winding is possible with any number of slots. If a lap winding is to be fitted with equaliser rings, the number of slots must be a multiple of the number of pairs of poles, but this is a problem that is beyond the scope of this volume.

119. Wave Windings. It was shown in Fig. 163 that the difference between lap and wave windings is due to the manner in which the ends of the coils are connected to the commutator. In a lap winding the ends of each coil are connected to adjacent segments, whereas in a wave winding they are bent in opposite directions and connected to segments some distance apart. Our next problem is to determine this spacing.

Let us again consider a 4-pole armature with 11 slots and 2 conductors per slot, and let us start with conductor 1 (Fig. 165) connected to segment 1. The coil span will be the same as that adopted in Fig. 164, namely 3. Consequently, if 1 occupies the outer half of slot 1, the other side 1' occupies the inner half of slot 4.

It is now necessary to connect the end of 1' to the beginning of a conductor, such as 6 or 7, moving under the second N pole in order that the e.m.f. generated in that conductor may assist the e.m.f.'s generated in 1 and

1'. If we select 6, then from Fig. 165 (b) it follows that the end of 1' must be connected to segment 6, giving a *commutator pitch* of 6 − 1, namely 5.

Once the spacing between the ends of 1 and 1' has been decided, the same value will apply to each of the other coils; therefore the end of 6' must go to segment

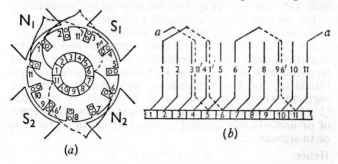

FIG. 165.—Portion of a wave winding with $y = 5$.

(6 + 5), namely 11. From the latter we go to coil 11–11', which lies adjacent to 1–1'.

Let us next consider the alternative method in which 1' is connected to the beginning of 7. From Fig. 166 it is seen that the end of 1' must now be connected to

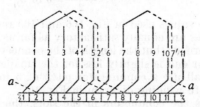

FIG. 166.—Portion of a wave winding with $y = 6$

segment 7, giving a **commutator pitch** of 7 − 1 = 6. Consequently, the end of 7' must go to segment (7 + 6) = 13. But there are only 11 segments; therefore the end of 7' is connected to segment 2 and thence to coil 2–2', which is adjacent to coil 1–1'.

9

From Fig. 165 and 166 it is evident that after following the coil connections once round the armature we
must arrive at a segment adjacent to the one from which
we started. Thus, in the above diagrams we started
from segment 1, and after going round coils 1–1' and 6–6'
(Fig. 165), we arrived at segment 11; while the path via
coils 1–1' and 7–7' (Fig. 166) brought us to segment 2.

Let us now derive a general expression for the commutator pitch of a 4-pole wave winding.

Let C=number of commutator segments, and y=com-
mutator pitch. If the beginning of coil 1–1' be joined
to segment 1, its end must be taken to segment $(1+y)$.
Similarly, for the coil whose beginning is joined to
segment $(1+y)$, its end must be taken to segment
$(1+y+y)$, namely $(1+2y)$, which is immediately in front
of or immediately beyond segment 1, i.e. to segment C
or to segment 2.

Hence $$1+2y=C \text{ or } C+2$$

$$\therefore \qquad y=\frac{C-1}{2} \text{ or } \frac{C+1}{2}$$

$$=\frac{C\pm1}{2}.$$

In the above example, $C=11$

$$\therefore \qquad y=\frac{11\pm1}{2}=6 \text{ or } 5,$$

namely the values used in Fig. 166 and 165 respectively.
These values are equally satisfactory as far as this winding is concerned; but the length of the connections at the
commutator end is slightly less for the smaller pitch, so
that we shall use a commutator pitch of 5 for drawing
the complete winding diagram in Fig. 167.

As far as the conductors in the slots, the back end-
connections and the poles are concerned, the procedure
is precisely the same as that for Fig. 164. The front end-
connections are then inserted by joining conductor 1 to
segment 1, 2 to segment 2, etc., and afterwards joining
1' to 6, 2' to 7, etc. The first brush A is inserted by
taking a conductor, such as 5, in which no e.m.f. is being
generated and following it to the nearest segment.

A second brush B is placed at a distance of $11/4 = 2\frac{3}{4}$ segment pitches from A. The polarities of A and B can be determined by starting with any conductor such as 1, and following the direction of the generated e.m.f.

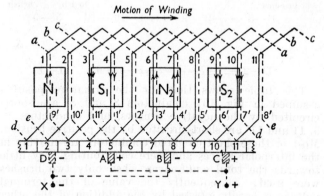

FIG. 167.—Developed diagram of a wave winding.

via $1', 6, 6', 11, 11'$ to A. Therefore A must be the positive brush.

Let us now trace the circuits between B and A:

$$\nearrow 3' - 3 - 9' - 9 - 4' - 4 - 10' - 10 - 5' - 5 \searrow$$

Brush →
B

$$\searrow 8 - 8' - 2 - 2' - 7 - 7' - 1 - 1' - 6 - 6' - 11 - 11' \nearrow$$

Brush
A

It will be seen that all the 22 conductors are included in the two parallel paths between A and B; and the arrows alongside the conductors that are generating e.m.f.'s indicate that in each path these e.m.f.'s are all acting from B towards A. Further, it is evident that for a wave winding, only two brushes are essential. Apart from small 4-pole motors, however, it is the practice to fit the machine with as many brushes as there are poles, thereby enabling the axial length of the commutator to be reduced and an appreciable saving of copper to be effected. In Fig. 167 the extra two brushes and the brush connections are shown dotted. By tracing the circuits between the brushes, starting from the negative brushes B and D, we have:

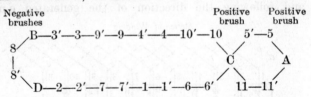

This table shows that for the armature position assumed in Fig. 167 conductors 8 and 8′ are short-circuited by the negative brushes, and conductors 5′, 5, 11 and 11′ are short-circuited by the positive brushes. Most of these short-circuited conductors are moving in the interpolar spaces and were contributing very little towards the total e.m.f. even when only two brushes were used; consequently the value of the terminal voltage is hardly affected by the addition of the other two brushes.

120. General Expression for the Commutation Pitch. It has been shown in connection with Fig. 165 and 166 that for a 4-pole armature

$$1 + 2y = C \quad \text{or} \quad C + 2$$

where C=number of commutator segments

and y=commutator pitch.

Similarly, for a 6-pole armature, it follows that:

$$(1 + 2y) + y = 1 + 3y = C \quad \text{or} \quad C + 2$$

and for a machine with p pairs of poles

$$1 + py = C \quad \text{or} \quad C + 2$$

$$\therefore \qquad y = \frac{C \pm 1}{p} \qquad . \quad . \quad . \quad . \quad . \quad (111)$$

Example 61. *A 6-pole wave-wound armature has 72 slots and 143 commutator segments. Find (a) a suitable coil span, (b) a suitable commutator pitch.*

(a) Number of slots per pole $= \dfrac{72}{6} = 12$.

If the coil span be made 12, such a coil is said to be *full-pitched* because the distance between the two sides would be exactly a pole-pitch. For reasons beyond the scope of this book it is found that the tendency for sparking to occur at the brushes is reduced by making the coil span one less than the number of slots per pole; for instance, 11 in this example.

(b) From expression (111),

$$\text{commutator pitch} = \frac{143 \pm 1}{3} = 48.$$

In this case there is only one alternative, since the value of the pitch must be an integer (or whole number).

It will be noticed that if the number of segments had been 144, namely 2 segments per slot, $y\left(=\dfrac{144 \pm 1}{3}\right)$ would not be an integer and therefore would not be practicable; hence the necessity of omitting one segment. Such an armature is wound with 72 identical coils, each having two pairs of wires projecting towards the commutator. After the 143 pairs of wires have been connected to the segments there is one pair still unused. These two wires are cut short and the ends insulated. The conductors of which these wires form the ends become dummies and merely assist in the mechanical balance of the armature.

121. Calculation of E.M.F. generated in an Armature Winding. When an armature is rotated through one revolution, each conductor cuts the lines of magnetic flux emanating from all the N poles and also those entering all the S poles. Consequently,

if Φ = total flux per pole, in webers, entering or leaving the armature

p = number of *pairs* of poles

and N = speed in r.p.m.

$$\text{time of 1 revolution} = \frac{60}{N} \text{ sec}$$

and time taken by a conductor to move one pole pitch $\left.\right\} = \dfrac{60}{N} \cdot \dfrac{1}{2p} \text{ sec.}$

$$\therefore \quad \left. \begin{array}{l} \text{average rate at which} \\ \text{conductor cuts the flux} \end{array} \right\} = \Phi \div \left(\frac{60}{N} \cdot \frac{1}{2p} \right)$$

$$= \frac{2\Phi Np}{60} \text{ webers/sec.}$$

and average e.m.f. generated in each conductor

$$= \frac{2\Phi Np}{60} \text{ volts.}$$

If Z = total number of armature conductors

c = number of parallel paths through winding between positive and negative brushes

= 2 for a wave winding

and   = $2p$ for a lap winding

$\therefore \quad \dfrac{Z}{c}$ = number of conductors in series in each path.

The brushes are assumed to be in contact with segments connected to conductors in which no e.m.f. is being generated, and the e.m.f. generated in each conductor, while it is moving between positions of zero e.m.f., varies as shown by curve OCDE in Fig. 108. Also, it has been shown that the *number* of conductors in series in each of the parallel paths between the brushes remains practically constant; hence

$$\left. \begin{array}{l} \text{total e.m.f.} \\ \text{between brushes} \end{array} \right\} = \left\{ \begin{array}{l} \text{average e.m.f. per conductor} \times \text{no.} \\ \text{of conductors in series per path} \end{array} \right.$$

$$= \frac{2\Phi Np}{60} \times \frac{Z}{c}$$

i.e. $$E = 2\frac{Z}{c} \times \frac{Np}{60} \times \Phi \text{ volts} \quad . \quad . \quad . \quad (112)$$

This is an extremely important equation and should be memorised.

Example 62. *A 4-pole wave-wound armature has 51 slots with 12 conductors per slot and is rotated at 900 r.p.m. If the useful flux per pole is 25 milliwebers, calculate the value of the generated e.m.f.*

Total number of conductors $= Z = 51 \times 12 = 612$; $c = 2$; $p = 2$; $N = 900$ r.p.m.; $\Phi = 0.025$ weber.

Using expression (112), we have:

$$E = 2 \times \frac{612}{2} \times \frac{900 \times 2}{60} \times 0.025$$

$$= 459 \text{ volts.}$$

Example 63. *An 8-pole lap-wound armature rotated at 350 r.p.m. is required to generate 260 V. The useful flux per pole is about 0.05 weber. If the armature has 120 slots, calculate a suitable number of conductors per slot.*

For an 8-pole lap winding, $c = 8$.

Hence, $260 = 2 \times \dfrac{Z}{8} \times \dfrac{350 \times 4}{60} \times 0.05$

and $Z = 890$ (approximately)

and number of conductors per slot $= \dfrac{890}{120} = 7.4$ (approx.).

This value must be an even number; hence 8 conductors per slot would be suitable.

Since this arrangement involves a total of $8 \times 120 = 960$ conductors, and since a flux of 0.05 weber per pole with 890 conductors gave 260 V, then with 960 conductors the same voltage is generated with a flux of $0.05 \times \dfrac{890}{960} = 0.0464$ weber per pole

122. Comparison of Lap and Wave Windings. In general it may be said that lap windings are used for low-voltage, heavy current machines owing to the fact that there are more paths in parallel than in a wave winding. Consequently, for a given size of conductor and therefore a given current per conductor, the total current from a lap winding is p times the current from a wave winding. On the other hand, for a given number of conductors and a given e.m.f. per conductor, the number of conductors in series per circuit in a wave winding and, therefore, the voltage between the negative and positive brushes are p times the corresponding values in a lap winding.

With a wave winding the conductors of each of the parallel circuits are distributed opposite all the poles simultaneously, so that the total e.m.f. generated in each circuit is independent of the distribution of the flux between the various poles. With a lap winding the e.m.f.'s generated in the parallel paths are unequal if the flux is not the same in all the poles; and in order that the circulating currents due to such unequal e.m.f.'s may be diverted from the brushes, the winding must be fitted with equaliser rings, otherwise sparking at some of the brushes may be excessive. Also, with a wave-wound armature, only two sets of brushes—one positive and one negative—are essential, a feature that can be utilised in small 4-pole machines to reduce the cost of the brush gear.

Summary of Important Formulae

Coil span $\simeq \dfrac{\text{total no. of slots}}{\text{total no. of poles}}$ and must be an integer.

For lap winding, commutator pitch $=y=1$.

,, wave ,, ,, ,, $=y=\dfrac{C \pm 1}{p}$ (111)

and must be an integer.

$$E = \frac{2Z}{c} \cdot \frac{Np}{60} \cdot \varPhi \text{ volts} \quad . \quad . \quad . \quad (112)$$

where $c=2$ for wave winding

$=2p$ for lap winding

and $p=$ no. of *pairs* of poles.

EXAMPLES XIV

1. Draw a developed diagram of a lap winding for a 4-pole armature having 16 slots with 2 conductors per slot. Show the poles and the brushes and indicate the polarity of the brushes for an assumed direction of rotation. Also, trace the parallel circuits between the negative and positive brushes.

2. Draw a developed diagram of a wave winding for a 4-pole armature having 15 slots with 2 conductors per slot. Show the poles and

the brushes and indicate the polarity of the brushes for an assumed direction of rotation. Also, trace the parallel circuits between the negative and positive brushes, and indicate the conductors that are short-circuited at that instant.

3. A 6-pole wave-wound armature has 78 slots and 155 commutator segments. Find suitable coil span and commutator pitch and draw a developed diagram showing the connections for the 6 coils, starting from segment 1 and extending twice round the armature.

4. State, giving reason, which of the following number of commutator segments can be used with a wave winding of a machine having (a) 4 poles, (b) 6 poles: 132, 87, 142.

5. A 6-pole armature is wound with 498 conductors. The flux and the speed are such that the average e.m.f. generated in each conductor is 2 V. Also each conductor is capable of carrying 120 A without excessive temperature rise. Find the total current and the generated e.m.f. of the armature if the winding is connected (a) wave, (b) lap. Also find the total power generated in each case.

6. A 4-pole armature is wound with 564 conductors and driven at 800 r.p.m., the flux per pole being 20 milliwebers. Each conductor is capable of carrying 60 A without excessive temperature rise. Calculate the total current, the e.m.f. and the electrical power generated in the armature if the armature conductors are connected (a) wave, (b) lap.

7. An 8-pole lap-wound armature has 96 slots with 6 conductors per slot and is driven at 500 r.p.m. The useful flux per pole is 0·09 weber. Calculate the generated e.m.f.

8. A 4-pole armature is lap-wound with 624 conductors and is driven at 1200 r.p.m. Calculate the useful flux per pole required to generate an e.m.f. of 250 V.

9. A 6-pole armature is wave-wound with 410 conductors. The flux per pole is 0·025 weber. Find the speed at which the armature must be driven to generate an e.m.f. of 485 V.

10. Distinguish between lap-connected and wave-connected armature windings and deduce the e.m.f. equation for a d.c. machine.

Calculate the flux in a 4-pole dynamo with 722 armature conductors generating 500 V when running at 1000 r.p.m., when the armature is (a) lap-connected and (b) wave-connected.

(C. & G., El. Eng. Pract., Int.)

CHAPTER XV

DIRECT-CURRENT GENERATORS

123. Armature Core. The armature core of a d.c. machine is built of sheet-steel laminations, each about 0·4 to 0·6 mm thick, insulated from one another by a thin layer of paper or varnish or by spraying the laminations with a mixture of flour, chalk and water which, when dried, adheres to the metal. If the core were made of solid iron, as shown in Fig. 168 (a) for a 2-pole machine, then if the armature were rotated clockwise

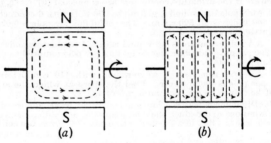

FIG. 168.—Eddy currents.

when viewed from the right-hand side of the machine, e.m.f.'s would be generated in the core in exactly the same way as they would be generated in conductors placed on the armature, and these e.m.f.'s would circulate currents—known as *eddy currents*—in the core, as shown dotted in Fig. 168 (a). Owing to the very low resistance of the core, these eddy currents would be very large and would cause a large loss of power and excessive heating of the armature.

By making the core of laminations insulated from one another, the eddy currents are confined to their respective sheets, as shown dotted in Fig. 168 (b), and the eddy-current loss is thereby reduced. Thus if the core is split up into five laminations, the e.m.f. per lamination is only a fifth of that generated in the solid core, and the cross-sectional area per path is also reduced to about a fifth, so that the resistance per path is roughly five times that of the solid core. Consequently the current per path is about 1/25th of that in the solid core. Hence:

$$\frac{I^2R \text{ loss per lamination}}{I^2R \text{ loss in solid core}} = \left(\frac{1}{25}\right)^2 \times 5 = \frac{1}{125} \text{ (approx.).}$$

Since there are five laminations, then:

$$\frac{\text{total eddy-current loss in laminated core}}{\text{total eddy-current loss in solid core}} = \frac{5}{125} = \left(\frac{1}{5}\right)^2.$$

It follows that the eddy-current loss is approximately proportional to the square of the thickness of the laminations. Hence the eddy-current loss can be reduced to any desired value, but if the thickness of the laminations is made less than about 0·4 mm, the reduction in the loss does not justify the extra cost of construction.

124. General Arrangement of a D.C. Generator or Dynamo.* In Chapter VII we discussed the magnetic circuit and the method of calculating the ampere-turns required to produce a given flux, while in Chapter XIV we considered armature windings and the relationship between the factors that determine the value of the e.m.f. generated in the armature. We shall now deal with the various methods of connecting the exciting winding and the armature winding.

Fig. 169 shows the general arrangement of a 4-pole machine. The four brushes B are making contact with the commutator; and it has been explained in Art. 118 and 119 that these brushes are consecutively positive and negative. Hence, the two positive brushes are connected together and to the positive terminal A. Similarly the negative brushes are connected together and to the negative terminal A_1. From Fig. 164 and 165 it will be seen that for both lap and wave windings

---

* According to the British Standard Glossary, No. 205, the terms "d.c. generator" and "dynamo" are synonymous.

the brushes are situated approximately in line with the
centres of the poles because this position enables them to
make contact with conductors in which little or no e.m.f.
is being generated since these conductors are then moving
between the poles.

The four exciting or field coils C are usually joined in
series and the ends are brought out to terminals F and F_1.
These coils must be so connected as to produce N and S

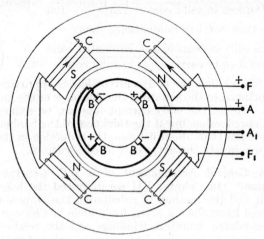

FIG. 169.—Armature and field connections.

poles alternately.   The arrowheads in Fig. 169 indicate
the direction of the field current when F is positive.

In general, we may divide the methods used for
connecting the field and armature windings into the
following groups:

(a) *Separately-excited dynamos*—the field winding being
connected to a source of supply other than the armature
of its own machine.

(b) *Self-excited dynamos*, which may be subdivided
into:

(i) *Shunt-wound dynamos*—the field winding being
connected across the armature terminals.

(ii) *Series-wound dynamos*—the field winding being connected in series with the armature winding.

(iii) *Compound-wound dynamos*—a combination of shunt and series windings.

We shall now consider these systems in greater detail.

125. Separately-excited Dynamos. Fig. 170 shows a simple method of representing the armature and field windings, A and A_1 being the armature terminals and F and F_1 the field terminals already referred to in Fig. 169. The field winding is connected in series with a variable resistance R and an ammeter A to a battery or another dynamo.

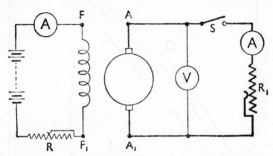

FIG. 170.—Separately-excited dynamo.

Suppose the armature to be driven at a *constant* speed on no load (i.e. with switch S open) and the exciting current to be increased from zero up to the maximum permissible value and then reduced to zero, the generated e.m.f. being noted for various values of the exciting current. It is found that the relationship between the two quantities is as indicated in Fig. 171, curve P being for increasing values of the excitation and Q for decreasing values. The difference between the curves is due to hysteresis (Art. 58), and OR represents the e.m.f. generated by the residual magnetism in the poles. If the test be repeated, the e.m.f. curve follows the dotted line and then merges into curve P. These curves are termed the *internal* or *open-circuit characteristics* of the machine.

From expression (112) it follows that for a given speed the e.m.f. generated in a given machine is proportional to the flux. Consequently curves P and Q in Fig. 171 indicate how the flux varies with the exciting current.

Let us next consider the effect of load upon the terminal voltage. This can be determined experimentally by closing switch S (Fig. 170), varying the value of

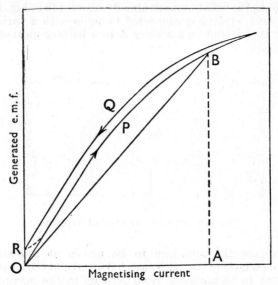

FIG. 171.—Open-circuit characteristic.

the load resistance and noting the terminal voltage for each load current. Curve M in Fig. 172 is typical of the relationship for such a machine. The decrease in the terminal voltage with increase of load is mainly due to the resistance drop in the armature circuit; thus, if the load current is 100 A and the resistance of the armature circuit is $0·08$ Ω, the voltage drop in the armature circuit is $100 \times 0·08 = 8$ V. Consequently, if the generated e.m.f. be 235 V, the terminal p.d. $=235-8$ $=227$ V. In general, if $E=$generated e.m.f., $I_a=$armature current, $R_a=$resistance of armature circuit and $V=$terminal p.d., then:

$$V = E - I_a R_a \quad . \quad . \quad . \quad . \quad (113)$$

The curve representing the variation of terminal voltage with load current is termed the *load* or *external characteristic* of the dynamo.

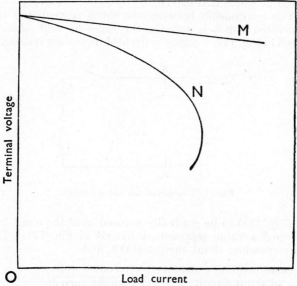

Fig. 172.—Load characteristics of separately-excited and shunt dynamos.

The separately-excited dynamo has the disadvantage of requiring a separate source of direct current and is therefore only employed in special cases, for instance when a wide range of terminal voltage is required (see Art. 136).

126. Shunt-wound Dynamo. The field winding is connected in series with a field regulating resistance R across the armature terminals as shown in Fig. 173, and is therefore in parallel or "shunt" with the load. The power absorbed by the shunt circuit is kept within reasonable limits by winding the field coils with a large number of turns of comparatively thin wire.

A shunt dynamo will not excite unless the poles have some residual magnetism and unless the resistance of the shunt circuit is less than some critical value, the actual value depending upon the machine and upon the speed at which it is driven.

The relationship between the shunt current and the generated e.m.f. is exactly the same as that already given in Fig. 171. Suppose the field regulating resistance

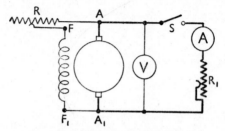

FIG. 173.—Shunt-wound dynamo.

R (Fig. 173) to be gradually reduced until the e.m.f. has reached a value represented by AB in Fig. 171. The corresponding shunt current is OA, and

$$\left.\begin{array}{c}\text{corresponding resistance} \\ \text{of shunt circuit}\end{array}\right\} = \frac{\text{terminal voltage}}{\text{shunt current}}$$

$$= \frac{AB}{OA} = \text{slope of OB.}$$

It follows that for a given resistance of the shunt circuit the value to which the e.m.f. grows is given by the intersection of the open-circuit characteristic P and a straight line OB having a slope corresponding to the resistance of the shunt circuit.

By taking a number of points on curves P and Q (Fig. 171) and calculating the corresponding shunt resistances, the curves of Fig. 174 can be derived. Graph P in the latter figure shows that as the regulating resistance is decreased, the generated e.m.f., being mainly due to residual magnetism, increases very slowly as represented by portion *ab* of the curve. But when the resistance has been reduced to a certain critical value, the generated e.m.f. becomes very sensitive to further change of resistance, a small decrease of resistance being accompanied by an increase of shunt current and of flux, followed by further increase of e.m.f. and of shunt current, etc. These changes cause the voltage

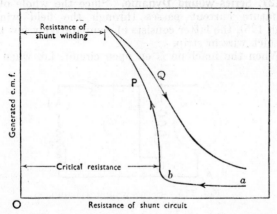

FIG. 174.—Variation of e.m.f. with shunt resistance.

to increase by a relatively large amount. A comparison of curves P in Fig. 171 and 174 shows that *the critical resistance of the shunt circuit is equal to the slope of the straight-line portion of the open-circuit characteristic with increasing excitation.*

It will be seen from curve Q in Fig. 174 that hysteresis causes the variation of voltage with increasing shunt resistance to be comparatively gradual.

The variation of terminal voltage with load current for a shunt dynamo is greater than that for the corresponding separately-excited dynamo, and is represented by curve N in Fig. 172. This greater variation is due to the decrease in the terminal voltage accompanying an increase of load causing a reduction of the shunt current and therefore of flux and of generated e.m.f. It is seen that as the load increases these variations become more marked. Ultimately, the load reaches an unstable value when the effect of reducing the load resistance still further is to cause the terminal voltage to fall so much that the load current decreases.

The shunt dynamo is the type of d.c. generator most commonly employed.

127. Series-wound Dynamo. Since the whole of the armature current passes through the field winding (Fig. 175), the latter consists of comparatively few turns of thick wire or strip.

When the machine is on open circuit, i.e. when S is

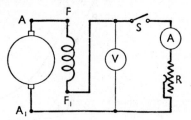

Fig. 175.—Series-wound dynamo.

open, the terminal voltage OP (Fig. 176) is very small, being due to the residual flux in the poles. If S is closed with the load resistance R comparatively large, the machine does not excite; but as R is reduced, a value is reached when a slight reduction of R is accompanied by a relatively large increase of terminal voltage. The full line in Fig. 176 shows the variation of terminal voltage with load current for a certain series dynamo driven at a constant speed; and the dotted line represents the generated e.m.f. of the same machine when driven at the same speed with the armature on open circuit and the field separately excited. Thus, for a current OA, AC is the generated e.m.f. and AB is the corresponding terminal voltage on load. The difference, BC, is mainly the voltage drop due to the resistance of the field and armature circuits.

It is obvious from Fig. 176 that a series-wound dynamo is quite unsuitable when the voltage is to be maintained

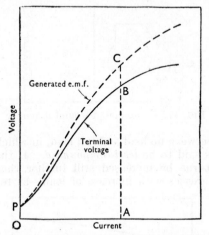

FIG. 176.—Characteristics of a series dynamo.

constant or even approximately constant over a wide range of load current.

128. Compound-wound Dynamo. In Fig. 177, C represents the shunt coils and S the series coils, these windings being usually connected * so that their ampere-turns assist one another. Consequently the larger the load, the greater are the flux and the generated e.m.f.

If curve S in Fig. 178 represents the load characteristic with shunt winding alone, then by the addition of a small series winding the fall of terminal voltage with increase

* In practice, it is of little consequence whether the shunt winding is connected "long-shunt" as in Fig. 177 or "short-shunt," i.e. directly across the armature terminals, since the shunt current is very small compared with the full-load current and the number of series turns is very small compared with the number of shunt turns.

of load is reduced as indicated by curve P. Such a
machine is said to be *under-compounded*. By increasing
the number of series turns we can arrange for the machine
to maintain its terminal voltage (curve Q) practically

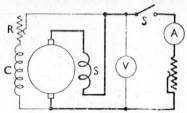

FIG. 177.—Compound-wound dynamo.

constant between no load and full load, in which case the
machine is said to be *level-compounded*. If the number
of series turns be increased still further, the terminal
voltage increases with increase of load—as represented

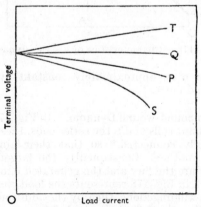

FIG. 178.—Load characteristics of shunt-wound and
compound-wound dynamos.

by curve T. The machine is then said to be *over-
compounded*.

An over-compounded dynamo may be used to compensate for the voltage drop in a feeder system (Art. 32).

For instance, if the voltage at the far end of a feeder is to be maintained constant at, say, 460 V and if the total resistance of the feeder is 0·2 Ω, the voltage drop due to a current of 100 A is 20 V.   Consequently the voltage at the transmitting end must be $(460+20)=480$ V. When there is no load on the feeder, the voltage at the transmitting end is the same as that at the far end, namely 460 V.   Hence a dynamo compounded to give 460 V on no load and 480 V with 100 A maintains the voltage at the far end of the feeder approximately constant over this range of load.

Example 64.   *A shunt dynamo is to be converted into a level-compound dynamo by the addition of a series field winding.   From a test on the machine with shunt excitation only, it is found that the shunt current is 4·1 A to give 440 V on no load and 5·8 A to give the same voltage when the machine is supplying its full load of 200 A. The shunt winding has 1200 turns per pole.   Find the number of series turns required per pole.*

Ampere-turns per pole required on no load

$$=4·1 \times 1200 = 4920.$$

Ampere-turns per pole required on full load

$$=5·8 \times 1200 = 6960.$$

Hence ampere-turns/pole to be provided by the series winding

$$=6960-4920=2040,$$

∴ number of series turns per pole

$$=\frac{2040}{200}=10.$$

The shunt current is so small compared with the full load current that it is of little consequence whether it is included in or omitted from the above calculation.

EXAMPLES XV

1. The following table gives the open-circuit voltages for different field currents of a shunt dynamo driven at a constant speed:

Open-circuit voltage .	120	240	334	400	444	470
Field current (amps) .	0·5	1·0	1·5	2·0	2·5	3·0

Plot a graph showing the variation of generated e.m.f. with exciting current and from this graph derive the value of the generated e.m.f. when the shunt circuit has a resistance of (a) 160, (b) 210 and (c) 300 Ω. Also, find the value of the critical resistance of the shunt circuit.

2. Sketch and explain the curves connecting (a) e.m.f. and speed at constant excitation and (b) e.m.f. and excitation at constant speed for a separately-excited generator. The curve of induced e.m.f. for a separately-excited generator when run at 1300 r.p.m. on open circuit is given by:

| E.m.f. (volts) . . | 12 | 44 | 73 | 98 | 113 | 122 | 127 |
| Exciting current (amps) | 0 | 0·2 | 0·4 | 0·6 | 0·8 | 1·0 | 1·2 |

Deduce the curve of e.m.f. and excitation when the generator is running separately excited at 1000 r.p.m. To what voltage will the generator build up on no load when shunt-excited and running at 1000 r.p.m. if the total resistance of the field is 100 Ω?
(N.C.T.E.C., S2)

3. Sketch neat graphs to show the internal or open-circuit character-istics of a separately-excited d.c. generator. Why is a field regulator used with such a machine?

A 4-pole d.c. generator gives 410 V on open circuit when driven at 900 r.p.m. Calculate the flux per pole if the wave-wound armature has 39 slots with 16 conductors per slot.   (U.E.I., S2)

4. Draw the connection diagram for a short-shunt compound dynamo and explain the shape of the p.d./current curve when the machine is under-compounded.

Such a machine has armature, shunt-field and series-field resistances of 0·8 Ω, 45 Ω and 0·6 Ω respectively and supplies a load of 5 kW at 250 V. Calculate the e.m.f. generated in the armature.
(C. & G., El. Eng. Pract., Prelim.)

5. A 6-pole dynamo having a lap-wound armature is required to give a terminal voltage of 240 V when supplying an armature current of 400 A. The armature has 84 slots and is driven at 700 r.p.m. The resistance of the armature circuit is 0·03 Ω and the useful flux per pole is about 0·03 weber. Calculate the number of conductors per slot and the actual value of the useful flux per pole.

6. Find the number of series turns per pole necessary on a compound dynamo to enable it to maintain the voltage constant at 460 V between no load and full load of 100 kW. Without any series winding, it is found that the shunt current has to be 2 A on no load and 2·65 A on full load to maintain the voltage constant at 460 V. Number of turns per pole on shunt winding =2000.

7. Explain, with the aid of a circuit diagram, how you would obtain experimentally the open-circuit characteristic (=magnetisation curve) of a shunt-connected generator, and sketch the kind of graph you would expect. How would the graph be altered if the speed of the machine were increased by 50 per cent?

Sketch also the load-voltage characteristic of a series generator and briefly explain its shape.   (E.M.E.U., S2)

8. A separately-excited d.c. generator has its excitation kept constant and the speed varied over a range of 3 to 1. The speed is then kept constant and the exciting current varied over a wide range. Plot graphs to indicate the results you would expect in each case. Draw a circuit diagram for the test, including all necessary meters.
(U.E.I., S2)

9. Describe the function of the commutator in a d.c. generator.

Draw a diagram showing how the field winding of a 2-pole shunt dynamo is arranged and explain how self-excitation is obtained in such a machine.   (I.Mech.E., Prin. of Elect.)

10. A shunt-wound battery-charging dynamo has been installed and has run satisfactorily for some time.   One morning the dynamo fails to develop its output voltage when driven at normal speed. Discuss possible causes of the failure and their remedies.

(C. & G., El. Inst. Work)

11. Describe with the aid of circuit diagrams the various methods of excitation used for d.c. generators.   Draw graphs showing how the terminal voltage varies with the output current in each case, and give reasons for the shapes of the graphs.   (I.Mech.E., Prin. of Elect.)

CHAPTER XVI

DIRECT-CURRENT MOTORS

129. A D.C. Machine as Generator or Motor. There is no difference of construction between a d.c. generator and a d.c. motor. In fact, the only difference is that in a dynamo the generated e.m.f. is greater than the terminal voltage, whereas in a motor the generated e.m.f. is less than the terminal voltage. For instance, suppose a shunt dynamo D (Fig. 179) to be driven by an

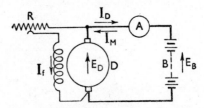

FIG. 179.—Shunt-wound machine as generator or motor.

engine and connected through a centre-zero ammeter A to a battery B. If the field regulator R is adjusted until the reading on A is zero, the e.m.f., E_D, generated in D is then exactly equal to the e.m.f., E_B, of the battery. If R is now reduced, the e.m.f. generated in D exceeds that of B, and the excess e.m.f. is available to circulate a current I_D through the resistance of the armature circuit, the battery and the connecting leads. Since I_D is in the same direction as E_D, machine D is a generator of electrical energy.

Next, suppose the supply of steam, oil or gas to the engine of D to be cut off. The speed of the set falls, and as E_D decreases, I_D becomes less, until when $E_D = E_B$ there is no circulating current. But E_D continues to decrease and becomes less than E_B, so that a current I_M

flows in the reverse direction. Hence B is now supplying electrical energy to drive D as an electric motor.

The speed of D continues to fall until the difference between E_D and E_B is sufficient to circulate the current necessary to maintain the rotation of D.

It will be noticed that the direction of the field current I_f is the same whether D is running as a generator or a motor.

The relationship between the current, the e.m.f., etc., for machine D may be expressed thus:

If $\qquad E=$e.m.f. generated in armature

$\qquad V=$terminal voltage

$\qquad R_a=$resistance of armature circuit

and $\qquad I_a=$current through armature,

then when D is operating as a generator it follows from expression (113) that:

$$E=V+I_aR_a \quad . \quad . \quad . \quad (114)$$

When the machine is operating as a motor, the e.m.f., E, is less than the applied voltage V, and the direction of the current I_a is the reverse of that when the machine is acting as a generator; hence

$$E=V-I_aR_a$$

or $\qquad V=E+I_aR_a \quad . \quad . \quad . \quad (115)$

Since the e.m.f. generated in the armature of a motor is in opposition to the applied voltage, it is frequently referred to as a *back e.m.f.*

Example 65. *The armature of a d.c. machine has a resistance of 0·1 Ω and is connected to a 230-V supply. Calculate the generated e.m.f. when it is running* (a) *as a generator giving 80 A,* (b) *as a motor taking 60 A.*

(a) Voltage drop due to armature resistance

$$=80\times0\cdot1=8\text{ V}.$$

From (114), generated e.m.f. $=230+8=238$ V.

(b) Voltage drop due to armature resistance

$$=60\times0\cdot1=6\text{ V}.$$

From (115) generated e.m.f. $=230-6=224$ V.

130. Speed of a Motor. In Art. 121 it was shown that the relationship between the generated e.m.f., speed, flux, etc., is represented by:

$$E = 2\frac{Z}{c} \cdot \frac{Np}{60} \cdot \Phi \quad . \quad . \quad . \quad . \quad (112)$$

For a given machine, Z, c and p are fixed; and in such a case we can write:

$$E = kN\Phi$$

where

$$k = 2\frac{Z}{c} \cdot \frac{p}{60}.$$

Substituting for E in expression (115) we have:

$$V = kN\Phi + I_a R_a$$

$$\therefore \qquad N = \frac{V - I_a R_a}{k\Phi} \quad . \quad . \quad . \quad . \quad (116)$$

The value of $I_a R_a$ is usually less than 5 per cent of the terminal voltage V, so that:

$$N = \frac{V}{k\Phi} \text{ (approximately)} \quad . \quad (117)$$

In words, this expression means that the speed of an electric motor is approximately proportional to the voltage applied to the armature and inversely proportional to the flux; and all methods of controlling the speed involve the use of either or both of these relationships.

Example 66. *A 4-pole motor is fed at 440 V and takes an armature current of 50 A. The resistance of the armature circuit is 0·28 Ω. The armature is wave-wound with 888 conductors and the useful flux per pole is 0·023 weber. Calculate the speed.*

From expression (115) we have:

$$440 = \text{generated e.m.f.} + 50 \times 0·28$$

$$\therefore \qquad \text{generated e.m.f.} = 440 - 14 = 426 \text{ V}.$$

Substituting in the e.m.f. equation (112), we have:

$$426 = 2 \times \frac{888}{2} \times \frac{N \times 2}{60} \times 0 \cdot 023$$

$$\therefore \qquad N = 626 \text{ r.p.m.}$$

Example 67. *A motor runs at 900 r.p.m. off a 460-V supply. Calculate the approximate speed when the machine is connected across a 200-V supply. Assume the new flux to be 0·7 of the original flux.*

If Φ be the original flux, then from expression (117):

$$900 \text{ r.p.m.} = \frac{460 \text{ volts}}{k\Phi}$$

$$\therefore \qquad k\Phi = 0 \cdot 511 \text{ volt/r.p.m.}$$

and new speed $= \dfrac{\text{new voltage}}{k \times \text{original flux} \times 0 \cdot 7}$ (approximately)

$$= \frac{200 \text{ volts}}{0 \cdot 7 \times 0 \cdot 511 \text{ volt/r.p.m.}} = 559 \text{ r.p.m.}$$

131. Torque of an Electric Motor. If we start with equation (115) and multiply each term by I_a, namely the total armature current, we have:

$$VI_a = EI_a + I_a^2 R_a.$$

But VI_a represents the total electrical power supplied to the armature, and $I_a^2 R_a$ represents the loss due to the resistance of the armature circuit. The difference between these two quantities, namely EI_a, therefore represents the mechanical power developed by the armature. All of this mechanical power is not available externally since some of it is absorbed as friction loss at the bearings and at the brushes and some is wasted as hysteresis loss (Art. 58) and in circulating eddy currents in the iron core (Art. 123).

If T lb-ft be the torque * exerted on the armature to

* In many textbooks, the value of the torque is derived from expression (23). This method gives the correct result; but it should be realised that with a slotted armature, the flux density in the slot is extremely low so that there is practically no force on the conductors. Practically the whole of the torque is exerted on the teeth.

develop the mechanical power just referred to, and if N be the speed in r.p.m., then:

mechanical power developed

$$= \frac{2\pi \times \text{speed (r.p.m.)} \times \text{torque (lb-ft)}}{33,000}$$

$$= \frac{2\pi \times N \times T}{33,000} \text{ h.p.}$$

$$= \frac{2\pi \times N \times T \times 746}{33,000} \text{ watts.}$$

Hence

$$\frac{2\pi N T \times 746}{33,000} = EI_a \quad . \quad . \quad . \quad . \quad . \quad . \quad (118)$$

$$= 2\frac{Z}{c} \cdot \frac{Np}{60} \cdot \Phi \cdot I_a$$

$$\therefore \qquad T = 0 \cdot 235 \frac{I_a}{c} \cdot Zp\Phi \text{ lb-ft} \quad . \quad . \quad (119)$$

For a given machine, Z, c and p are fixed; in which case:

$$T \propto I_a \times \Phi \quad . \quad . \quad . \quad . \quad (120)$$

Or, in words, the torque of a given d.c. motor is proportional to the product of the armature current and the flux per pole.

If the torque T is expressed in newton-metres, then from expression (5), we have

$$\frac{2\pi TN}{60} = EI_a \quad . \quad . \quad . \quad . \quad . \quad . \quad . \quad . \quad (121)$$

$$= 2\frac{Z}{c} \cdot \frac{Np}{60} \cdot \Phi \cdot I_a$$

$$\therefore \qquad T = 0 \cdot 318 \frac{I_a}{c} \cdot Zp\Phi \text{ newton-metres} . \quad (122)$$

Example 68. *Calculate the torque* (a) *in lb-ft,* (b) *in newton-metres and* (c) *in kg-m for the motor referred to in Example* 66 :

Armature current $=50$ A

and back e.m.f. $=426$ V

$\therefore$ mechanical power developed by armature

$$=50 \times 426 = 21,300 \text{ W.}$$

From Ex. 66,   speed $=626$ r.p.m.

(a) If T is the torque in lb-ft, then from (118),

$$\frac{2\pi T \times 626 \times 746}{33,000} = 21,300$$

$\therefore$ $T = 240$ lb-ft.

(b) If T is the torque in newton-metres, then from (121),

$$\frac{2\pi T \times 626}{60} = 21,300$$

$\therefore$ $T = 325$ newton-metres.

(c) If T is the torque in kilogram-metres, then since a force of 1 kg $= 9 \cdot 81$ newtons,

$\therefore$ $T = \dfrac{325}{9 \cdot 81} = 33 \cdot 1$ kg-m.

132. Starting Resistance. If the armature referred to in Example 66 were stationary and then switched directly across a 440-V supply, there would be no back e.m.f. and the current would tend to grow to $\dfrac{440}{0 \cdot 28}$ $=1572$ A. Such a current would blow the fuses, thereby disconnecting the supply from the motor. It is therefore necessary (except with very small motors) to connect a variable resistance in series with the armature, this resistance being reduced as the armature accelerates. Such an arrangement is termed a *starter*. If the starting current in the above example is to be limited to, say, 80 A, the total resistance of the starter and armature must be $\dfrac{440}{80} = 5 \cdot 5$ Ω, so that the resistance of the starter alone must be $(5 \cdot 5 - 0 \cdot 28) = 5 \cdot 22$ Ω.

Fig. 180 shows a starting resistance R subdivided between four contact-studs S and connected to a shunt-wound motor.   One end of the shunt winding is joined to stud 1;   consequently when arm A is moved from "Off" to that stud, the full voltage is applied to the shunt winding and the whole of R is in series with the

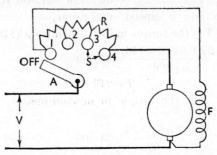

Fig. 180.—Shunt-wound motor with starter.

armature.   The armature current instantly grows to a value I_1 (Fig. 181) where:

$$I_1 = \frac{\text{supply voltage } V}{\text{resistance of (armature+starter)}}$$

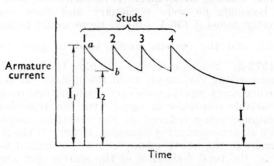

Fig. 181.—Variation of starting current.

Since the torque is proportional to (armature current ×flux), it follows that the maximum torque is immediately available to accelerate the armature.

As the armature accelerates, its back e.m.f. grows and the armature current decreases as indicated by curve ab. When the current has fallen to some pre-arranged value I_2, arm A is moved over to stud 2, thereby cutting out sufficient resistance to allow the current to rise once more to I_1. This operation is repeated until A is on stud 4 and the whole of the starting resistance is cut out of the armature circuit. The motor continues to accelerate and the current to decrease until it settles down at some value I (Fig. 181) such that the torque due to this current is just sufficient to enable the motor to cope with its load.

It is evident from Fig. 180 that when A is on stud 4 the whole of R is in the field circuit. The effect upon the

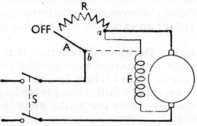

FIG. 182.—Wrong methods of connecting the shunt winding.

field current, however, is almost negligible. Thus, taking the example considered at the beginning of this article, the shunt current of such a machine would not exceed 2 A, so that the resistance of shunt winding F would be at least $\frac{440}{2}$, namely 220 Ω. Consequently the addition of 5·22 Ω means a decrease of only 2·4 per cent in the field current.

If the field winding were connected to a as in Fig. 182, then at the instant of starting, the voltage across the field winding would be very small, namely that across the armature winding. In the above example, for instance, this p.d. is only $80 \times 0.28 = 22.4$ V. Consequently the torque would be extremely small and the machine would probably refuse to start. On the other hand, if the field were connected to b, as shown dotted in Fig. 182, it would be directly across the supply; but if the motor were stopped by moving the starter arm back to "Off," the field would still remain excited. If such a field current were switched off by opening switch S quickly, the sudden collapse of the flux would induce a very high e.m.f. in F and might result in a breakdown of the insulation.

With the connections shown in Fig. 180 it is obvious that the armature winding, the starting resistance and the field winding form a closed circuit. Consequently when A is returned to "Off," the kinetic energy of the machine and its load maintains rotation for an appreciable period, and during most of that time the machine continues to excite as a shunt dynamo. The field current therefore decreases comparatively slowly and there is no risk of an excessive e.m.f. being induced.

133. Protective Devices on Starters.
It is very desirable to provide the starter with protective devices to enable the starter arm to return to "Off":

(a) when the supply fails, thus preventing the armature being directly across the mains when the voltage is restored; and

(b) when the motor becomes overloaded or develops a fault causing the machine to take an excessive current.

Fig. 183 shows a starter fitted with such features. The no-volt release NVR consists of a coil wound on a U-shaped iron core. The starter arm carries an iron plate B, so that when it is in the "On" position, as shown, the core of NVR is magnetised by the field current and holds B against the tendency of a spiral spring G to return A to "Off." Should the supply fail, the motor stops, NVR is de-energised, and the residual magnetism in it is not sufficient to hold A against the counter-clockwise torque of G.

If a connection C be made between the core of NVR and the supply side of the coil, the shunt current flows from A via B and C, and the starting resistance is thereby short-circuited.

The coil of the *overload release* OLR is wound on an

iron core and connected in series with the motor.   An
iron plate L, pivoted at one end, carries an extension
which, when lifted, connects together two pins *p*, *p*.
When the current taken by the motor exceeds a certain
value the magnetic pull on L is sufficient to lift it,
thereby short-circuiting the coil of NVR and releasing
the starter arm A.   The critical value of the overload
current is dependent upon the length of air-gap between

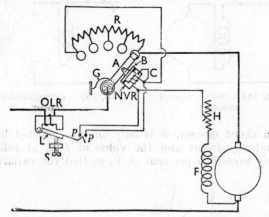

FIG. 183.—Starter with no-volt and overload releases.

L and the core of OLR and is controlled by a screw
adjustment S.

**134. Speed Characteristics of Electric Motors.   With
very few exceptions, d.c. motors are shunt-, series- or
compound-wound.   The connections of a shunt motor
have already been given in Fig. 180 and 183, and Fig.
184 and 185 show the connections for series and compound motors respectively, the starter in each case being
shown in the "On" position.   (Students should always
make a practice of including starters in diagrams of
motor connections.)   In compound motors, the series
and shunt windings almost invariably assist each other,
as indicated in Fig. 185.
10

The speed characteristic of a motor represents the variation of speed with load, and its shape can be easily derived from expression (116), Art. 130, namely:

$$N = \frac{V - I_a R_a}{k\Phi}.$$

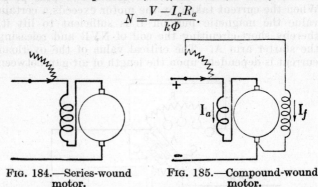

FIG. 184.—Series-wound motor.   FIG. 185.—Compound-wound motor.

In shunt motors, Φ is only slightly affected by the armature current and the value of $I_a R_a$ at full load rarely exceeds 5 per cent of V, so that the variation of

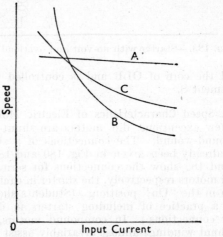

FIG. 186.—Speed characteristics.

speed with input current is represented by curve A in Fig. 186. Hence shunt motors are suitable where the speed has to remain approximately constant over a wide range of load.

In series motors, Φ increases at first in proportion to the current and then less rapidly owing to magnetic saturation (Fig. 171). Also R_a in the above expression now includes the resistance of the field winding. Hence the speed is roughly inversely proportional to the current, as indicated by curve B in Fig. 186. It will be seen that if the load falls to a very small value, the speed may become dangerously high. A series motor should therefore not be employed when there is any such risk; for instance, it should never be belt-coupled to its load.

Since the compound motor has a combination of shunt and series excitations, its characteristic (curve C in Fig. 186) is intermediate between those of the shunt and series motors, the exact shape depending upon the values of the shunt and series ampere-turns.

135. Torque Characteristics of Electric Motors. In Art. 131 it was shown that for a given motor:

$$\text{torque} \propto \text{armature current} \times \text{flux per pole.}$$

Since the flux in a shunt motor is practically independent of the armature current:

$$\therefore \quad \text{torque of a shunt motor} \propto \text{armature current}$$

and is represented by the straight line A in Fig. 187.

In a series motor the flux is approximately proportional to the current up to full load, so that:

$$\text{torque of a series motor} \propto (\text{armature current})^2, \text{ approx.}$$

Above full load, magnetic saturation becomes more marked and the torque does not increase so rapidly.

Curves A, B and C in Fig. 187 show the relative shapes of torque curves for shunt, series and compound motors having the same full-load torque OQ with the same full-load armature current OP, the exact shape of curve C depending upon the relative value of the shunt and series ampere-turns at full load.

From Fig. 187 it is evident that for a given current below the full-load value the shunt motor exerts the largest torque; but for a given current above that value the series motor exerts the largest torque.

The maximum permissible current at starting is usually about 1·5 times the full-load current. Consequently where a large starting torque is required,

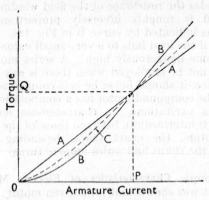

FIG. 187.—Torque characteristics.

such as for hoists, cranes, electric trains, etc., the series motor is the most suitable machine.

Example 69. *A series motor runs at* 600 *r.p.m. when taking* 110 *A off a* 230-*V supply. The resistance of the armature circuit is* 0·12 Ω *and that of the series winding is* 0·03 Ω. *Calculate the speed when the current has fallen to* 50 *A, assuming the useful flux per pole for* 110 *A to be* 0·024 *weber and that for* 50 *A to be* 0·0155 *weber.*

Total resistance of armature and series windings

$$=0·12+0·03=0·15 \ \Omega,$$

∴ back e.m.f. when current is 110 A

$$=230-110\times0·15=213·5 \ V.$$

In Art. 130 it was shown that for a given machine:

back e.m.f. = a constant (say k) × speed × flux.

Hence with 110 A, $213{\cdot}5 = k \times 600 \times 0{\cdot}024$

$\therefore \qquad k = 14{\cdot}82.$

With 50 A,   back e.m.f. $= 230 - 50 \times 0{\cdot}15 = 222{\cdot}5$ V.

But the new back e.m.f. $= k \times$ new speed $\times$ new flux

$\therefore \qquad 222{\cdot}5 = 14{\cdot}82 \times$ new speed $\times 0{\cdot}0155$

$\therefore \qquad$ speed for 50 A $= 969$ r.p.m.

136. Speed Control of D.C. Motors. It has been explained in Art. 130 that the speed of a d.c. motor can be altered by varying either the flux or the armature voltage (or both); and the methods most commonly employed are:

(a) A variable resistance, termed a *field regulator*, in series with the shunt winding—only applicable to shunt and compound motors. Such a field regulator is indicated by H in Fig. 183. When the resistance is increased, the field current, the flux and the back e.m.f. are reduced. Consequently more current flows through the armature and the increased torque enables the armature to accelerate until the back e.m.f. is again nearly equal to the applied voltage (see Example 70).

With this method it is possible to increase the speed to three or four times that at full excitation, but it is not possible to reduce the speed below that value. Also, with any given setting of the regulator, the speed remains approximately constant between no load and full load.

(b) A variable resistance, termed a *diverter*, in parallel with the field winding—only applicable to series-wound motors. In Fig. 188, R represents the variable portion of the diverter and r the fixed portion, the function of r being to prevent the series winding being short-circuited. The smaller the value of R, the greater is the amount of current diverted from the series winding and the higher is the speed of the motor. The minimum speed for a given input current is obtained by moving the slider on to the off-stud S, thereby breaking the circuit through the diverter.

(c) A variable resistance—termed a *controller*—in series with the armature. The electrical connections for a controller are exactly the same as for a starter, the only difference being that in a controller the resistance elements are designed to carry the armature current indefinitely, whereas in a starter they can only do so for a comparatively short time without getting excessively hot.

For a given armature current, the larger the controller resistance in circuit, the smaller is the p.d. across the armature and the lower, in consequence, is the speed.

This system has several disadvantages: (1) the relatively high cost of the controller; (2) much of the input energy may be dissipated in the controller and the overall efficiency of the motor considerably reduced

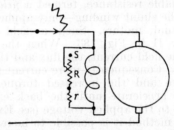

FIG. 188.—Speed control of series-wound motor by a diverter.

thereby; (3) the speed may vary greatly with variation of load due to the change in the p.d. across the controlling resistance causing a corresponding change in the p.d. across the armature.

The principal advantage of the system is that speeds from zero upwards are easily obtainable, and the method is chiefly used for controlling the speed of cranes, hoists, trains, etc., where the motors are frequently started and stopped and where efficiency is of secondary importance.

(d) Exciting the field winding off a constant-voltage system and supplying the armature from a separate dynamo, as shown in Fig. 189. M represents the motor whose speed is to be controlled; M_1D is a motor-generator set consisting of a shunt motor coupled to a separately-excited dynamo. The voltage applied to the armature of M can be varied between zero and a maximum by means of R. If provision is made for reversing the excitation of D, the speed of M can then be varied from a maximum in one direction to the same maximum in the reverse direction.

This method is often referred to as the *Ward-Leonard* system and is used for controlling the speed of motors driving colliery winders, rolling mills, etc. The advantages of the system are:

(1) Starting and speed control are easily effected with a single regulator.

(2) There is no resistance in series with the armature circuit to absorb any power; consequently the efficiency

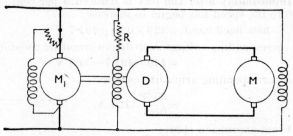

FIG. 189.—Ward-Leonard system of speed control.

at low speeds is much higher than that obtainable with the controller system.

(3) For a given value of R and therefore a given e.m.f. generated in D, the speed of M is almost independent of its load.

(4) Retardation of M may be effected by increasing R so that the e.m.f. generated in D is less than that of M. Consequently much of the kinetic energy of M and its load is transferred electrically to D, which then runs as a motor driving M₁ as a generator, thereby sending electrical energy back into the mains. Where M has to be started and stopped frequently, the total energy *regenerated* may amount to a considerable percentage of the total energy absorbed from the mains.

The main disadvantage of the system is the initial cost of the motor-generator set.

Example 70. *A shunt motor is running at 626 r.p.m. (Example 66) when taking an armature current of 50 A off a 440-V supply. The armature circuit has a resistance of 0·28 Ω. If the flux is suddenly reduced by 5 per cent find: (a) the maximum value to which the current increases momentarily and the ratio of the corresponding torque to the initial torque, (b) the ultimate steady value of the armature current, assuming the torque due to the load to remain unaltered.*

(a) From Example 66:

initial back e.m.f. $=440-50\times0\cdot28=426$ V.

Immediately after the flux is reduced 5 per cent, i.e. before the speed has begun to increase:

new back e.m.f. $=426\times0\cdot95=404\cdot7$ V

∴ corresponding voltage drop due to armature resistance
$$=440-404\cdot7=35\cdot3 \text{ V}$$

and corresponding armature current

$$=\frac{35\cdot3}{0\cdot28}=126 \text{ A.}$$

From expression (120):

torque of a given machine ∝ armature current × flux

$$\therefore \frac{\text{new torque}}{\text{initial torque}}=\frac{\text{new current}}{\text{initial current}}\times\frac{\text{new flux}}{\text{initial flux}}$$

$$=\frac{126 \text{ A}}{50 \text{ A}}\times0\cdot95=2\cdot394.$$

Hence the sudden reduction of 5 per cent in the flux is accompanied by more than a twofold increase of torque; this is the reason why the motor accelerates.

(b) After the speed and current have attained steady values, the torque will have decreased to the original value, so that:

new current × new flux = original current × original flux

∴ new armature current $=50\times\dfrac{1}{0\cdot95}=52\cdot6$ A.

Example 71. *A series motor is taking 30 A when running off a 230-V supply. The armature and field circuits have a total resistance of 0·6 Ω. Find the resistance to be connected in series with the armature to reduce the speed by 40 per cent if the current at the new speed is 18 A. Assume the flux to be proportional to the current.*

When the motor is taking 30 A:

$$\text{back e.m.f.} = 230 - 30 \times 0·6 = 212 \text{ V}.$$

But the back e.m.f. is proportional to (speed ×flux) and the flux is proportional to the current:

∴ back e.m.f. at the new speed

$$= 212 \text{ V} \times \frac{60}{100} \times \frac{18 \text{ A}}{30 \text{ A}}$$

$$= 76·3 \text{ V}.$$

Corresponding voltage across motor terminals

$$= 76·3 + 18 \times 0·6 = 87·1 \text{ V}$$

∴ p.d. across the series resistance

$$= 230 - 87·1 = 142·9 \text{ V}$$

and value of the series resistance

$$= \frac{142·9}{18} = 7·94 \text{ Ω}.$$

136A. Applications of Shunt, Series and Compound Motors. In the preceding articles the characteristics of the three types of motors have been dealt with, and we may summarise the discussion thus:

Shunt motors are used—

(a) When the speed has to be maintained approximately constant between no load and full load; e.g. for driving a line of shafting.

(b) When it is required to drive the load at various speeds, any one speed being maintained constant for a relatively long period; e.g. for individual driving of such machines as lathes, etc. The shunt regulator enables the required speed control to be obtained easily and economically.

10*

Series motors are used—

(a) When a large starting torque is required; e.g. for driving hoists, cranes, trains, etc.

(b) When the motor can be direct-coupled to a load, such as a fan, whose torque increases with speed.

Where constancy of speed is not essential the decrease of speed with increase of load has the advantage that the power absorbed by the motor does not increase as rapidly as the torque; for instance, when the torque is doubled, the power usually increases by only about 50 or 60 per cent.

A series motor should not be used when there is a possibility of the load decreasing to a very small value; thus it should not be used for driving a centrifugal pump or for a belt-drive of any kind.

Compound motors are used—

(a) When a large starting torque is required but where the load may fall to such a small value that a series motor would reach a dangerously high speed.

(b) When the load is of a fluctuating nature; e.g. for driving stamping presses, etc. The shunt excitation prevents the speed becoming excessive on light load and the decrease of speed with increase of load enables the flywheel usually fitted to such a machine to give up some of its kinetic energy, thereby assisting the motor in dealing with the peak load.

(c) When the supply voltage is subject to fluctuations; for instance, on a traction system. The series winding reduces the fluctuation of armature current, partly by its inductance and partly by its influence on the value of the flux and therefore on that of the back e.m.f.

(d) When regeneration is required on a traction system; thus trolley-buses are usually fitted with compound motors. If the shunt excitation is increased until the generated e.m.f. exceeds the supply voltage, the bus sends electrical power back into the mains and can thereby be retarded.

Summary of Important Formulae

For a dynamo, $E = V + I_a R_a$ . . . . (114)

For a motor, $V = E + I_a R_a$ . . . . (115)

For a given motor, $N = \dfrac{V - I_a R_a}{k\Phi}$ . . . . (116)

$\simeq \dfrac{V}{k\Phi}$ . . . . . (117)

$T = 0.235 \dfrac{I_a}{c} \cdot Zp\Phi$ lb-ft . . . . (119)

$= 0.318 \dfrac{I_a}{c} \cdot Zp\Phi$ newton-metres . (122)

For a given motor, $T \propto I_a \Phi$ . . . . . . (120)

EXAMPLES XVI

1. A shunt machine has armature and field resistances of $0.02\ \Omega$ and $50\ \Omega$ respectively. When connected to constant 500-V bus-bars and driven as a dynamo at 400 r.p.m. it delivers 100 kW. Calculate its speed when running as a motor and taking 100 kW from the same bus-bars.

Show that the direction of rotation of the machine as a dynamo and as a motor under these conditions is unchanged.

(C. & G., El. Eng. Pract., Prelim.)

2. A shunt machine driven as a generator at 700 r.p.m. is supplying an armature current of 60 A at a terminal voltage of 220 V. If the same machine runs as a motor with the same terminal voltage and an armature current of 40 A, calculate the speed. Resistance of armature circuit $= 0.2\ \Omega$. Neglect any change of flux due to armature reaction.

3. A shunt machine is running as a motor off a 500-V system, taking an armature current of 50 A. If the field current is suddenly increased so as to increase the flux by 20 per cent, calculate the current which will momentarily be fed back into the mains. Neglect the shunt current and assume the resistance of the armature circuit to be $0.5\ \Omega$.

4. A shunt motor is running off a 220-V supply taking an armature current of 15 A, the resistance of the armature circuit being $0.8\ \Omega$. Calculate the value of the back e.m.f.

If the flux is suddenly reduced by 10 per cent, to what value will the armature current increase momentarily?

5. A 4-pole motor has its armature lap-wound with 1040 conductors and runs at 1200 r.p.m. when taking an armature current of 60 A off a 230-V supply. The resistance of the armature circuit is $0.2\ \Omega$. Calculate the useful flux per pole and the torque in pound-feet and in newton-metres.

6. A series traction motor runs at 700 r.p.m. off a 500-V supply when taking 70 A. What will be the speed when the load is such that the motor takes only 30 A? Assume the resistance of the armature and field circuits to be 0·6 Ω, the useful flux per pole with 70 A to be 0·03 weber and that with 30 A to be 0·022 weber. Also find the torque with 70 A (a) in lb-ft, (b) in newton-metres, (c) in kg-m.

7. A 6-pole, 460-V shunt motor has its armature wave-wound with 936 conductors. The useful flux per pole is 0·02 weber, and the resistance of the armature circuit is 0·7 Ω. Calculate (a) the speed and (b) the torque in lb-ft and in kg-m when the armature current is 30 A.

8. A shunt motor runs at 800 r.p.m. off a 460-V supply when taking an armature current of 50 A. Calculate the speed at which it will run off a 230-V supply when the armature current is 30 A. The resistance of the armature circuit is 0·4 Ω. Assume the flux to have decreased to 75 per cent of the original value.

9. Explain briefly why a shunt-wound motor needs a starter instead of a plain switch.

A shunt-wound motor has a field resistance of 400 Ω and an armature resistance of 0·1 Ω, and runs off a 240-V supply. The armature current is 50 A and the motor speed is 900 r.p.m. Assuming a straight-line magnetisation curve, calculate (a) the additional resistance in the field to increase the speed to 1000 r.p.m. for the same armature current, and (b) the speed with the original field current and an armature current of 200 A.   (E.M.E.U., S2)

10. A 250-V shunt motor has an armature resistance of 0·5 Ω and runs at 1200 r.p.m. when the armature current is 80 A. If the torque remains unchanged, find the speed and the armature current if the field is strengthened by 25 per cent.
                              (C. & G., El. Eng. Pract., Prelim.)

11. A 230-V series motor runs at 500 r.p.m. with a current of 30 A. Find the speed when the current is 20 A, assuming the resistance to be 0·8 Ω and the flux to be proportional to the current.

12. A shunt motor is running at 900 r.p.m. off 440 V with no resistance in series with the armature, the armature current being 80 A. Calculate the resistance to be connected in series with the armature to reduce the speed to 500 r.p.m., if the armature current has then decreased to 45 A. Resistance of the armature circuit = 0·25 Ω. Assume the flux to remain constant.

13. Give an explanation of the speed control of a shunt motor by variation of the field current.

A 250-V shunt motor with an armature resistance of 0·5 Ω takes an armature current of 20 A when running on load at 1000 r.p.m. If the load torque remains unchanged, find the approximate value of the armature current and the speed if the field be weakened by 10 per cent.   (C. & G., El. Eng. Pract., Prelim.)

14. A 500-V motor having an efficiency of 90 per cent runs at 900 r.p.m. Calculate the current taken from the mains when the torque on the shaft is 150 lb-ft.

Find also the current and the approximate speed if the flux were reduced by 20 per cent and the torque unchanged. Neglect any change in the losses.   (C. & G., El. Eng. Pract., Prelim.)

15. Deduce an expression for the back e.m.f. generated in the armature of a shunt motor in terms of the constants of the motor and the speed of rotation.

A d.c. shunt motor has an armature resistance of 0·1 Ω and is connected to a 100-V supply. If the armature current taken by the motor is 25 A, what is the back e.m.f. generated by the armature? Explain the effect of (a) inserting a resistance in the field circuit, (b) inserting a resistance in the armature circuit, if the armature current is maintained at 25 A.   (N.C.T.E.C., S2)

16. Sketch and explain the speed-current curve of a shunt motor.

Find the approximate percentage change of speed of a 250-V shunt motor having an armature resistance of $0·2\ \Omega$ when, as a result of decreased load, the armature current changes from 100 A to 50 A. State the assumptions made in the calculation.

(C. & G., El. Eng. Pract., Prelim.)

17. A 20-b.h.p. shunt motor runs off a 230-V supply. Calculate the value of the starting resistance necessary to limit the starting current to 1·5 times the full-load current if the full-load efficiency of the motor is 88 per cent and the resistance of the armature circuit is $0·2\ \Omega$. Neglect the shunt current.

Also, find the back e.m.f. of the motor when the current has fallen to the full-load value, assuming that the whole of the starting resistance is still in circuit.

18. The starter for a certain shunt motor has a resistance of $2·75\ \Omega$. The armature and shunt windings have resistances of $0·25$ and $200\ \Omega$ respectively. Calculate the armature and shunt currents when the armature is at standstill with the starter arm on the first stud with the field winding connected (a) correctly, (b) to the junction of the starting resistance and the armature. Supply voltage $=230$ V.

19. The static torque characteristic of a series motor is as follows:

Current (amperes)	.	10	20	30	40
Torque (lb-ft)	.	60	150	250	340

If the resistance of the armature and field circuit is $0·5\ \Omega$, deduce the speed/torque curve of the motor when supplied at 500 V. Ignore iron and friction losses.   (Joint Section A)

20. Sketch the speed/torque characteristics of (a) a shunt motor and (b) a series motor.

A series motor exerts a steady torque when driving a load at 1000 r.p.m. A diverter resistor is connected across the field, such that 30 per cent of the current is diverted from the field winding. When the speed has settled down, the load torque is 15 per cent more than the original torque. Calculate the new speed, and the ratio between the final motor current and the original current. Neglect the effects of magnetic saturation and internal resistance drops.

(Joint Section A)

21. Explain why a shunt-connected d.c. motor cannot normally be switched straight on to the supply, but requires a "starter."

In a brake test on such a machine, the following results were obtained:

Supply: 230 V; armature current: 22 A; field resistance: 115 Ω; speed: 1390 r.p.m.; effective diameter of brake drum: 18 in; difference between pulls on the two ends of brake rope: 27 lb. Calculate the efficiency of the motor.   (E.M.E.U., S2)

CHAPTER XVII

ELECTRICAL MEASUREMENTS

137. Electrical Indicating Instruments. An indicating instrument is almost invariably fitted with a pointer which indicates on a scale the value of the quantity being measured. The moving system of such an instrument is carried by a spindle of hardened steel, having its ends tapered and highly polished * to form pivots which rest in hollow-ground bearings, usually of sapphire, set in steel screws. Indicating instruments possess three essential features:

(a) a *deflecting device* whereby a mechanical force is produced by the electric current, voltage or power,

(b) a *controlling device* whereby the value of the deflection is dependent upon the magnitude of the quantity being measured,

(c) a *damping device* to prevent oscillation of the moving system and enable the latter to reach its final position quickly.

The action of the deflecting device depends upon the type of instrument, and the principle of operation of each of the instruments most commonly used in practice will be described in later articles.

138. Controlling Devices. There are two types of controlling devices, namely:

(a) spring control,
(b) gravity control.

The most common arrangement of spring control utilises two phosphor-bronze spiral hairsprings, A and B

* The necessity of handling measuring instruments with care may be realised from the fact that if a pivot point has a circle of contact 0·002 inch in diameter and supports a weight of 3 grams (a normal weight for the moving system of an ammeter or voltmeter), the pressure is nearly 1 ton/square inch.

(Fig. 190), the inner ends of which are attached to the
spindle S. The outer end of B is fixed, whereas that of
A is attached to one end of a lever L, pivoted at P,
thereby enabling zero adjustment to be easily effected.

The two springs, A and B, are wound in opposite
directions so that when the moving system is deflected,
one spring winds up while the other unwinds, and the
controlling torque is due to the combined torsions of the
springs. Since the torsional torque of a spiral spring is
proportional to the angle of twist, the controlling torque

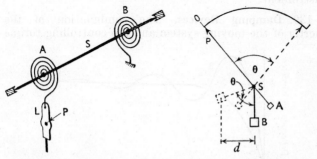

FIG. 190.—Spring control.   FIG. 191.—Gravity control.

is directly proportional to the angular deflection of the
pointer.

With gravity control, weights A and B are attached to
the spindle S (Fig. 191), the function of A being to balance
the weight of pointer P. Weight B therefore provides
the controlling torque. When the pointer is at zero,
B hangs vertically downwards. When P is deflected
through an angle θ, the controlling torque is proportional
to distance d and therefore to the sine of the angular
deflection. This has the disadvantage that with deflections of the order of 70° or 80°, the controlling torque
increases very slowly with increase of deflection; thus:

$$\frac{\text{controlling torque for 80° deflection}}{\text{controlling torque for 70° deflection}} = \frac{\sin 80°}{\sin 70°} = 1 \cdot 048.$$

whereas with spring control:

$$\frac{\text{controlling torque for } 80° \text{ deflection}}{\text{controlling torque for } 70° \text{ deflection}} = \frac{80}{70} = 1 \cdot 143.$$

Hence, with gravity control, the scale at the top end is more open than with spring control and the total deflection is limited to about 80°. A further disadvantage of gravity control is that the instrument must be correctly levelled before being used. The only advantage of the gravity-controlled instrument is that it is cheaper than the corresponding spring-controlled instrument.

139. Damping Devices. The combination of the inertia of the moving system and the controlling torque

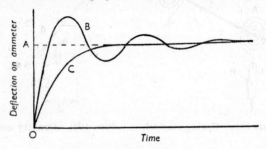

FIG. 192.—Damping curves.

of the spiral springs or of gravity gives the moving system a natural frequency of oscillation (Art. 113). Consequently, if the current through an undamped ammeter were increased suddenly from zero to OA (Fig. 192), the pointer would oscillate about its mean position, as shown by curve B, before coming to rest. Similarly every fluctuation of current would cause the pointer to oscillate and it would be difficult to read the instrument accurately. It is therefore desirable to damp the motion of the moving system, thereby causing the pointer to move over the scale less rapidly but to reach its steady position without oscillation, as indicated by curve C. Such an instrument is said to be *dead-beat*

The two methods of damping commonly employed are:

   (a) eddy-current damping,

   (b) air damping.

One form of eddy-current damping is shown in Fig. 193, where a copper or aluminium disc D, carried by a

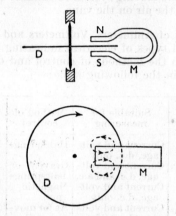

FIG. 193.—Eddy-current damping.

spindle, can move between the poles of a permanent magnet M. If the disc moves clockwise, the e.m.f.'s induced in the disc circulate eddy currents as shown dotted. It follows from Lenz's Law that these currents

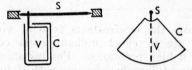

FIG. 194.—Air damping.

exert a force opposing the motion producing them, namely the clockwise movement of the disc.

Another arrangement, used in moving-coil instruments (Art. 141), is to wind the coil on an aluminium former. When the latter moves across the magnetic field, eddy currents are induced in the former in such a direction as to damp the movement of the coil.

Air damping is usually obtained by means of a thin metal vane V attached to the spindle S, as shown in Fig. 194. This vane moves in a sector-shaped box C, and any tendency of the moving system to oscillate is damped by the action of the air on the vane.

140. Types of Ammeters, Voltmeters and Wattmeters. The principal types of electrical indicating instruments, together with the methods of control and damping, are summarised in the following table:

Type of instrument	Suitable for measuring	Method of control	Method of damping
Moving coil .	Current and voltage, d.c. only	Hairsprings	Eddy current
Moving iron .	Current and voltage, d.c. and a.c.	Gravity or hairsprings	Air
Polarised moving-iron	Current and voltage, d.c. only	Magnetic pull	None
Thermo-couple *	Current and voltage, d.c. and a.c.	As for moving coil	As for moving coil
Electro-dynamic † or dynamometer	Current, voltage and power, d.c. and a.c.	Hairsprings	Air
Electrostatic	Voltage only, d.c. and a.c.	Gravity or hairsprings	Air
Rectifier .	Current and voltage, a.c. only	As for moving coil	As for moving coil

Apart from the electrostatic type of voltmeter, all voltmeters are in effect milliammeters connected in series with a high resistance. For instance, if a milliammeter has a full-scale deflection with 10 mA and has a resistance of 10 Ω and if this milliammeter is connected in series with a resistance of 9990 Ω, then the p.d.

* The hot-wire instrument is obsolete and only of historic interest. Its principle of action is described in Art. 7.
† "Electrodynamic" is the term recommended by the British Standards Institution, but "dynamometer" is the term more frequently used in practice.

required for full-scale deflection is $\frac{10}{1000} \times 10{,}000$, namely 100 V, and the scale of the milliammeter can be calibrated to give the p.d. directly in volts.

141. Moving-Coil Ammeters and Voltmeters. The moving-coil instrument consists of a rectangular coil C (Fig. 195) of insulated copper wire wound on a light aluminium frame which is carried by spindles resting in jewelled bearings. Current is led into and out of the coil by spiral hairsprings A, which also provide the controlling torque. The coil is free to move in the gaps between soft-iron pole-pieces P and a central iron cylinder B carried by a non-magnetic bridge attached to P. The magnetism in the gap is provided by a permanent magnet NS. The functions of the centre core B are (1) to intensify the magnetic field by reducing the length of airgap across which magnetic flux has to pass and (2) to give a radial magnetic field of uniform density.

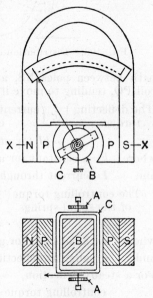

FIG. 195.—Moving-coil instrument.

The manner in which a torque is produced when the coil is carrying a current may be understood more easily by considering a single turn PQ, as in Fig. 196. Suppose P to carry current outwards from the paper; then Q is carrying current towards the paper. Current in P tends to set up a magnetic field in a counter-clockwise direction around P and thus strengthens the magnetic field on the lower side and weakens it on the upper side. The current in Q, on the other hand, strengthens the field on the upper side while weakening it on the lower side. Hence, the effect is to distort the magnetic flux as shown in Fig. 196. Since these lines of flux behave like stretched elastic strings, they try to take the shortest

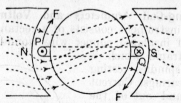

FIG. 196.—Distribution of resultant magnetic field.

path between poles NS, and thus exert forces FF on coil PQ, tending to move it out of the magnetic field.

$$\left.\begin{array}{c}\text{The deflecting}\\\text{torque}\end{array}\right\} \propto \left(\begin{array}{c}\text{current through}\\\text{coil}\end{array}\right) \times \left(\begin{array}{c}\text{flux density}\\\text{in gap}\end{array}\right)$$

$$=kI \text{ for uniform flux density,}$$

where　$k=$a constant for a given instrument

and　　$I=$current through coil.

$$\left.\begin{array}{c}\text{The controlling torque}\\\text{of the spiral springs}\end{array}\right\} \propto \text{angular deflection}$$

$$=c\theta$$

where　$c=$a constant for given springs

and　　$\theta=$angular deflection.

For a steady deflection,

$$\text{controlling torque}=\text{deflecting torque}$$

∴　　　　　　　$c\theta=kI$

and　　　　　　$\theta=\dfrac{k}{c}I,$

i.e. the deflection is proportional to the current and the scale is therefore uniformly divided.

As already mentioned in Art. 139, damping is effected by eddy currents induced in the metal former on which the coil is wound.

Owing to the delicate nature of the moving system,

this type of instrument is only suitable for measuring currents up to about 50 milliamperes directly. When larger currents have to be measured, a low resistance S (Fig. 197), termed a *shunt*, is connected in parallel with

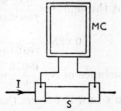

FIG. 197.—Moving-coil instrument as an ammeter.

the moving coil MC, and the instrument scale may be calibrated to read directly the total current I.

The moving-coil instrument may be made into a voltmeter by connecting a high resistance R in series, as

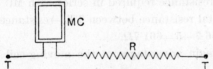

FIG. 198.—Moving-coil instrument as a voltmeter.

in Fig. 198. Again, the scale may be calibrated to read directly the voltage applied to the terminals TT.

Example 72. *A moving coil gives full-scale deflection with 15 mA and has a resistance of 5 Ω. Calculate the resistance to be connected (a) in parallel to enable the instrument to read up to 1 A, (b) in series to enable it to read up to 10 V.*

(a) From Ohm's Law,

$$\text{current through MC} = \frac{\text{p.d. across MC}}{\text{resistance of MC}}$$
(Fig. 197)

$$\therefore \quad \frac{15}{1000} = \frac{\text{p.d. (in volts) across MC}}{5}$$

so that p.d. across MC when carrying 15 mA $=0.075$ V.

From Fig. 197 it follows that

current through S = total current − current through MC

$$= 1 - 0.015 = 0.985 \text{ A.}$$

Similarly, current through S $= \dfrac{\text{p.d. across S}}{\text{resistance of S}}$

$$\therefore \qquad 0.985 = \frac{0.075}{\text{resistance of S (in ohms)}}$$

and resistance of S $= \dfrac{0.075}{0.985} = 0.07614\,\Omega.$

(b) From Ohm's Law it follows that for Fig. 198

current through MC $= \dfrac{\text{p.d. across TT}}{\text{resistance between TT}}$

$$\therefore \qquad \frac{15}{1000} = \frac{10}{\text{resistance between TT}}$$

so that resistance between TT $= 666.7\,\Omega.$

Hence, resistance required in series with MC

= total resistance between TT − resistance of MC

$$= 666.7 - 5 = 661.7\,\Omega.$$

The main advantages of the moving-coil instrument are:

(1) high sensitivity,
(2) uniform scale,
(3) well shielded from any stray magnetic field.

Its main disadvantages are:

(1) more expensive than the moving-iron instrument,
(2) only suitable for direct currents and voltages.

142. Moving-Iron Ammeters and Voltmeters.
Moving-iron instruments can be divided into two types:

(a) the *attraction* type, namely those in which a sheet of iron is attracted towards a solenoid,
(b) the *repulsion* type, namely those in which two parallel rods or strips of soft iron, magnetised inside a solenoid, repel each other.

Type (a).   Fig. 199 shows an end elevation and a

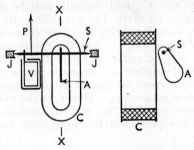

FIG. 199.—Attraction-type moving-iron instrument.

sectional front view (taken on XX) of the attracted-iron
type. A soft-iron disc A is attached to a spindle S
carried by jewelled centres J.
Disc A is so placed that it is
attracted towards solenoid C
carrying the current to be
measured. Damping is provided
by vane V attached to the spindle
and moving in an air chamber,
as already mentioned in Art. 139 ;
and in Fig. 199, gravity control is
assumed.

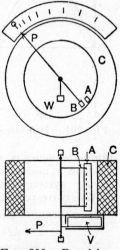

Type (b). This type depends
upon the force of repulsion
between two soft-iron rods or
strips magnetised in the same
direction by a solenoid carrying
the current to be measured. In
Fig. 200, C represents the solenoid.
An iron rod A is attached to the
bobbin on which the coil is wound
and another rod B is carried by
the spindle. When a current
passes through C, A and B are
magnetised in the same direction.

FIG. 200.—Repulsion-
type moving-iron in-
strument.

But poles of the same polarity repel each other (Art. 33) ;
consequently B tries to move away from A.   In Fig. 200

the controlling torque is due to a weight W attached to the spindle but it could equally well be obtained by spiral springs, as described in Art. 138. Air damping is provided by vane V moving in an air chamber.

For both the attraction and the repulsion types it is found that for a given position of the moving system, the value of the deflecting torque is proportional to the square of the current, so long as the iron disc or rods are working below saturation. Hence, if the current waveform is as shown in Fig. 201, the variation of the deflecting torque is represented by the dotted wave. If the

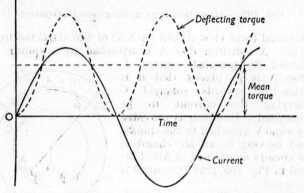

FIG. 201.—Deflecting torque in a moving-iron instrument.

supply frequency is, say, 50 c/s, the torque varies between zero and a maximum 100 times a second, so that the moving system—owing to its inertia—takes up a position corresponding to the mean torque, where

mean torque ∝ mean value of the square of the current

$$=kI^2$$

$k=$ a constant for a given instrument

and $I=$ r.m.s. value of the current (Art. 89).

Hence the moving-iron instrument can be used to measure both direct current and alternating current, and in the latter case the instrument gives the r.m.s.

value of the current. Owing to the deflecting torque being proportional to the square of the current, the scale divisions are not uniform, being cramped at the beginning and open at end of the scale.

Since the strength of the magnetic field and therefore the magnitude of the deflecting torque depend upon the number of ampere-turns on the solenoid, it is possible to arrange different instruments to have different ranges by merely winding different number of turns on the solenoids. For example, suppose that full-scale deflection is obtained with 400 ampere-turns, then for

full-scale reading with 100 A, no. of turns $=400/100=4$,

,, ,, ,, 5 A, ,, ,, $=400/5=80$.

A moving-iron voltmeter is a moving-iron milliam-meter connected in series with a suitable non-inductive resistance.

Example 73. *A moving-iron instrument requires* 400 *ampere-turns to give full-scale deflection. Calculate* (a) *the number of turns required if the instrument is to be used as an ammeter reading up to* 50 *A,* (b) *the number of turns and the total resistance if the instrument is to be arranged as a voltmeter reading up to* 300 *V with a current of* 20 *mA.*

(a) No. of turns $=400/50=8$.

(b) No. of turns $=400/0\cdot02=20{,}000$.

Total resistance $=300/0\cdot02=15{,}000\ \Omega$.

The advantages of moving-iron instruments are:

(1) robust construction,

(2) relatively cheap,

(3) can be used to measure direct and alternating currents and voltages.

The disadvantages of moving-iron instruments are:

(1) Affected by stray magnetic fields. Error due to this cause is minimised by the use of a magnetic screen such as an iron casing.

(2) Liable to hysteresis error when used in a d.c. circuit; i.e. for a given current, the instrument reads higher with decreasing than with increasing values of

current.   This error is reduced by making the iron strips
of nickel-iron alloy such as mumetal (Art. 58).

(3) Owing to the inductance of the solenoid, the reading on moving-iron voltmeters may be appreciably
affected by variation of frequency.   This error is reduced
by arranging for the resistance of the voltmeter to be
large compared with the reactance of the solenoid.

(4) Moving-iron voltmeters are liable to a temperature
error owing to the solenoid being wound with copper
wire.   This error is minimised by connecting in series
with the solenoid a high resistance of a material such as
manganin (copper, manganese and nickel) having a
negligible temperature coefficient of resistance.

143. Polarised Moving-Iron Ammeters and Voltmeters.

This type of instrument is chiefly used for motor-car
dashboards to indicate the charging and discharging
currents of the accumulators and for radio instruments
where cheapness is a prime factor and where an accuracy
of only 3 to 5 per cent is required.   The instrument *
consists of a permanent magnet NS (Fig. 202) with a
large airgap in which is pivoted a soft-iron armature
disc B, carrying pointer P.   The armature is "butterfly"
shape to give approximately a straight-line calibration.
A coil C (shown in section in Fig. 202) of one or more
turns is fixed alongside the gap.   When there is no
current through C, B is magnetised by NS and takes up
a position, Fig. 202 (a), such that the reluctance of the
airgaps is a minimum and the flux in B is a maximum.
Pointer P should then be indicating zero on the scale.

* In the modern instrument, the cobalt-steel permanent
magnet NS is in the form of a small bar, 2 cm × 0·5 cm × 0·2 cm,
situated below coil C, as shown in Fig. 202A, where the dotted
line represents the path of that part of the flux due to NS
which passes through the soft-iron armature disc B, inducing
in the latter the polarities marked n and s. The principle of
action is exactly the same as that of the arrangement shown
in Fig. 202. The student who does not have a modern instrument available for inspection may find some difficulty in
forming a mental picture of it and will probably be able to
understand more easily the construction shown in Fig. 202.
The authors are indebted to Messrs. Joseph Lucas, Ltd., for
information concerning this instrument.

When a current is flowing through C in the direction indicated by the dot and cross in Fig. 202 (b), the direc-

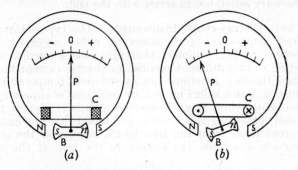

FIG. 202.—Polarised moving-iron instrument.

tion of the magnetic field due to C is upwards through C and the effect is to try to deflect B so that the n pole of the latter is also pointing upwards. Hence B is deflected anti-clockwise until the deflecting torque due to the current in C is balanced by the controlling torque exerted on B by the permanent magnet NS. No springs are required and the damping is practically automatic owing to the lightness of the moving system and the strong controlling torque available.

If the direction of the current through C is reversed, B is deflected clockwise; hence this instrument can only be used in d.c. circuits. Since the magnetic effect of C depends upon its ampere-turns, it follows that this instrument can be arranged as an

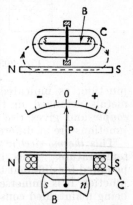

FIG. 202A.—Polarised moving-iron instrument.

ammeter reading up to any desired current by merely winding coil C with suitable number of turns. Similarly, the instrument can be arranged as a voltmeter by winding C with a large number of turns and connecting the necessary resistance in series with the coil.

144. Thermo-couple Instruments. This type of instrument utilises the thermo-electric effect observed by Seebeck in 1821, namely that in a closed circuit consisting of two different metals, an electric current flows when the two junctions are at different temperatures. Thus, if A and B in Fig. 203 are junctions of copper and iron wires, each being immersed in water, then if the vessel containing B is heated, it is found that an electric current flows from the iron to the copper at the cold junction and from the copper to the iron at the hot

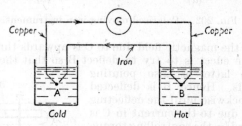

FIG. 203.—A thermo-couple.

junction, as indicated by the arrowheads. A pair of metals arranged in this manner is termed a *thermo-couple* and gives rise to a *thermo-e.m.f.* when the two junctions are at different temperatures.

This *thermo-electric effect* may be utilised to measure temperature. Thus, if the reading on galvanometer G be noted for different temperatures of the water in which junction B is immersed, the temperature of junction A being maintained constant, it is possible to calibrate the galvanometer in terms of the difference of temperature between A and B. The materials used in practice depend upon the temperature range to be measured; thus, copper-constantan couples are suitable for temperatures up to about 400° C and iron-constantan couples up to about 900° C, constantan being an alloy of copper and nickel. For temperatures up to about 1400° C, a couple made of platinum and platinum-iridium alloy is suitable.

A thermo-couple can be used to measure the r.m.s. value of an alternating current by arranging for one of the junctions of wires of dissimilar material, B and C (Fig. 204), to be placed near or welded to a resistor H carrying the current I to be measured. The current due to the thermo-e.m.f. is measured by a moving-coil microammeter A. The heater and the thermo-couple can be enclosed in an evacuated glass bulb D, shown dotted in Fig. 204, to shield them from draughts.

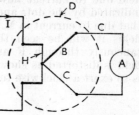

FIG. 204.—A thermo-couple ammeter.

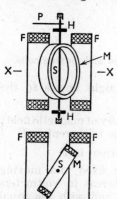

FIG. 205.—Electro-dynamic or dyna-mometer instrument.

Ammeter A may be calibrated by noting its reading for various values of direct current through H and it can then be used to measure the r.m.s. value of alternating currents of frequencies up to several megacycles per second.

145. Electrodynamic or Dynamometer Instruments. The action of this type of instrument depends upon the electromagnetic force exerted between fixed and moving coils carrying current. The upper diagram in Fig. 205 shows a sectional elevation through fixed coils FF and the lower diagram represents a sectional plan on XX. The moving coil M is carried by a spindle S and the controlling torque is exerted by spiral hairsprings H, which may also serve to lead the current into and out of M.

The deflecting torque is due to the interaction of the

magnetic fields produced by currents in the fixed and moving coils; thus Fig. 206 (a) shows the magnetic field due to current flowing through F in the direction indicated by the dots and crosses and Fig. 206 (b) shows that due to current in M.   By combining these magnetic fields it will be seen that when currents flow simultaneously through F and M, the resultant magnetic field is distorted as shown in Fig. 206 (c) and the effect is to exert a clockwise torque on M.

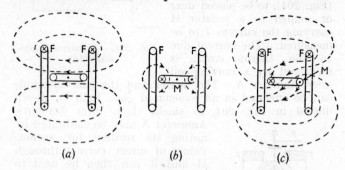

(a) (b) (c)

FIG. 206.—Magnetic fields due to fixed and moving coils.

Since M is carrying current at right angles to the magnetic field produced by F,

$$\text{deflecting torque} \propto \left(\begin{array}{c} \text{current} \\ \text{in M} \end{array} \right) \times \left(\begin{array}{c} \text{density of magnetic field} \\ \text{due to current in F} \end{array} \right)$$

$$\propto \text{current in M} \times \text{current in F.}$$

In dynamometer ammeters, the fixed and moving coils are connected in parallel, whereas in voltmeters they are in series with each other and with the usual high resistance.   In each case, the deflecting torque is proportional to the square of the current or the voltage; hence the dynamometer instrument, when used in an a.c. circuit, reads the r.m.s. value.

Owing to the higher cost and lower sensitivity of dynamometer ammeters and voltmeters compared with moving-iron instruments, the former are seldom used commercially, but *electrodynamic* or *dynamometer wattmeters* are very important because they are commonly employed for measuring the power in a.c. circuits. The fixed coils F are connected in series with the load, as shown in Fig. 207. The moving coil M is connected in series with a high non-inductive resistance R across the supply, so that the current through M is proportional to and practically in phase with the supply voltage V; hence:

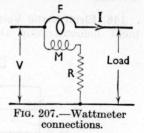

FIG. 207.—Wattmeter connections.

$$\left.\begin{array}{l}\text{instantaneous}\\\text{torque on the}\\\text{moving coil}\end{array}\right\} \propto \left(\begin{array}{c}\text{instantaneous}\\\text{current}\\\text{through F}\end{array}\right) \times \left(\begin{array}{c}\text{instantaneous}\\\text{current}\\\text{through M}\end{array}\right)$$

$$\propto \left(\begin{array}{c}\text{instantaneous}\\\text{current}\\\text{through load}\end{array}\right) \times \left(\begin{array}{c}\text{instantaneous}\\\text{p.d. across}\\\text{load}\end{array}\right)$$

$$\propto \text{instantaneous power taken by load}$$

$$\therefore \quad \left.\begin{array}{l}\text{average deflecting}\\\text{torque on M}\end{array}\right\} \propto \text{average value of the power}$$

$$=aP$$

where P is the power in watts and a is a constant for a given instrument.

The controlling torque is invariably provided by spiral hairsprings. If θ be the deflection corresponding to power P watts,

$$\text{controlling torque} \propto \text{deflection}$$

$$=c\theta$$

where c is a constant for a given instrument. For a steady deflection,

$$\text{controlling torque} = \text{deflecting torque}$$

$$\therefore \qquad c\theta = aP$$

and $\qquad \theta = \dfrac{a}{c}P.$

Hence the deflection is proportional to the power and the scale of the dynamometer wattmeter is uniformly divided.

146. Electrostatic Voltmeters. In Art. 68 an experiment demonstrating the mutual attraction between

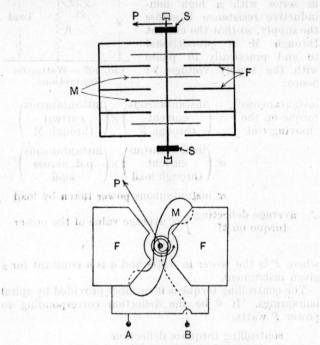

FIG. 208.—Electrostatic voltmeter.

positive and negative charges was described. This phenomenon is utilised in the electrostatic voltmeter. This instrument consists of fixed metal plates F, shaped as indicated in the lower part of Fig. 208, and very light metal vanes M attached to a spindle controlled by spiral springs S and carrying a pointer P.

The voltage to be measured is applied across terminals

A and B, and it is found that the force of attraction between F and M is proportional to the square of the applied voltage; hence this instrument can be used to measure either direct or alternating voltage, and when used in an a.c. circuit it reads the r.m.s. value.

The main advantages of the electrostatic voltmeter are: (a) it takes no current from a d.c. circuit (apart from the small initial charging current) and the current taken from an a.c. circuit is usually negligible. Hence it can be used to measure the p.d. between points in a circuit where the current taken by other types of voltmeter might considerably modify the value of that p.d. —for instance, to measure the p.d. between two points in a radio receiver. (b) It is particularly suitable for measuring high voltages, since the electrostatic forces are then so large that its construction can be greatly simplified.

147. Rectifier Ammeters and Voltmeters. In this type of instrument a copper-oxide rectifier is used to convert the alternating current into a unidirectional current, the mean value of which is measured on a moving-coil instrument. This rectifier consists of a copper disc, having on one side a layer of cuprous oxide formed by special heat treatment, and possesses the property * of offering a low resistance to current in one direction and a very high resistance to current in the reverse direction.

Rectifier ammeters usually consist of four rectifier elements arranged in the form of a bridge, as shown in Fig. 209, where the apex of the black triangle indicates the direction in which the resistance is low, and A represents a moving-coil ammeter. During the half-cycles that the current is flowing from left to right in Fig. 209, current flows through elements B and D, as shown by the full arrows. During the other half-cycles, the current flows through C and E, as shown by the dotted arrows. The waveform of the current through A is therefore as shown in Fig. 210. Consequently, the deflection of A depends upon the average value of the current, and the

---

* The behaviour of the copper-oxide rectifier is discussed in Art. 129 of *Applied Electricity*.

11

scale of A can be calibrated to read the r.m.s. value of
the current on the assumption that the waveform of the
latter is sinusoidal with a form factor of 1·11.

In a rectifier voltmeter, A is a milliammeter and the
bridge circuit of Fig. 209 is connected in series with a
high non-reactive resistance.

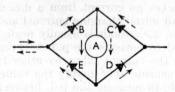

FIG. 209.—Bridge circuit for full-wave rectification.

The main advantage of the rectifier voltmeter is that
it is far more sensitive than other types of voltmeter
suitable for measuring alternating voltages.   Also, metal
rectifiers can be incorporated in universal instruments,
such as the Avometer, thereby enabling a moving-coil

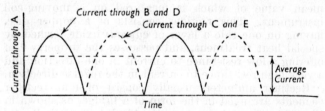

FIG. 210.—Waveform of current through moving-coil
ammeter.

milliammeter to be used in combination with shunt and
series resistances to measure various ranges of direct
current and voltage, and in combination with a bridge
rectifier and suitable resistances to measure various
ranges of alternating current and voltage.

**148. Measurement of Resistance by the Voltmeter-
Ammeter Method.**   The most obvious way of measuring
a resistance is to measure the current through and the

p.d. across the resistor and then apply Ohm's Law. This method, however, must be used with care; for instance if the instruments be connected as in Fig. 211, and if the voltmeter V be other than the electrostatic type, the current taken by V passes through A and may be comparable with that through R if the resistance of the latter is fairly high. If the resistance of V is known, its current can be calculated and subtracted from the reading on A to give the current through R.

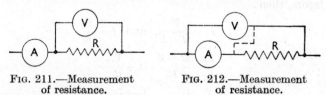

FIG. 211.—Measurement of resistance.   FIG. 212.—Measurement of resistance.

A better method is to connect the voltmeter across R and A as in Fig. 212, then :

$$\frac{\text{reading on V}}{\text{reading on A}} = \text{resistance of (R + A)}.$$

The resistance of A can be easily calculated from the p.d. across A—obtained by connecting V as shown dotted —and the corresponding current through A.

149. Measurement of Resistance by Substitution. (a) *Series method.* The unknown resistance X (Fig. 213) is connected in series with a variable resistance R, such

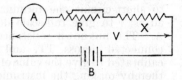

FIG. 213.—Measurement of resistance.

as a decade resistance box, which can be varied in steps of 1 or 0·1 Ω. The total resistance of R must exceed that of X. R is adjusted to give a convenient reading on ammeter A—preferably a reading such that the pointer is exactly over a scale mark near the top end of the scale. X is then removed and R readjusted to give the same reading on A. The increase of R gives the resistance of X.

If the known resistance R is fixed, it is necessary to note the current I_1 with R and X in series and the current I_2 with X removed. If V be the terminal voltage, which may be assumed constant if the current is very small compared with the rated current of the accumulators, then:

$$I_1 = \frac{V}{R+X}, \text{ and } I_2 = \frac{V}{R}$$

$$\therefore \qquad \frac{I_2}{I_1} = \frac{R+X}{R} = 1 + \frac{X}{R}$$

$$\therefore \qquad \frac{X}{R} = \frac{I_2}{I_1} - 1 = \frac{I_2 - I_1}{I_1}$$

and

$$X = R\left(\frac{I_2 - I_1}{I_1}\right).$$

If the resistance of the ammeter is appreciable, it must be included with R in the above calculation.

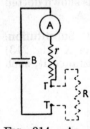

FIG. 214.—An ohmmeter circuit.

A modification of this arrangement is frequently used in universal instruments. A moving-coil milliammeter A is connected in series with a variable resistance r and a battery B to terminals TT, as in Fig. 214. The procedure is to short-circuit the terminals TT and adjust r to give full-scale deflection on A. The unknown resistance R is then connected across TT, and A can be calibrated to give the value of R directly, thereby making the instrument into an ohmmeter. Thus, suppose A to have full-scale deflection with 1 mA and battery B to be a dry cell having an e.m.f. of 1·5 V. With TT short-circuited, the total resistance of r and the cell must be 1·5 ÷ 1/1000, namely 1500 Ω. If a resistance of 1000 Ω is connected across TT, the current is 1·5 × 1000/2500, namely 0·6 mA; i.e. a scale deflection of 0·6 mA corresponds to a resistance of 1000 Ω, etc., as shown in Fig. 215.

Resistance r in Fig. 214 is made variable to allow for variation of the e.m.f. and internal resistance of battery B. It should be mentioned, however, that if the e.m.f.

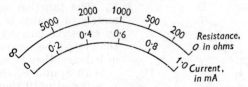

FIG. 215.—Ammeter and ohmmeter scales.

of B falls appreciably below its rated value, the resistance scale will only be approximately correct.

(b) *Alternative-circuit method.* In Fig. 216, X is the unknown resistance, R a known variable resistance and S a two-way switch. The reading on A is noted when S is on *a*. The switch is then moved over to *b* and R adjusted to give the same reading on A. The value of X is obviously the same as that of R.

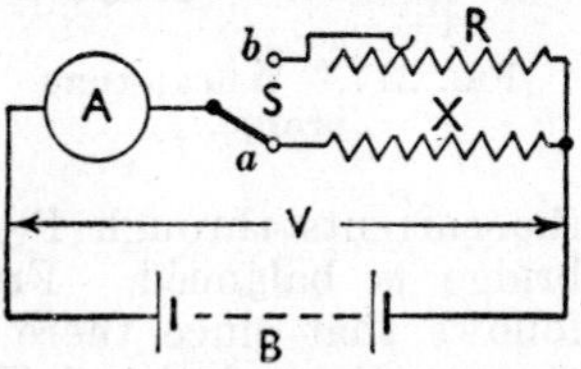

If R is a fixed resistance, it is necessary to note the current I_1 through X when S is on *a* and the current I_2 through R when switch is on *b*. If V is the terminal voltage and if the resistances of the battery and ammeter are negligible compared with those of X and R, then:

FIG. 216.—Measurement of resistance.

$$I_1 = \frac{V}{X}, \text{ and } I_2 = \frac{V}{R}$$

∴

$$\frac{I_2}{I_1} = \frac{X}{R}$$

and

$$X = R \times \frac{I_2}{I_1}.$$

150. Measurement of Resistance by the Wheatstone Bridge.

Two known resistances P and Q, a known variable resistance R and the unknown resistance X are connected as in Fig. 217. A battery B is connected through a switch S_1 to junctions C and F; and a galvanometer G, a variable high resistance A and a switch S_2

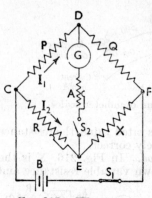

are in series across D and E. The function of A is merely to protect G against an excessive current should the system be seriously out of balance when S_2 is closed.

With S_1 and S_2 closed, R is adjusted until there is no deflection on G even with A reduced to zero. Junctions D and E are then at the same potential, so that the p.d. between C and D is the same as that between C and E, and the p.d. between D and F is the same as that between E and F.

FIG. 217.—Wheatstone bridge.

Suppose I_1 and I_2 to be the currents through P and R respectively when the bridge is balanced. From Kirchhoff's First Law it follows that since there is no current through G the currents through Q and X are also I_1 and I_2 respectively.

But   p.d. across $P = PI_1$
and   p.d. across $R = RI_2$
∴ $PI_1 = RI_2$ . . . . . . (123)
Also   p.d. across $Q = QI_1$
and   p.d. across $X = XI_2$
∴ $QI_1 = XI_2$ . . . . . (124)

Dividing (124) by (123), we have:

$$\frac{Q}{P} = \frac{X}{R}$$

and $X = R \times \dfrac{Q}{P}$ . . . . . (125)

The resistances P and Q may take the form of a slide-wire, in which case R may be a fixed value and balance obtained by moving a sliding contact along the wire. If the wire is homogeneous and of uniform section, the ratio of P to Q is the same as the ratio of the lengths of wire in the respective arms. A more convenient method, however, is to arrange P and Q so that each may be made 10, 100 or 1000 Ω. For instance, if P$=$1000 Ω and Q$=$10 Ω, and if R has to be 476 Ω to give a balance, then from (125):

$$X = 476 \times \frac{10}{1000} = 4 \cdot 76 \ \Omega.$$

On the other hand, if P and Q had been 10 and 1000 Ω respectively, then for the same value of R:

$$X = 476 \times \frac{1000}{10} = 47,600 \ \Omega$$

Hence it is seen that with this arrangement it is possible to measure a wide range of resistance with considerable accuracy and to derive the actual resistance very easily from the reading on R.

At one time, resistance boxes fitted with plugs to short-circuit the respective resistance elements were commonly employed; and in one pattern, known as the Post Office box, the ratio arms P and Q and the variable resistance R were constructed on this principle in one compact unit, complete with battery and galvanometer switches. Due partly to the trouble experienced with badly-fitting plugs or plugs inadequately pressed into their sockets and partly to the labour involved in removing and replacing plugs when balancing the bridge and in the subsequent adding up of the resistances left in circuit, plugs have been superseded by rotary dial switches, as shown in Fig. 8.

151. The Potentiometer. One of the most useful instruments for the accurate measurement of p.d., current and resistance is the potentiometer; and its importance has been increased by the fact that under the Electricity Supply (Meters) Act, 1936, it has been adopted as the standard method of measuring direct currents and voltages.

The potentiometer in its simplest form is shown in Fig. 218. MN is a wire of uniform section, stretched alongside a scale and connected across an accumulator B of ample capacity. A standard cell of known e.m.f. E_1, for example a Weston cell having an e.m.f. of 1·0186 V (Art. 20), is connected in series with a galvanometer G between sliding contacts P and Q, care being taken to check the polarity of the standard cell relative to that of B.

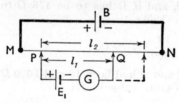

FIG. 218.—A simple potentiometer.

One or both sliders are moved along MN until the galvanometer deflection is reduced to zero. Let l_1 be the corresponding distance between P and Q. The fall of potential over a length l_1 of the wire must therefore be the same as the e.m.f., E_1, of the standard cell.

The standard cell is then replaced by another cell, such as a Leclanché cell, the e.m.f., E_2, of which is required. Q or P (or both) is again adjusted to give zero deflection on G. If l_2 be the new distance between P and Q, then:

$$\frac{E_1}{E_2}=\frac{l_1}{l_2}$$

$$\therefore \qquad E_2=E_1 \times \frac{l_2}{l_1}=1\cdot0186 \times \frac{l_2}{l_1} \quad . \quad . \quad (126)$$

152. A Commercial Form of Potentiometer. The simple arrangement described in the preceding article has two disadvantages: (a) the arithmetical calculation involved in expression (126) may introduce an error, and in any case takes an appreciable time; (b) the accuracy is limited by the length of slide-wire that is practicable and by the difficulty of ensuring exact uniformity over a considerable length.

In the commercial type of potentiometer shown in Fig. 219 these disadvantages are practically eliminated. R consists of fourteen equal resistors in series, the resistance of each unit being equal to that of the slide-wire S. The value of the current supplied by accumulator B is

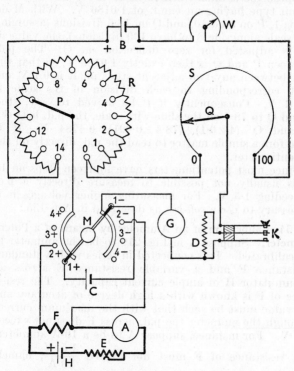

FIG. 219.—A commercial potentiometer.

controlled by a slide-wire resistance W. A multi-way 2-pole switch M enables various circuits to be connected in turn through a galvanometer G to the sliding contacts P and Q. K is a special key which, when slightly depressed, inserts a high resistance D in series with G. When K is depressed further, D is short-circuited.   The

11*

galvanometer is thereby protected against an excessive current should the potentiometer be appreciably out of adjustment when K is depressed.

153. Method of Standardising the Potentiometer. Suppose the standard cell to be of the Weston or cadmium type having an e.m.f. of 1·0186 V. With M on studs 1, P on stud 10, and Q on 18·6 divisions (assuming the scale alongside S to have 100 divisions), the value of W is adjusted for zero deflection on G. The p.d. between P and Q is then exactly 1·0186 V, so that the p.d. between any two adjacent studs on R is 0·1 V and that corresponding to each division of S's scale is 0·001 V. Consequently if P be moved to, say, stud 4 and Q to 78·4 on the slide-wire scale, the p.d. between P and Q $= (4 \times 0·1) + (78·4 \times 0·001) = 0·4784$ V. It is therefore a simple matter to read the p.d. directly off the potentiometer.

Since most potentiometers have fourteen steps on R, it is usually not possible to measure directly a p.d. exceeding 1·5 V. For measuring higher voltages it is necessary to use a *volt-box* as described in Art. 155.

154. Calibration of an Ammeter by means of a Potentiometer. Suppose A in Fig. 219 to be the ammeter to be calibrated. It is connected in series with a standard resistance F and a variable resistance E across an accumulator H of ample current capacity. The resistance of F is known with a high degree of accuracy and its value must be such that with the maximum current through the ammeter the p.d. across F does not exceed 1·5 V. For instance, suppose A to be a 10-A ammeter; the resistance of F must not exceed $\dfrac{1·5 \text{ V}}{10 \text{ A}}$, namely 0·15 Ω. Further, the resistance of F should preferably be a round figure, such as 0·1 Ω in this case, in order that the current may be quickly and accurately deduced from the potentiometer readings.

By means of switch M the connections from P and Q may be quickly transferred from the standard cell C to the standard resistance F. With some convenient current through A, P and Q are adjusted to give zero deflection on G and their positions noted.   For example, suppose the reading on A to have been adjusted to 6 A by means of E, and suppose the readings on P and Q, when balanced, to be 5 and 86·7 respectively. The p.d. across F is therefore 0·5867 V; and since F is assumed to be 0·1 Ω, the true value of the current through F is 0·5867/0·1, namely 5·867 A.   Hence the ammeter is reading high by 0·133 A.

The test is repeated for various values of the current.

155. Calibration of a Voltmeter by means of a Potentiometer. Suppose the voltmeter to be calibrated to have a range of 0–100 V.   It is therefore necessary to

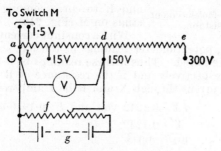

FIG. 220.—Voltmeter calibration.

use a *volt-box* to enable an accurately known fraction—not exceeding 1·5 V—to be obtained.   The volt-box consists of a high resistance *ae*, Fig. 220, with tappings at accurately determined points.   This arrangement enables voltmeters of various ranges to be calibrated; thus the 100-V voltmeter is connected across the 150-V tappings, the resistance between *ad* being 100 times that between *ab*.   The 1·5-V tappings are connected via switch M to sliders P and Q of the potentiometer (Fig. 219).   Various voltages can be applied to the voltmeter by moving the slider along a resistance *f* connected across a suitable battery *g*.

Let us suppose that the voltmeter reading has been adjusted to 70 V and that the corresponding readings on P and Q to give a balance are 7 and 8·4 respectively. The p.d. across *ab* is 0·7084 V, and the true value of the p.d. across *ad* is therefore 70·84 V.   Hence the voltmeter is reading low by 0·84 V.

156. Measurement of Resistance by means of a Potentiometer. The unknown resistance X (Fig. 221)

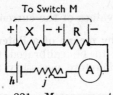

FIG. 221.—Measurement of resistance.

is connected in series with a known standard resistance R, an ammeter A and a variable resistance *j* across a battery *h*. The function of A is simply to check the value of the current. Connections are taken from X and R to corresponding pairs of studs on M (Fig. 219).

With a constant current through X and R, potentiometer readings of the p.d.'s across X and R are noted.   Thus if these readings be 0·1242 and 0·648 V respectively and if the resistance of R be 0·1 Ω and the current through X and R be I amperes, then:

$$IX = 0.1242 \text{ volt and } I \times 0.1 = 0.648 \text{ volt,}$$

$$\therefore \quad \frac{X}{0.1} = \frac{0.1242}{0.648}$$

and $$X = 0.01917 \ \Omega.$$

This method is particularly suitable for the accurate measurement of low resistances.

EXAMPLES XVII

1. A milliammeter gives full-scale deflection with 5 mA and has a resistance of 12 Ω.   Calculate the resistance necessary (a) in parallel, to enable the instrument to read up to 10 A, (b) in series, to enable it to read up to 100 V.

2. If the shunt for Question 1 (a) is to be made of manganin strip having a resistivity of 50 microhm-cm, a thickness of 0·5 mm and a length of 6 cm, calculate the width of the strip.

3. The rectangular moving-coil of an ammeter is wound with 30½ turns.   The effective axial length of the magnetic field is 2 cm and the effective radius of the coil is 0·8 cm.   The flux density in the gap is 0·12 Wb/m² and the controlling torque of the hairsprings is 0.5×10^{-6} newton-metre per degree of deflection.   Calculate the current to give a deflection of 60°.

4. The coil of a moving-coil instrument is wound with $36\frac{1}{2}$ turns on a former having an effective length of 2·5 cm and an effective breadth of 2 cm. The flux density in the gap is 0·08 Wb/m². Calculate the torque in newton-metres when the current is 25 mA.

5. The movement of a d.c. ammeter of 3-Ω resistance is adjusted so that a full-scale reading is produced by a current of 25 mA. Determine the value of shunts required to enable full-scale deflections to be obtained with currents of (a) 2 A, (b) 10 A. (N.C.T.E.C., S1)

6. What is meant by the multiplying power of a shunt?
A galvanometer with a resistance of 990 Ω is shunted so that 1/100 of the current in the main circuit passes through the instrument. Find the resistance of the shunt and the combined resistance of galvanometer and shunt. (C. & G., El. Eng. Pract., Prelim.)

7. What is meant by the terms "control" and "damping" as applied to electrical measuring instruments? Describe *one* method of each.
The coil of a moving-coil instrument has a resistance of 5 Ω and gives full-scale deflection when 0·015 A passes through it. What modification must be made to convert the instrument to a voltmeter reading to 150 V? (U.L.C.I., S2)

8. Describe with the aid of a sketch the principle of a Wheatstone bridge.
A galvanometer having a resistance of 5 Ω gives full-scale deflection with a current of 30 mA. Find the value of the necessary additional resistance for this instrument to be used as (a) an ammeter reading up to 2 A, (b) a voltmeter indicating up to 50 V. Give the diagram of connections for the added resistance in each case. (U.E.I., S2)

9. Compare the advantages and disadvantages of the following types of ammeters: (a) moving coil, (b) moving iron, (c) dynamometer and (d) thermal. Describe briefly the most suitable method of damping for each type.
A moving-iron ammeter is wound with 40 turns and gives full-scale deflection with 5 A. How many turns would be required on the same bobbin to give full-scale deflection with 20 A?
(I.Mech.E., Prin. of Elect.)

10. The coil of a moving-iron voltmeter has an inductance of 0·35 H and the total resistance of the instrument when made to read up to 20 V is 400 Ω. If the instrument is calibrated with direct voltage, calculate the percentage error when it is used on (a) a 50-c/s supply, (b) a 500-c/s supply.

11. Give a summary of four different types of voltmeters commonly used in practice. State whether they can be used on a.c. or d.c. circuits.
In *one* case give a sketch showing the construction with the method of control and damping employed. A d.c. voltmeter has a resistance of 28,600 Ω. When connected in series with an external resistance across a 480-V d.c. supply, the instrument reads 220 V. What is the value of the external resistance? (U.E.I., S2)

12. An unknown resistor R is measured by means of an ammeter (resistance 0·5 Ω), a voltmeter (resistance 65 Ω) and a battery, the voltmeter being connected directly across R. Draw a diagram of connections. If the ammeter reads 5·2 A and the voltmeter 13 V, calculate the value of R (a) approximately, (b) accurately. What change in connections would you make in order to measure a resistance of about 100 Ω, and why? (E.M.E.U., S1)

13. In a Wheatstone bridge arranged as in Fig. 217, P = 100 Ω, Q = 40 Ω and R = 156 Ω when the bridge is balanced. Calculate the value of the unknown resistance. Also find the value of the current in each circuit if the battery B has an e.m.f. of 4 V and an internal resistance of 20 Ω.

14. Draw a neat diagram showing how you would connect a slide-wire Wheatstone bridge in order to measure the value of an unknown resistance.

An unknown resistance is placed in the left-hand side and a standard resistance of 12 Ω in the right-hand side of a metre slide-wire Wheatstone bridge. Balance is obtained at a point on the slide-wire 41·7 cm from the left-hand side.

(a) Calculate the value of the unknown resistance.

(b) If the standard resistance were to be reduced to 8 Ω, at what distance from the left-hand end of the slide-wire would balance then be obtained?   (E.M.E.U., S1)

15. Four resistors are connected in series to form a closed circuit ABCD. The resistances AB, BC, CD and DA respectively are 16, 14, 7 and 3 Ω. If a p.d. of 3 V is applied between A and C, being positive with respect to C, calculate the value and the direction of the p.d. between points B and D. What value of resistance should be connected in parallel with resistor AB to give zero p.d. between B and D?
                                                            (U.E.I., S2)

16. Describe the principle of the Wheatstone bridge and deduce the balance condition.

It is required to use a Wheatstone bridge and a 2-V cell to measure the resistance of a voltmeter scaled 0 to 2 V. Two of the branches, adjacent to each other, are set to values of 100 Ω and 1000 Ω. The meter is connected adjacent to the 1000-Ω branch, and the fourth branch has a value of 202 Ω when the balance is obtained. Draw a diagram of connections. Calculate the resistance of the meter and estimate the reading which the meter might be expected to indicate, if connected as in your diagram. You may neglect the internal resistance of the cell.   (Joint Section A)

17. State Kirchhoff's Laws.

The arms of a Wheatstone bridge have the following resistances: AB, 10 Ω; BC, 20 Ω; CD, 30 Ω; and DA, 10 Ω. A galvanometer having a resistance of 40 Ω is connected between B and D and a cell having an e.m.f. of 2 V and negligible internal resistance is connected across A and C, its positive end being connected to A. Calculate the current through the galvanometer and state its direction.
                                                (I.Mech.E., Prin. of Elect.)

18. Explain how resistance may be measured if a d.c. supply, a voltmeter and an ammeter are available. Draw a circuit diagram showing the connections when the resistance is about 0·5 Ω and carries 20 A.

In a Wheatstone bridge arrangement the 2-V battery is connected between terminals A and B, and a galvanometer of resistance 10 Ω is connected between terminals C and D. If terminals A and C, C and B, A and D, and D and B are joined by resistances of 10, 5, 5 and 20 Ω respectively, calculate the current in the galvanometer.
                                                        (Joint Section A)

19. The current through an ammeter connected in series with a standard shunt of 0·01 Ω, as in Fig. 219, is adjusted to 40 A; and the readings on the studs and the slide-wire of the potentiometer, when balanced, are 4 and 12·3 respectively. Calculate the percentage error of the ammeter and state whether the instrument is reading high or low.

20. The reading on a voltmeter connected across the 0/300-V range of a volt-box (Fig. 220) is adjusted to 250 V, and the readings on the studs and the slide-wire of the potentiometer, when balanced, are 12 and 34·7 respectively. Calculate the percentage error of the voltmeter and state whether the instrument is reading high or low.

21. Explain the principle of operation of a simple potentiometer when used to measure the e.m.f. of a cell.

In an experiment with a simple potentiometer, a balance was obtained on a length of 60 cm of the wire when using a standard cell of electromotive force 1·0183 V. When a dry cell was substituted for the standard cell, a balance was obtained with a length of 85 cm. Calculate the e.m.f. of the dry cell. (U.L.C.I., S2)

22. Show how a potentiometer can be used to calibrate a d.c. ammeter with the aid of a standard cell.

Using a Weston cadium cell (e.m.f. 1·0183) and a standard 0·1-Ω resistance, the potentiometer was adjusted so that 1·0183 metres was equivalent to the e.m.f. of the cell. When a certain direct current was flowing through the standard resistance, the voltage across it corresponded to 150 cm. What was the value of the current?
(C. & G., Telecom. Prin. I)

23. Explain the theory of the simple potentiometer. What are the advantages of this method of measuring a p.d.?

A standard cell (e.m.f. 1·018 V) gives a balance at 50·9 cm, and a cell X of unknown e.m.f. gives a balance at 93 cm, when each is tested on a certain potentiometer. When the cell X is connected to a voltmeter whose resistance is 200 Ω, the voltmeter reads 1·84 V. Determine the internal resistance of X. (E.M.E.U., S2)

24. Explain how a moving-coil milliammeter, having a range 0–10 mA, can be adapted, by means of metal rectifiers and resistors, to measure alternating voltages up to 10 V. Does the meter reading depend on peak, r.m.s. or mean value of the voltage?

If such an instrument had been calibrated with a sinusoidal supply, by what factor must the scale readings be multiplied when measuring the effective value of a square wave? (C. & G., Telecom. Prin. II)

CHAPTER XVIII

ACCUMULATORS

157. Introductory. In Art. 6 it was shown that an electric current is capable of producing a chemical action when passed through an electrolyte; and that if the electrodes consist of lead plates immersed in a dilute solution of sulphuric acid, the passage of an electric current for a little while produces a chocolate-colour coating on the positive plate. It was also found that the plates could then produce sufficient current to light a lamp. In this case the chemical action is of a reversible kind, electrical energy being converted into and stored as chemical energy when the cell is charged, and chemical energy being transformed back into electrical energy when the cell is discharged. Such an arrangement is termed an *accumulator* or *secondary* cell.

A *primary* cell is an arrangement whereby it is only possible to transform chemical energy into electrical energy, and the cell can only be replenished by renewal of the active materials. By far the commonest type of primary cell is the Leclanché pattern, in which the active materials are carbon (+), zinc (−) and ammonium chloride (salammoniac). Manganese dioxide is added as a *depolariser* to prevent hydrogen accumulating round the carbon rod. In the so-called "dry" cell, zinc chloride is added to absorb moisture, thereby maintaining the mixture of carbon powder, salammoniac and manganese dioxide as a damp paste. Students should dissect exhausted cells and sketch their construction.

A primary cell has a relatively high internal resistance, so that when more than a small current is required, secondary cells must be used. These may be divided into two types:

(a) the lead-acid cell, in which lead plates covered with compounds of lead are immersed in a dilute solution of sulphuric acid in water,

(b) the nickel-cadmium and the nickel-iron alkaline cells.

These cells will now be considered in detail.

158. Lead-Acid Accumulators. The plates used in this type of cell may be grouped thus:

(a) *Formed* or *Planté* plates, namely those formed from lead plates by charging, discharging, charging in the reverse direction, etc., a number of times, the forming process being accelerated by the use of suitable chemicals. The main difficulty with this type of construction is to secure as large a working surface as possible for a given weight of plate. One method of increasing the surface area is to make the plates with deep corrugations, as in Fig. 222, with reinforcing ribs at intervals.

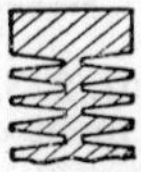

(b) *Pasted* or *Faure* plates, namely those in which a paste of the active material is either pressed into recesses in a lead-antimony grid or held between two finely perforated lead sheets cast with ribs and flanges so that the two sheets, when riveted together, form in effect a number of boxes which hold the paste securely in position. The paste is usually sulphuric acid mixed with red lead (Pb_3O_4) for the positives and with litharge (PbO) for the negatives. A small percentage of a material such as powdered pumice is added to increase the porosity of the paste. For a given ampere-hour capacity (Art. 160), the weight of a pasted plate is only about a third of that of a formed plate.

FIG. 222.— Section of a Planté plate.

Students are advised to examine specimen plates or plates taken from disused accumulators.

When weight is of no importance it is common practice to make the positive plates of the "formed" type and the negative plates of the "pasted" type. The active material on the positive plates expands when it is subjected to chemical changes; consequently it is found that the greater mechanical stiffness of the "formed" construction is an important advantage in reducing the tendency of the plates to buckle. This

tendency to buckle is reduced still further by constructing the cell with an odd number of plates, as shown in
Fig. 223, the outer plates being always negative. This
arrangement enables both sides of each positive plate
to be actively employed, and the tendency of one side
of a plate to expand and cause buckling is neutralised
by a similar tendency on the other side.

The plates are assembled in glass, celluloid, vulcanised
rubber or lead-lined wood containers and separated by
insulating rods or porous diaphragms.

The most suitable specific gravity of the acid depends
upon the type of cell and the state of charge of the cell.
An average value, however, is
about 1·21.

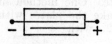

FIG. 223.—Arrange-
ment of plates.

When accumulators are used for
car lighting and starting they must
be capable of giving a very heavy
current for very short periods. It
is then necessary to keep the in-
ternal resistance as low as possible. This is done by
making the ratio of the active surface to the weight of
the plate as high as possible, partly by using pasted
plates for both positives and negatives and partly by
making each plate relatively thin and using a large
number of plates.

In the Exide-Ironclad battery the weakness of the
pasted positive is overcome by constructing each
positive plate of a row of thin vertical ebonite tubes
assembled in a lead frame. Each tube has a lead rod
down its centre and is packed with the active material,
the electrolyte having access to the latter through a
large number of narrow slits in the ebonite cylinder.

159. Chemical Reactions in a Lead-Acid Accumulator.
The chemical reactions taking place during charge and
discharge are complicated, and all we can do here is to
indicate the most important reactions and to account
for the variation in the density of the electrolyte.

When the cell is fully charged, the active material on
the positive plate is lead peroxide (PbO_2) and that on
the negative is spongy or porous lead (Pb). During

discharge the lead peroxide and the spongy lead are gradually converted into lead sulphate ($PbSO_4$). The SO_4 portion of the lead sulphate has to be supplied from the sulphuric acid (H_2SO_4), and the hydrogen (H) thereby released from the acid combines with the oxygen (O) of the lead peroxide to form water (H_2O). Since one atom of oxygen (O) replaces one atom of sulphur and four atoms of oxygen (SO_4) in each molecule of the electrolyte that undergoes chemical change, the weight of such molecules is reduced and consequently the specific gravity of the electrolyte falls as the cell discharges.

During charge the chemical reactions are reversed and the active material is converted back to lead peroxide on the positive and to spongy lead on the negative plates. The SO_4 released from the lead sulphate combines with hydrogen from the water to form H_2SO_4, and the corresponding quantity of oxygen from the water is absorbed to form the lead peroxide on the positive plates. Hence the specific gravity of the electrolyte is restored to its original value.

The above reactions may be summarised thus:

	Positive plate	Electrolyte	Negative plate	
Dis-charge	Lead peroxide (PbO_2)	Sulphuric acid ($2H_2SO_4$)	Lead (Pb)	Charge
	Lead sulphate ($PbSO_4$)	Water ($2H_2O$)	Lead sulphate ($PbSO_4$)	

160. Characteristics of a Lead-Acid Accumulator. When a cell is discharged, its terminal voltage falls at a rate that depends upon the discharge current; and the normal capacity of the cell is taken as the number of ampere-hours it can give on a 10-hour discharge at a constant current before its p.d. falls to about 1·85 V. Such a condition is represented by curve A in Fig. 224. Curve B represents the variation of p.d. when the cell is discharged at about 2·4 times the normal rate. The higher the rate of discharge, the smaller is the number of ampere-hours obtainable from the cell before its p.d. falls below the permissible value—a value that depends upon the discharge rate. The lower curve in Fig. 225 represents the capacity in ampere-hours obtainable at different discharge rates, and the upper curve represents the corresponding rates, the values for both curves being expressed as percentages of the 10-hour values.

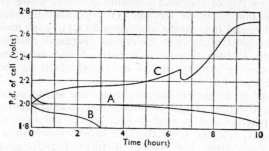

FIG. 224.—Characteristics of a lead-acid cell.

The reduction in the capacity at high rates of discharge is due to the chemical reactions being at first confined to the outer layers of the active material.

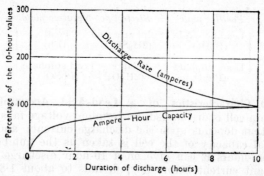

FIG. 225.—Variation of capacity with discharge rate.

Consequently the acid in the pores of these outer layers is used up before fresh acid can take its place. Owing to the relatively high resistance of very weak acid the voltage falls rapidly, though there may be plenty of unchanged active material still left in the inner layers. If a cell is discharged at a very high rate to the permissible final voltage and then left on open circuit, the weakened acid becomes strengthened by diffusion of the electrolyte; and a further discharge can be obtained from the cell.

The first portion of curve C in Fig. 224 represents the variation of p.d. during charge at normal rate, but the actual value of the p.d. varies appreciably for different types of cells. It is seen that after about 5 hours the p.d. increases more rapidly, and in order to prevent the temperature exceeding about 100° F (38° C), it is necessary to reduce the charging rate; thus the second portion of curve C represents the variation of p.d. with the charging current reduced to half the normal rate.

The ampere-hour efficiency of an accumulator is the ratio of the number of ampere-hours obtainable during discharge to that required to restore it to its original condition. The value for a lead-acid cell is about 90 per cent. The watt-hour efficiency takes the voltage variation into account, and its value is about 75 per cent.

161. Care of a Lead-Acid Battery. The principal difficulty in the maintenance of this type of cell in a healthy condition is the tendency for the lead sulphate to become hard and form a white incrustation on the plates. This white sulphate has a relatively high resistance and reduces the porosity of the plates so that the acid has greater difficulty in penetrating into the active material. The capacity of the cell is thereby reduced.

The following are the chief precautions to be taken in the maintenance of a lead-acid battery:

(a) The cells should be recharged as soon as possible after discharge. White sulphate forms more readily the lower the state of charge of a cell.

(b) The rates of charge and discharge specified by the makers should not be exceeded.

(c) Records should be kept of the p.d. of each cell and of the specific gravity of the electrolyte; and if either becomes abnormal, the trouble should be immediately rectified.

(d) If it is possible, the plates should be examined periodically for colour and for clearance between the positive and negative plates and between the plates and any sediment at the bottom of the container. When healthy, the positive plates are chocolate-brown and the negative plates are slate-grey.

(e) The level of the electrolyte must be kept above the tops of the plates, and the loss of water by evaporation and decomposition during gassing should be made up by the addition of distilled water. Tap water should only be used if it has been found by analysis to be free of injurious chemicals. The "make-up" water should preferably be added when the cells are gassing, so that it may mix thoroughly with the electrolyte.

(f) Any sulphuric acid added to the electrolyte should be of the pure colourless variety. No acid should be added until it has been checked that the low density is not due to white sulphate on the plates or to the cell being undercharged.

(g) The cells should be given a periodic overcharge at about half the normal rate, the latter being maintained until the cells are gassing freely and until half-hourly readings of the terminal voltage and of the specific gravity of each cell show no further increase. This ensures the removal of any white sulphate and restores the whole of the active material to its normal condition.

(h) If a battery has a relatively light duty it is advisable to discharge it occasionally through an artificial load at its normal rate and then immediately recharge it.

(i) If the battery is being used as a standby source to give emergency lighting, etc., it should be connected across a d.c. supply so as to receive a continuous trickle-charge.

(j) The temperature of the cells should not exceed about 100° F (38° C), otherwise the plates deteriorate rapidly.

162. Alkaline Accumulators. In both the nickel-iron and the nickel-cadmium types, the positive plates are made of nickel hydroxide enclosed in finely perforated steel tubes or pockets, the electrical resistance being reduced by the addition of flakes of pure nickel or graphite. These tubes or pockets are assembled in nickelled-steel plates. In the nickel-iron cell the negative plate is made of iron oxide with a little mercuric oxide to reduce the resistance, the mixture being enclosed in perforated steel pockets, also assembled in nickelled-steel plates. In the nickel-cadmium cell the active material is cadmium mixed with a little iron, the purpose of the latter being to prevent the active material caking and losing its porosity.

In both types of cell, the electrolyte is a solution of potassium hydroxide (KOH) having a specific gravity of about 1·17. The electrolyte does not undergo any chemical change; consequently the quantity of electrolyte can be reduced to the minimum necessitated by adequate clearance between the plates.

The plates are separated by ebonite rods and assembled in sheet-steel containers, the latter being mounted in wooden crates to insulate the cells from one another.

163. Chemical Reactions in an Alkaline Accumulator.

When the nickel-cadmium cell is in a charged condition the active material on the positive plates appears to be a hydroxide of nickel having the chemical formula $Ni(OH)_3$ and that on the negative is pure cadmium. During discharge, the $Ni(OH)_3$ is converted into the lower hydroxide $Ni(OH)_2$ and the cadmium is converted into cadmium hydroxide $Cd(OH)_2$. During charge, the chemical reactions are reversed. These reactions may be summarised thus:

Positive plate	*Negative plate*		*Positive plate*	*Negative plate*
$2Ni(OH)_3$	$+ \ Cd$	$\xrightarrow[\text{Charge}]{\text{Discharge}}$	$2Ni(OH)_2$	$Cd(OH)_2$

In the nickel-iron cell the reactions are exactly similar, except that iron replaces cadmium.

164. Characteristics of the Alkaline Accumulator.

Curve A in Fig. 226 represents the terminal voltage of a

nickel-cadmium cell during discharge at the 10-hour rate, while curve B shows the variation for a 3-hour rate. Owing to the fact that no change occurs in the composition of the electrolyte during discharge, the number of ampere-hours obtainable from an alkaline

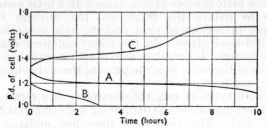

FIG. 226.—Characteristics of an alkaline cell.

cell is much less affected by the discharge rate than is the case with the lead-acid cell. Fig. 227 shows the capacity of a nickel-cadmium cell—expressed as a percentage of the 10-hour capacity—for different rates of discharge. It is seen that for a 1-hour rate it is possible to obtain

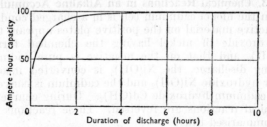

FIG. 227.—Capacity of an alkaline cell.

about 84 per cent of the 10-hour capacity, compared with about 50 per cent for the lead-acid cell (Fig. 225).

Curve C of Fig. 226 represents the variation of the terminal voltage when the cell is charged at 1·5 times the 10-hour discharge rate.

The ampere-hour efficiency of the nickel-cadmium cell is about 75–80 per cent, while its watt-hour efficiency is about 60–65 per cent.

Alkaline cells capable of giving the heavy current required for car starting, etc., have been developed, the low internal resistance being obtainable by making the plates and the separators as thin as practicable, thereby enabling more plates to be used.

The advantages of the alkaline accumulator are: (a) its mechanical construction enables it to withstand considerable vibration and (b) it is free from "sulphating" or any similar trouble and can therefore be left in any state of charge without damage. Its disadvantages are: (a) its cost is greater than that of the corresponding lead cell, (b) its average discharge p.d. is about 1·2 V compared with 2 V for the lead cell, so that for a given voltage the number of alkaline cells is about 67 per cent greater than that of lead cells.

EXAMPLES XVIII

1. What is the difference between a primary and a secondary cell? Six cells, each of 2 V and internal resistance 2 Ω, are connected in two groups of three in series, and the two groups connected in parallel to an external resistance of 30 Ω. Sketch the arrangement and calculate the current which will flow through the external resistance.
(U.E.I., S1)

2. Explain the cause of gassing during charging of a lead-acid battery.

An accumulator is overcharged by 5 A for 20 hours. If the electrochemical equivalents of hydrogen and oxygen are 0·01045 and 0·08295 mg per coulomb respectively, find the volume of water in cubic centimetres required to be added to compensate for gassing.
(C. & G., El. Eng. Pract., Prelim.)

3. If the terminal voltage of a lead-acid cell varies between 2·1 and 1·85 V during discharge, calculate the number of cells required to give 230 V (a) at beginning of discharge, (b) at end of discharge.

4. A battery of 50 cells in series is charged through a resistance of 4 Ω from a 230-V supply. If the terminal voltage per cell is 2 and 2·7 V respectively at the beginning and end of the charge, calculate the charging current (a) at the beginning and (b) at the end of the charge.

5. A battery of 40 cells in series is to be charged from a 220-V supply. If the average p.d. per cell during charge is 2·2 V, calculate the resistance to be connected in series with the battery to give an average charging current of 5 A.

6. Explain the differences between the constant-current and the constant-voltage methods of charging secondary batteries.

Thirty-five lead-acid secondary cells, each of discharge capacity 100 ampere-hours at the 10-hour rate, are to be fully charged at constant current for 8 hours. The d.c. supply is 120 V, the ampere-hour efficiency is 80 per cent and the e.m.f. of each cell at beginning and end of charge is respectively 1·9 V and 2·6 V.   Calculate the maximum and minimum values of the necessary charging resistance.   Ignore internal resistance of cells.   (C. & G., El. Inst. Work)

7. Explain the terms "ampere-hour efficiency" and "watt-hour efficiency" with reference to secondary cells; which is the greater, and why?

A battery of 12 cells is charged, through a resistor, from a constant 30-V supply.   When charging commences, the e.m.f. per cell is 1·85 V and the charging current is 4 A.   At the end of the charge the e.m.f. per cell has risen to 2·25 V.   If each cell has a constant internal resistance of 0·05 Ω, calculate the value of the external resistor, and the current at the end of the charge.   (E.M.E.U., S2)

8. Describe the construction of a lead-acid accumulator.   What are the indications that an accumulator requires recharging?

How many identical accumulators may be charged in series from a 230-V supply if the terminal voltage of each is 2·0 V and 2·7 V at the beginning and end respectively when the charging current is 5 A. What value of resistance is required in series with the circuit at the beginning of charge if the current is 5 A?   (Joint Section A)

9. What are the relative advantages and disadvantages of lead-acid and alkaline secondary cells?

An alkaline cell is discharged at a steady current of 4 A for 12 hours, the average terminal voltage being 1·2 V.   To restore it to its original state of charge, a steady current of 3 A for 20 hours is required, the average terminal voltage being 1·44 V.   Calculate the ampere-hour and watt-hour efficiencies in this particular case.   (U.L.C.I., S2)

10. State two advantages and two disadvantages of the nickel alkaline accumulator compared with the lead acid type.   An emergency battery has 175 alkaline cells connected in series and the input capacity per cell is 1000 Ah.   If the quantity efficiency is 80 per cent, calculate the average horsepower during an 8-hour discharge if the average voltage during discharge is 1·2 V per cell.   (U.E.I., S2)

11. Describe the construction of a lead-acid cell and account for the variation in the density of the acid during charge and discharge.

A cell is discharged at a constant current of 5 A for 10 hours, the average value of the terminal voltage being 1·92 V.   The cell is then recharged at a constant rate of 3 A for 20 hours, with an average terminal voltage of 2·2 V.   Calculate (a) the ampere-hour efficiency, (b) the watt-hour efficiency.   (I.Mech.E., Prin. of Elect.)

12. Sketch the graphs, approximately to scale, showing the change of voltage with the time of charge and of discharge of a lead-acid cell at constant current.

A battery of 56 cells in series takes a constant charging current of 8 A, the e.m.f. rising from 1·8 to 2·4 V per cell.   If each cell has an internal resistance of 0·008 Ω, find the p.d. across the battery at the beginning and at the end of charge.

If the battery is completely discharged in 40 hours at 4 A at an average voltage of 1·96 V per cell after being charged for 24 hours at 8 A with an average voltage of 2·2 V per cell, find the ampere-hour and the watt-hour efficiencies of the battery.

                    (C. & G., El. Eng. Pract., Prelim.)

13. An alkaline cell is discharged at a constant current of 5 A for 10 hours, the average terminal voltage being 1·2 V.   A charging current of 3 A maintained for 21 hours is required to bring the cell back to the same state of charge, the average terminal voltage being 1·48 V.   Calculate the ampere-hour and the watt-hour efficiencies.

14. The 10-hour capacity of a certain accumulator is 60 Ah. From Fig. 225 and 227 find the number of ampere-hours obtainable on a half-hour discharge rate if the accumulator is of (a) the lead-acid type and (b) the alkaline type.

15. An accumulator has a terminal voltage of 1·9 V when supplying a current of 8 A. The terminal voltage rises to 2·03 V immediately the load is switched off. Calculate the internal resistance of the accumulator.

16. Describe the construction of an alkaline cell and compare the advantages and disadvantages of this type of cell with those of the lead-acid cell.

A certain alkaline cell had a terminal voltage of 1·24 V when supplying a load of 3 A. Immediately after the load was disconnected, the terminal voltage was 1·28 V. Calculate the internal resistance of the cell.   (I.Mech.E., Prin. of Elect.)

17. Describe a method for determining the internal resistance of a battery.

The terminals of an accumulator, e.m.f. 2 V and internal resistance 0·05 Ω, are joined directly to those of a dry battery, e.m.f. 1·5 V and internal resistance 1·7 Ω, so that the cells are in series. Determine the reading on a moving-coil voltmeter connected to the terminals of the dry battery and show clearly on a diagram the necessary polarity of the instrument for this reading.   (U.E.I., S2)

18. A shunt dynamo is used to charge a battery of 50 cells in series. If each cell has a terminal p.d. of 2·6 V at completion of charge, calculate the e.m.f. to be generated in the dynamo to give a charging current of 40 A at the end of the charge. Assume the armature circuit to have a resistance of 0·1 Ω and the cables connecting the dynamo to the battery to have a resistance of 0·08 Ω. The shunt current of the dynamo may be neglected.

COMPARISON OF M.K.S. AND C.G.S. UNITS

Term	M.K.S. unit (Rationalized system)	Equivalent in C.G.S. units	
		Electromagnetic	Electrostatic
Length . .	1 metre	100 cm	100 cm
Mass . .	1 kg	1000 g	1000 g
Time . .	1 sec	1 sec	1 sec
Force . .	1 newton	10^5 dynes	10^5 dynes
Work . .	1 joule	10^7 ergs	10^7 ergs
Power . .	1 watt	10^7 ergs/sec	10^7 ergs/sec
Current .	1 ampere	0·1 unit	3×10^9 units
Charge . .	1 coulomb	0·1 unit	3×10^9 units
E.M.F. and P.D.	1 volt	10^8 units	1/300 unit
Resistance .	1 ohm	10^9 units	—
Inductance .	1 henry	10^9 units	—
Capacitance .	1 farad	—	9×10^{11} units
Magnetomotive force	1 ampere-turn	$0·4\pi$ gilberts	—
Magnetising force	1 ampere-turn per metre	$4\pi \times 10^{-3}$ oersted	—
Magnetic flux	1 weber	10^8 maxwells	—
Magnetic flux density	1 weber/metre^2	10^4 gauss	—
Permeability of free space	$4\pi \times 10^{-7}$ unit	1 unit	—
Electric force	1 volt/metre	—	$\frac{1}{3} \times 10^{-4}$ unit/cm
Electric flux density	1 coulomb/metre^2	—	$12\pi \times 10^5$ units/cm^2
Permittivity of free space	$8·85 \times 10^{-12}$ unit	—	1 unit

MATHEMATICAL CONSTANTS

Constant	Number	Reciprocal
π	3·1416	0·3183
$\pi/4$	0·7854	1·2732

CONVERSION FACTORS

To convert	Multiply by	Reciprocal
Radian to degrees . . .	57·30	0·01745
Inches to metres . . .	0·0254	39·37
Yards to metres . . .	0·9144	1·094
Miles/hour to metres/sec .	0·447	2·237
Pounds to kilograms .	0·4536	2·205
Pounds (force) to newtons .	4·45	0·225
Kilograms (force) to newtons .	9·81	0·1019
Horsepower to ft-lb/min . .	33,000	$3·031 \times 10^{-5}$
Horsepower to ft-lb/sec . .	550	0·001818
Horsepower to kilowatts . .	0·746	1·341
Therms to B.Th.U. . .	100,000	10^{-5}
B.Th.U. to kilogram-calories .	0·252	3·97
B.Th.U. to kWh . . .	$2·934 \times 10^{-4}$	3,409
Ft-lb to B.Th.U. . . .	0·001285	778
Ft-lb to joules . .	1·356	0·7374
Kilogram-calories to joules .	4,187	$2·388 \times 10^{-4}$
Joules to kWh . . .	$0·2778 \times 10^{-6}$	3,600,000

	0	1	2	3	4	5	6	7	8	9	1	2	3	4	5	6	7	8	9
10	0000	0043	0086	0128	0170	0212	0253	0294	0334	0374	4	9	13	17	21	26	30	34	38
											4	8	12	16	20	24	28	32	37
11	0414	0453	0492	0531	0569	0607	0645	0682	0719	0755	4	8	12	15	19	23	27	31	35
											4	7	11	15	19	22	26	30	33
12	0792	0828	0864	0899	0934	0969	1004	1038	1072	1106	3	7	11	14	18	21	25	28	32
											3	7	10	14	17	20	24	27	31
13	1139	1173	1206	1239	1271	1303	1335	1367	1399	1430	3	7	10	13	16	20	23	26	30
											3	7	10	12	16	19	22	25	29
14	1461	1492	1523	1553	1584	1614	1644	1673	1703	1732	3	6	9	12	15	18	21	24	28
											3	6	9	12	15	17	20	23	26
15	1761	1790	1818	1847	1875	1903	1931	1959	1987	2014	3	6	9	11	14	17	20	23	26
											3	5	8	11	14	16	19	22	25
16	2041	2068	2095	2122	2148	2175	2201	2227	2253	2279	3	5	8	11	14	16	19	22	24
											3	5	8	10	13	15	18	21	23
17	2304	2330	2355	2380	2405	2430	2455	2480	2504	2529	3	5	8	10	13	15	18	20	23
											2	5	7	10	12	15	17	19	22
18	2553	2577	2601	2625	2648	2672	2695	2718	2742	2765	2	5	7	9	12	14	16	19	21
											2	5	7	9	11	14	16	18	21
19	2788	2810	2833	2856	2878	2900	2923	2945	2967	2989	2	4	7	9	11	13	16	18	20
											2	4	6	8	11	13	15	17	19
20	3010	3032	3054	3075	3096	3118	3139	3160	3181	3201	2	4	6	8	11	13	15	17	19
21	3222	3243	3263	3284	3304	3324	3345	3365	3385	3404	2	4	6	8	10	12	14	16	18
22	3424	3444	3464	3483	3502	3522	3541	3560	3579	3598	2	4	6	8	10	12	14	15	17
23	3617	3636	3655	3674	3692	3711	3729	3747	3766	3784	2	4	6	7	9	11	13	15	17
24	3802	3820	3838	3856	3874	3892	3909	3927	3945	3962	2	4	5	7	9	11	12	14	16
25	3979	3997	4014	4031	4048	4065	4082	4099	4116	4133	2	3	5	7	9	10	12	14	15
26	4150	4166	4183	4200	4216	4232	4249	4265	4281	4298	2	3	5	7	8	10	11	13	15
27	4314	4330	4346	4362	4378	4393	4409	4425	4440	4456	2	3	5	6	8	9	11	13	14
28	4472	4487	4502	4518	4533	4548	4564	4579	4594	4609	2	3	5	6	8	9	11	12	14
29	4624	4639	4654	4669	4683	4698	4713	4728	4742	4757	1	3	4	6	7	9	10	12	13
30	4771	4786	4800	4814	4829	4843	4857	4871	4886	4900	1	3	4	6	7	9	10	11	13
31	4914	4928	4942	4955	4969	4983	4997	5011	5024	5038	1	3	4	6	7	8	10	11	12
32	5051	5065	5079	5092	5105	5119	5132	5145	5159	5172	1	3	4	5	7	8	9	11	12
33	5185	5198	5211	5224	5237	5250	5263	5276	5289	5302	1	3	4	5	6	8	9	10	12
34	5315	5328	5340	5353	5366	5378	5391	5403	5416	5428	1	3	4	5	6	8	9	10	11
35	5441	5453	5465	5478	5490	5502	5514	5527	5539	5551	1	2	4	5	6	7	9	10	11
36	5563	5575	5587	5599	5611	5623	5635	5647	5658	5670	1	2	4	5	6	7	8	10	11
37	5682	5694	5705	5717	5729	5740	5752	5763	5775	5786	1	2	3	5	6	7	8	9	10
38	5798	5809	5821	5832	5843	5855	5866	5877	5888	5899	1	2	3	5	6	7	8	9	10
39	5911	5922	5933	5944	5955	5966	5977	5988	5999	6010	1	2	3	4	5	7	8	9	10
40	6021	6031	6042	6053	6064	6075	6085	6096	6107	6117	1	2	3	4	5	6	8	9	10
41	6128	6138	6149	6160	6170	6180	6191	6201	6212	6222	1	2	3	4	5	6	7	8	9
42	6232	6243	6253	6263	6274	6284	6294	6304	6314	6325	1	2	3	4	5	6	7	8	9
43	6335	6345	6355	6365	6375	6385	6395	6405	6415	6425	1	2	3	4	5	6	7	8	9
44	6435	6444	6454	6464	6474	6484	6493	6503	6513	6522	1	2	3	4	5	6	7	8	9
45	6532	6542	6551	6561	6571	6580	6590	6599	6609	6618	1	2	3	4	5	6	7	8	9
46	6628	6637	6646	6656	6665	6675	6684	6693	6702	6712	1	2	3	4	5	6	7	7	8
47	6721	6730	6739	6749	6758	6767	6776	6785	6794	6803	1	2	3	4	5	6	7	8	8
48	6812	6821	6830	6839	6848	6857	6866	6875	6884	6893	1	2	3	4	4	5	6	7	8
49	6902	6911	6920	6928	6937	6946	6955	6964	6972	6981	1	2	3	4	4	5	6	7	8
50	6990	6998	7007	7016	7024	7033	7042	7050	7059	7067	1	2	3	3	4	5	6	7	8

	0	1	2	3	4	5	6	7	8	9	1	2	3	4	5	6	7	8	9
51	7076	7084	7093	7101	7110	7118	7126	7135	7143	7152	1	2	3	3	4	5	6	7	8
52	7160	7168	7177	7185	7193	7202	7210	7218	7226	7235	1	2	2	3	4	5	6	7	7
53	7243	7251	7259	7267	7275	7284	7292	7300	7308	7316	1	2	2	3	4	5	6	6	7
54	7324	7332	7340	7348	7356	7364	7372	7380	7388	7396	1	2	2	3	4	5	6	6	7
55	7404	7412	7419	7427	7435	7443	7451	7459	7466	7474	1	2	2	3	4	5	5	6	7
56	7482	7490	7497	7505	7513	7520	7528	7536	7543	7551	1	2	2	3	4	5	5	6	7
57	7559	7566	7574	7582	7589	7597	7604	7612	7619	7627	1	2	2	3	4	5	5	6	7
58	7634	7642	7649	7657	7664	7672	7679	7686	7694	7701	1	1	2	3	4	4	5	6	7
59	7709	7716	7723	7731	7738	7745	7752	7760	7767	7774	1	1	2	3	4	4	5	6	7
60	7782	7789	7796	7803	7810	7818	7825	7832	7839	7846	1	1	2	3	4	4	5	6	6
61	7853	7860	7868	7875	7882	7889	7896	7903	7910	7917	1	1	2	3	4	4	5	6	6
62	7924	7931	7938	7945	7952	7959	7966	7973	7980	7987	1	1	2	3	3	4	5	6	6
63	7993	8000	8007	8014	8021	8028	8035	8041	8048	8055	1	1	2	3	3	4	5	5	6
64	8062	8069	8075	8082	8089	8096	8102	8109	8116	8122	1	1	2	3	3	4	5	5	6
65	8129	8136	8142	8149	8156	8162	8169	8176	8182	8189	1	1	2	3	3	4	5	5	6
66	8195	8202	8209	8215	8222	8228	8235	8241	8248	8254	1	1	2	3	3	4	5	5	6
67	8261	8267	8274	8280	8287	8293	8299	8306	8312	8319	1	1	2	3	3	4	5	5	6
68	8325	8331	8338	8344	8351	8357	8363	8370	8376	8382	1	1	2	3	3	4	4	5	6
69	8388	8395	8401	8407	8414	8420	8426	8432	8439	8445	1	1	2	2	3	4	4	5	6
70	8451	8457	8463	8470	8476	8482	8488	8494	8500	8506	1	1	2	2	3	4	4	5	6
71	8513	8519	8525	8531	8537	8543	8549	8555	8561	8567	1	1	2	2	3	4	4	5	5
72	8573	8579	8585	8591	8597	8603	8609	8615	8621	8627	1	1	2	2	3	4	4	5	5
73	8633	8639	8645	8651	8657	8663	8669	8675	8681	8686	1	1	2	2	3	4	4	5	5
74	8692	8698	8704	8710	8716	8722	8727	8733	8739	8745	1	1	2	2	3	4	4	5	5
75	8751	8756	8762	8768	8774	8779	8785	8791	8797	8802	1	1	2	2	3	3	4	5	5
76	8808	8814	8820	8825	8831	8837	8842	8848	8854	8859	1	1	2	2	3	3	4	5	5
77	8865	8871	8876	8882	8887	8893	8899	8904	8910	8915	1	1	2	2	3	3	4	4	5
78	8921	8927	8932	8938	8943	8949	8954	8960	8965	8971	1	1	2	2	3	3	4	4	5
79	8976	8982	8987	8993	8998	9004	9009	9015	9020	9025	1	1	2	2	3	3	4	4	5
80	9031	9036	9042	9047	9053	9058	9063	9069	9074	9079	1	1	2	2	3	3	4	4	5
81	9085	9090	9096	9101	9106	9112	9117	9122	9128	9133	1	1	2	2	3	3	4	4	5
82	9138	9143	9149	9154	9159	9165	9170	9175	9180	9186	1	1	2	2	3	3	4	4	5
83	9191	9196	9201	9206	9212	9217	9222	9227	9232	9238	1	1	2	2	3	3	4	4	5
84	9243	9248	9253	9258	9263	9269	9274	9279	9284	9289	1	1	2	2	3	3	4	4	5
85	9294	9299	9304	9309	9315	9320	9325	9330	9335	9340	1	1	2	2	3	3	4	4	5
86	9345	9350	9355	9360	9365	9370	9375	9380	9385	9390	1	1	2	2	3	3	4	4	5
87	9395	9400	9405	9410	9415	9420	9425	9430	9435	9440	0	1	1	2	2	3	3	4	4
88	9445	9450	9455	9460	9465	9469	9474	9479	9484	9489	0	1	1	2	2	3	3	4	4
89	9494	9499	9504	9509	9513	9518	9523	9528	9533	9538	0	1	1	2	2	3	3	4	4
90	9542	9547	9552	9557	9562	9566	9571	9576	9581	9586	0	1	1	2	2	3	3	4	4
91	9590	9595	9600	9605	9609	9614	9619	9624	9628	9633	0	1	1	2	2	3	3	4	4
92	9638	9643	9647	9652	9657	9661	9666	9671	9675	9680	0	1	1	2	2	3	3	4	4
93	9685	9689	9694	9699	9703	9708	9713	9717	9722	9727	0	1	1	2	2	3	3	4	4
94	9731	9736	9741	9745	9750	9754	9759	9763	9768	9773	0	1	1	2	2	3	3	4	4
95	9777	9782	9786	9791	9795	9800	9805	9809	9814	9818	0	1	1	2	2	3	3	4	4
96	9823	9827	9832	9836	9841	9845	9850	9854	9859	9863	0	1	1	2	2	3	3	4	4
97	9868	9872	9877	9881	9886	9890	9894	9899	9903	9908	0	1	1	2	2	3	3	4	4
98	9912	9917	9921	9926	9930	9934	9939	9943	9948	9952	0	1	1	2	2	3	3	4	4
99	9956	9961	9965	9969	9974	9978	9983	9987	9991	9996	0	1	1	2	2	3	3	3	4

	0	1	2	3	4	5	6	7	8	9	1	2	3	4	5	6	7	8	9
·00	1000	1002	1005	1007	1009	1012	1014	1016	1019	1021	0	0	1	1	1	1	2	2	2
·01	1023	1026	1028	1030	1033	1035	1038	1040	1042	1045	0	0	1	1	1	1	2	2	2
·02	1047	1050	1052	1054	1057	1059	1062	1064	1067	1069	0	0	1	1	1	1	2	2	2
·03	1072	1074	1076	1079	1081	1084	1086	1089	1091	1094	0	0	1	1	1	1	2	2	2
·04	1096	1099	1102	1104	1107	1109	1112	1114	1117	1119	0	1	1	1	1	2	2	2	2
·05	1122	1125	1127	1130	1132	1135	1138	1140	1143	1146	0	1	1	1	1	2	2	2	2
·06	1148	1151	1153	1156	1159	1161	1164	1167	1169	1172	0	1	1	1	1	2	2	2	2
·07	1175	1178	1180	1183	1186	1189	1191	1194	1197	1199	0	1	1	1	1	2	2	2	2
·08	1202	1205	1208	1211	1213	1216	1219	1222	1225	1227	0	1	1	1	1	2	2	2	3
·09	1230	1233	1236	1239	1242	1245	1247	1250	1253	1256	0	1	1	1	1	2	2	2	3
·10	1259	1262	1265	1268	1271	1274	1276	1279	1282	1285	0	1	1	1	1	2	2	2	3
·11	1288	1291	1294	1297	1300	1303	1306	1309	1312	1315	0	1	1	1	2	2	2	2	3
·12	1318	1321	1324	1327	1330	1334	1337	1340	1343	1346	0	1	1	1	2	2	2	2	3
·13	1349	1352	1355	1358	1361	1365	1368	1371	1374	1377	0	1	1	1	2	2	2	3	3
·14	1380	1384	1387	1390	1393	1396	1400	1403	1406	1409	0	1	1	1	2	2	2	3	3
·15	1413	1416	1419	1422	1426	1429	1432	1435	1439	1442	0	1	1	1	2	2	2	3	3
·16	1445	1449	1452	1455	1459	1462	1466	1469	1472	1476	0	1	1	1	2	2	2	3	3
·17	1479	1483	1486	1489	1493	1496	1500	1503	1507	1510	0	1	1	1	2	2	2	3	3
·18	1514	1517	1521	1524	1528	1531	1535	1538	1542	1545	0	1	1	1	2	2	2	3	3
·19	1549	1552	1556	1560	1563	1567	1570	1574	1578	1581	0	1	1	1	2	2	3	3	3
·20	1585	1589	1592	1596	1600	1603	1607	1611	1614	1618	0	1	1	1	2	2	3	3	3
·21	1622	1626	1629	1633	1637	1641	1644	1648	1652	1656	0	1	1	2	2	2	3	3	3
·22	1660	1663	1667	1671	1675	1679	1683	1687	1690	1694	0	1	1	2	2	2	3	3	3
·23	1698	1702	1706	1710	1714	1718	1722	1726	1730	1734	0	1	1	2	2	2	3	3	4
·24	1738	1742	1746	1750	1754	1758	1762	1766	1770	1774	0	1	1	2	2	2	3	3	4
·25	1778	1782	1786	1791	1795	1799	1803	1807	1811	1816	0	1	1	2	2	2	3	3	4
·26	1820	1824	1828	1832	1837	1841	1845	1849	1854	1858	0	1	1	2	2	3	3	3	4
·27	1862	1866	1871	1875	1879	1884	1888	1892	1897	1901	0	1	1	2	2	3	3	3	4
·28	1905	1910	1914	1919	1923	1928	1932	1936	1941	1945	0	1	1	2	2	3	3	4	4
·29	1950	1954	1959	1963	1968	1972	1977	1982	1986	1991	0	1	1	2	2	3	3	4	4
·30	1995	2000	2004	2009	2014	2018	2023	2028	2032	2037	0	1	1	2	2	3	3	4	4
·31	2042	2046	2051	2056	2061	2065	2070	2075	2080	2084	0	1	1	2	2	3	3	4	4
·32	2089	2094	2099	2104	2109	2113	2118	2123	2128	2133	0	1	1	2	2	3	3	4	4
·33	2138	2143	2148	2153	2158	2163	2168	2173	2178	2183	0	1	1	2	2	3	3	4	4
·34	2188	2193	2198	2203	2208	2213	2218	2223	2228	2234	1	1	2	2	3	3	4	4	5
·35	2239	2244	2249	2254	2259	2265	2270	2275	2280	2286	1	1	2	2	3	3	4	4	5
·36	2291	2296	2301	2307	2312	2317	2323	2328	2333	2339	1	1	2	2	3	3	4	4	5
·37	2344	2350	2355	2360	2366	2371	2377	2382	2388	2393	1	1	2	2	3	3	4	4	5
·38	2399	2404	2410	2415	2421	2427	2432	2438	2443	2449	1	1	2	2	3	3	4	4	5
·39	2455	2460	2466	2472	2477	2483	2489	2495	2500	2506	1	1	2	2	3	3	4	5	5
·40	2512	2518	2523	2529	2535	2541	2547	2553	2559	2564	1	1	2	2	3	4	4	5	5
·41	2570	2576	2582	2588	2594	2600	2606	2612	2618	2624	1	1	2	2	3	4	4	5	5
·42	2630	2636	2642	2649	2655	2661	2667	2673	2679	2685	1	1	2	2	3	4	4	5	6
·43	2692	2698	2704	2710	2716	2723	2729	2735	2742	2748	1	1	2	3	3	4	4	5	6
·44	2754	2761	2767	2773	2780	2786	2793	2799	2805	2812	1	1	2	3	3	4	4	5	6
·45	2818	2825	2831	2838	2844	2851	2858	2864	2871	2877	1	1	2	3	3	4	5	5	6
·46	2884	2891	2897	2904	2911	2917	2924	2931	2938	2944	1	1	2	3	3	4	5	5	6
·47	2951	2958	2965	2972	2979	2985	2992	2999	3006	3013	1	1	2	3	3	4	5	5	6
·48	3020	3027	3034	3041	3048	3055	3062	3069	3076	3083	1	1	2	3	4	4	5	6	6
·49	3090	3097	3105	3112	3119	3126	3133	3141	3148	3155	1	1	2	3	4	4	5	6	6

	0	1	2	3	4	5	6	7	8	9	1	2	3	4	5	6	7	8	9
·50	3162	3170	3177	3184	3192	3199	3206	3214	3221	3228	1	1	2	3	4	4	5	6	7
·51	3236	3243	3251	3258	3266	3273	3281	3289	3296	3304	1	2	2	3	4	5	5	6	7
·52	3311	3319	3327	3334	3342	3350	3357	3365	3373	3381	1	2	2	3	4	5	5	6	7
·53	3388	3396	3404	3412	3420	3428	3436	3443	3451	3459	1	2	2	3	4	5	6	6	7
·54	3467	3475	3483	3491	3499	3508	3516	3524	3532	3540	1	2	2	3	4	5	6	6	7
·55	3548	3556	3565	3573	3581	3589	3597	3606	3614	3622	1	2	2	3	4	5	6	7	7
·56	3631	3639	3648	3656	3664	3673	3681	3690	3698	3707	1	2	3	3	4	5	6	7	8
·57	3715	3724	3733	3741	3750	3758	3767	3776	3784	3793	1	2	3	3	4	5	6	7	8
·58	3802	3811	3819	3828	3837	3846	3855	3864	3873	3882	1	2	3	4	4	5	6	7	8
·59	3890	3899	3908	3917	3926	3936	3945	3954	3963	3972	1	2	3	4	5	5	6	7	8
·60	3981	3990	3999	4009	4018	4027	4036	4046	4055	4064	1	2	3	4	5	6	6	7	9
·61	4074	4083	4093	4102	4111	4121	4130	4140	4150	4159	1	2	3	4	5	6	7	8	9
·62	4169	4178	4188	4198	4207	4217	4227	4236	4246	4256	1	2	3	4	5	6	7	8	9
·63	4266	4276	4285	4295	4305	4315	4325	4335	4345	4355	1	2	3	4	5	6	7	8	9
·64	4365	4375	4385	4395	4406	4416	4426	4436	4446	4457	1	2	3	4	5	6	7	8	9
·65	4467	4477	4487	4498	4508	4519	4529	4539	4550	4560	1	2	3	4	5	6	7	8	9
·66	4571	4581	4592	4603	4613	4624	4634	4645	4656	4667	1	2	3	4	5	6	7	9	10
·67	4677	4688	4699	4710	4721	4732	4742	4753	4764	4775	1	2	3	4	5	7	8	9	10
·68	4786	4797	4808	4819	4831	4842	4853	4864	4875	4887	1	2	3	4	6	7	8	9	10
·69	4898	4909	4920	4932	4943	4955	4966	4977	4989	5000	1	2	3	5	6	7	8	9	10
·70	5012	5023	5035	5047	5058	5070	5082	5093	5105	5117	1	2	4	5	6	7	8	9	11
·71	5129	5140	5152	5164	5176	5188	5200	5212	5224	5236	1	2	4	5	6	7	8	10	11
·72	5248	5260	5272	5284	5297	5309	5321	5333	5346	5358	1	2	4	5	6	7	9	10	11
·73	5370	5383	5395	5408	5420	5433	5445	5458	5470	5483	1	3	4	5	6	8	9	10	11
·74	5495	5508	5521	5534	5546	5559	5572	5585	5598	5610	1	3	4	5	6	8	9	10	12
·75	5623	5636	5649	5662	5675	5689	5702	5715	5728	5741	1	3	4	5	7	8	9	10	12
·76	5754	5768	5781	5794	5808	5821	5834	5848	5861	5875	1	3	4	5	7	8	9	11	12
·77	5888	5902	5916	5929	5943	5957	5970	5984	5998	6012	1	3	4	5	7	8	10	11	12
·78	6026	6039	6053	6067	6081	6095	6109	6124	6138	6152	1	3	4	6	7	8	10	11	13
·79	6166	6180	6194	6209	6223	6237	6252	6266	6281	6295	1	3	4	6	7	9	10	11	13
·80	6310	6324	6339	6353	6368	6383	6397	6412	6427	6442	1	3	4	6	7	9	10	12	13
·81	6457	6471	6486	6501	6516	6531	6546	6561	6577	6592	2	3	5	6	8	9	11	12	14
·82	6607	6622	6637	6653	6668	6683	6699	6714	6730	6745	2	3	5	6	8	9	11	12	14
·83	6761	6776	6792	6808	6823	6839	6855	6871	6887	6902	2	3	5	6	8	9	11	13	14
·84	6918	6934	6950	6966	6982	6998	7015	7031	7047	7063	2	3	5	6	8	10	11	13	15
·85	7079	7096	7112	7129	7145	7161	7178	7194	7211	7228	2	3	5	7	8	10	12	13	15
·86	7244	7261	7278	7295	7311	7328	7345	7362	7379	7396	2	3	5	7	8	10	12	13	15
·87	7413	7430	7447	7464	7482	7499	7516	7534	7551	7568	2	3	5	7	9	10	12	14	16
·88	7586	7603	7621	7638	7656	7674	7691	7709	7727	7745	2	4	5	7	9	11	12	14	16
·89	7762	7780	7798	7816	7834	7852	7870	7889	7907	7925	2	4	5	7	9	11	13	14	16
·90	7943	7962	7980	7998	8017	8035	8054	8072	8091	8110	2	4	6	7	9	11	13	15	17
·91	8128	8147	8166	8185	8204	8222	8241	8260	8279	8299	2	4	6	8	9	11	13	15	17
·92	8318	8337	8356	8375	8395	8414	8433	8453	8472	8492	2	4	6	8	10	12	14	15	17
·93	8511	8531	8551	8570	8590	8610	8630	8650	8670	8690	2	4	6	8	10	12	14	16	18
·94	8710	8730	8750	8770	8790	8810	8831	8851	8872	8892	2	4	6	8	10	12	14	16	18
·95	8913	8933	8954	8974	8995	9016	9036	9057	9078	9099	2	4	6	8	10	12	15	17	19
·96	9120	9141	9162	9183	9204	9226	9247	9268	9290	9311	2	4	6	8	11	13	15	17	19
·97	9333	9354	9376	9397	9419	9441	9462	9484	9506	9528	2	4	7	9	11	13	15	17	20
·98	9550	9572	9594	9616	9638	9661	9683	9705	9727	9750	2	4	7	9	11	13	16	18	20
·99	9772	9795	9817	9840	9863	9886	9908	9931	9954	9977	2	5	7	9	11	14	16	18	20

12

Angle.		Chord	Sine	Tangent	Co-tangent	Cosine			
De-grees.	Radians								
0°	0	0	0	0	∞	1	1·414	1·5708	90°
1	·0175	·017	·0175	·0175	57·2900	·9998	1·402	1·5533	89
2	·0349	·035	·0348	·0349	28·6363	·9994	1·389	1·5359	88
3	·0524	·052	·0523	·0524	19·0811	·9986	1·377	1·5184	87
4	·0698	·070	·0698	·0699	14·3007	·9976	1·364	1·5010	86
5	·0873	·087	·0872	·0875	11·4301	·9962	1·351	1·4835	85
6	·1047	·105	·1045	·1051	9·5144	·9945	1·338	1·4661	84
7	·1222	·122	·1219	·1228	8·1443	·9925	1·325	1·4486	83
8	·1396	·140	·1392	·1405	7·1154	·9903	1·312	1·4312	82
9	·1571	·157	·1564	·1584	6·3138	·9877	1·299	1·4137	81
10	·1745	·174	·1736	·1763	5·6713	·9848	1·286	1·3963	80
11	·1920	·192	·1908	·1944	5·1446	·9816	1·272	1·3788	79
12	·2094	·209	·2079	·2126	4·7046	·9781	1·259	1·3614	78
13	·2269	·226	·2250	·2309	4·3315	·9744	1·245	1·3439	77
14	·2443	·244	·2419	·2493	4·0108	·9703	1·231	1·3265	76
15	·2618	·261	·2588	·2679	3·7321	·9659	1·218	1·3090	75
16	·2793	·278	·2756	·2867	3·4874	·9613	1·204	1·2915	74
17	·2967	·296	·2924	·3057	3·2709	·9563	1·190	1·2741	73
18	·3142	·313	·3090	·3249	3·0777	·9511	1·176	1·2566	72
19	·3316	·330	·3256	·3443	2·9042	·9455	1·161	1·2392	71
20	·3491	·347	·3420	·3640	2·7475	·9397	1·147	1·2217	70
21	·3665	·364	·3584	·3839	2·6051	·9336	1·133	1·2043	69
22	·3840	·382	·3746	·4040	2·4751	·9272	1·118	1·1868	68
23	·4014	·399	·3907	·4245	2·3559	·9205	1·104	1·1694	67
24	·4189	·416	·4067	·4452	2·2460	·9135	1·089	1·1519	66
25	·4363	·433	·4226	·4663	2·1445	·9063	1·075	1·1345	65
26	·4538	·450	·4384	·4877	2·0503	·8988	1·060	1·1170	64
27	·4712	·467	·4540	·5095	1·9626	·8910	1·045	1·0996	63
28	·4887	·484	·4695	·5317	1·8807	·8829	1·030	1·0821	62
29	·5061	·501	·4848	·5543	1·8040	·8746	1·015	1·0647	61
30	·5236	·518	·5000	·5774	1·7321	·8660	1·000	1·0472	60
31	·5411	·534	·5150	·6009	1·6643	·8572	·985	1·0297	59
32	·5585	·551	·5299	·6249	1·6003	·8480	·970	1·0123	58
33	·5760	·568	·5446	·6494	1·5399	·8387	·954	·9948	57
34	·5934	·585	·5592	·6745	1·4826	·8290	·939	·9774	56
35	·6109	·601	·5736	·7002	1·4281	·8192	·923	·9599	55
36	·6283	·618	·5878	·7265	1·3764	·8090	·908	·9425	54
37	·6458	·625	·6018	·7536	1·3270	·7986	·892	·9250	53
38	·6632	·651	·6157	·7813	1·2799	·7880	·877	·9076	52
39	·6807	·668	·6293	·8098	1·2349	·7771	·861	·8901	51
40	·6981	·684	·6428	·8391	1·1918	·7660	·845	·8727	50
41	·7156	·700	·6561	·8693	1·1504	·7547	·829	·8552	49
42	·7330	·717	·6691	·9004	1·1106	·7431	·813	·8378	48
43	·7505	·733	·6820	·9325	1·0724	·7314	·797	·8203	47
44	·7679	·749	·6947	·9657	1·0355	·7193	·781	·8029	46
45°	·7854	·765	·7071	1·0000	1·0000	·7071	·765	·7854	45°
			Cosine	Co-tangent	Tangent	Sine	Chord	Radians	De-grees
									Angle.

ANSWERS TO EXAMPLES

EXAMPLES I. Page 6

1. 27 lb, 0·343 m/sec^2.   2. 138·2 newtons.
3. 80 kg.   4. 0·03 newton, 3·06 g, 2·7 J.
5. 8950 J, 298 W.   6. 37·35 kW, 1778 J.
7. 438 lb-ft, 594 newton-metres, 60·5 kg-metres.
8. 12,320 W; 16·5 h.p., 58,860 J; 0·01635 kWh.
9. 36·3 newtons, 654 J, 109 W.
10. 520 newtons, 4905 J, 27·25 W.
11. 397·3 newtons, 7946 J, 993 W.
12. 8010 newtons, 1·72 × 10^8 J, 47·8 kWh, 143·3 kW, 6·76 kWh.
13. 114·8 kW; 83,800 kWh; £262.   14. £27 13s.
15. 7·5d, 14·8d.   16. 12·98 kW, 4·33d.
17. 4·96 minutes, 0·132d.   18. 112.
19. 3·14 kW, 7s 10d.

EXAMPLES II. Page 18

1. 0·05 A high.   2. 2·78 A.   3. 0·0222 mm.
4. 21·2 minutes.   5. 3·22 g, 2880 C, 0·8 Ah.
6. 3·02 hours, 87,000 C, 24·16 Ah.   7. 3·22 g.
8. 3·6 A, negative.   9. 0·0095 mm.
10. 0·00033 g/C.   11. 1628 sec.   12. −0·0354 A.
13. 3 A.   14. 0·01225 mm.
15. 0·0000932 g/C, 0·000681 g/C, 0·0003675 g/C.
16. 16·08 hours.

EXAMPLES III. Page 31

1. 11·35 min, 0·769 kW, 0·29d.   2. 3·57 Ω, 24·1 W.
3. 18·4° C.   4. 2·97 A, 77·5 Ω, 0·1365d.
5. 5·11 A, 45 Ω, 1·175 kW, 0·392 kWh.
6. 300 Ah, 40·5 kWh.   7. 80·7 A.
8. 24 A, 19·2 kWh, 7·57 b.h.p.
9. 107·4 A, 47·25 kW, £1 8s 4d.   10. 10 h.p.; 3,300,000 ft-lb.
11. 161·3 Ω, 25 Wh, 0·446 pint.   12. 225 A, £11 19s 3d.
13. 8·88 kWh, 13·04 A.   14. 9·17 A, 550 C, 211·2 kWh.
15. 2160 g.   16. 1·232 kW.
17. 0·435 A, 529 Ω.   18. 53·8 Ω, 19 per cent.
19. 9·5 Ω, 1·52 W.   20. 201·7 Ω, 0·496 A, 49·6 W.
21. 36,000,000 coulombs.   22. 15·33 mA, 7·05 W.
23. 6·39 μA, 735 μW.   24. 0·24 A, 1·44 W, 1728 J.
25. 4·08 V, 19·6 mW.

EXAMPLES IV. Page 61

1. 32 Ω, 7·875 Ω.   2. 1·8 A, 1·2 A, 81 V, 243 W.
3. 0·793 A, 1·24 A, 2·033 A.
4. 2·945 A, 1·718 A, 1·227 A, 34·35 V.   5. 17·25 Ω, 13·8d.
6. 9·6 A, 0·01458 Ω, 19·776 W, 18·432 W, 1·344 W.
7. 0·4 A, 0·75 Ω, 4·8 W.   8. 0·847 A, 116·5 V, 103·5 V.
9. 30 coulombs.
10. 5 A; 2A, 1·8 A, 1·2 A, 2·5 A, 2·5 A; 22·5 W; 36 V.
11. 20·83 Ω, 27·78 Ω, 90 W. 12. 44 per cent, 16 Ω, 115·2 Ω.
13. 0·833 Ω.   14. 0·182 A.   15. 0·3 A, 0·2 A, 0·278 A.
16. 0·5 A, 5 V, 300 J.   17. 0·25 V, 1·2 V.
18. 0·54 A, 0·225 A, 0·315 A, 0·852 V, 0·722 V.
19. 44 Ω, 4 Ω, 1 A, 11 A.   20. 5 Ω.
21. 7·2 Ω, 55·5 W.   22. 0·986 Ω.
23. 84·9 Ω.   24. 0·0718 Ω.
25. 15·3 Ω, 10·71 V, 7·5 W.   26. 0·000847 in², 0·572 kW.
27. 3·56 cm².   28. 1·696 μΩ-cm, 0·668 μΩ-inch
29. 17·33 μΩ-inch.   30. 840 Ω.
31. 50·6° C.   32. 61·1° C.
33. 253·5 Ω.   34. 0·00393 Ω.
35. 2390° C.   36. −0·0002655.
37. 5·27 A.   38. 29·05 Ω.
39. 150 MW; 12,500 Ω, 50 Ω/V; 600 MΩ; 52·1° C.
40. 13·45 V, 78·45 A, 3s 9d.
41. 455·4 V, 36·43 kW, 0·768 kW.   42. 90·1 A, 7·78 V.
43. 451·2 V, 8·8 V, 0·598 kW, 36·2 b.h.p.
44. 236·53 V, 235·61 V, 976 W.   45. 209·95 V, 2s 7½d.
46. 237·31 V, 236·2 V, 235·3 V.
47. 100 A, 35 A, 15 A; 4032 W, 98·8 W, 27·1 W; 524·95 V.
48. 3·79 MΩ, 60·7 μA, 0·1223 kWh.
49. 227·4 V, 234·4 V; 2·93 kW.
50. 156 A, 36 A, 114 A; 111·88 V, 110·44 V; 1·058 kW.
51. 118·7 A, 38·7 A, 81·3 A; 234·3 V, 232·68 V; 1·334 kW.
52. 245·3 V at A, 245·8 V at B.
53. 0·261 A, charge; 1·609 A, discharge; 10·78 V.
54. 4·91 A, 6·14 A, 11·05 A.

EXAMPLES V. Page 88

6. 300 newtons/m; 30·6 kg/m.   7. 0·486 Wb/m².
8. 46·1 g.   9. 0·756 g-cm.   10. 12·4 mA.
11. 173 newton-metres, 127·5 lb-ft; 12·7 kW, 17 h.p.
12. 1·15 Wb/m².   13. 160 μWb.

EXAMPLES VI. Page 101

1. 24 V, 224 V.   2. 37·5 V.   3. 90 V.
4. 0·32 V.   5. 5·87 V.   6. 1305 V.
7. 0·1635 V.   8. 2·33 mV.
9. 0·333 Wb/m²; 0·267 newton, 27·2 g.
11. 4·24 μV.   12. 5·6 V.   13. 1400 r.p.m.

Examples VII.   Page 124

1. 318 AT/m, 0·0004 Wb/m².   2. 6000 A.
3. 6370 AT/m, 0·008 Wb/m²; 7580 AT/m, 0·00952 Wb/m²;
   0, 0; 3030 AT/m, 0·00381 Wb/m².
4. 382,000; 306 AT; 255,000 AT/m.
5. 394,000 AT/m; 0·0016 Wb.   6. 557,000; 334 AT.
7. 500 AT/m, 955; 1500 AT/m, 637.   8. 750,000; 2090.
9. 750 AT; 1875 AT/m; 0·00106 Wb; 707,000.
10. 1·5 Wb/m², 1910.   11. 0·731 Wb/m², 1828.
12. 10·05.   13. 11·8 A.   14. 355 μWb.
15. 3 A.   16. 12·05 A.
17. 0·86 A; 1·92 A; 2,880,000.   18. 2·2 A.
19. 3·65 A.   20. 990 AT.   21. 4·15 A.
22. 3·77 A.   23. 1·48 A.

Examples VIII.   Page 144

1. 0·375 H.   2. 0·15 H.   3. 160 A/sec.
4. 3·5 V.   5. 1·25 mH, 0·1 V.
6. 0·129 mH, 0·0258 V.   7. 0·0833 H, 0·04165 sec, 1·667 V.
9. 2·85 A.
11. 12·5 A/sec, 0·984 A, 0·183 sec, 12·5 J.
14. 125 microjoules.   15. 0·4 H, 0·1 H.
16. 125 μH, 80 μH, 100 μH; 405 or 5 μH; increased 10 times.
17. 16 J.   18. 12 V.   19. 0·0625 H.
20. -10 V.   21. 0·0344 H.   22. 1·35 mH.
23. 100·5 μH, 40·2 mV.

Examples IX.   Page 171

1. 0·0885 μF.
2. 4·71 metres per strip, neglecting outer surface of outer
   layer.
3. 1200 μC; 120 V, 80 V; 6 μF.   4. 48 V; 960 μC, 240 μC.
5. 300 V; 4 μJ, 16 μJ.
6. 177 $\mu\mu$F, 1062 $\mu\mu$F, 66·7 V, 0·0708 μC, 14·16 μJ, 2·36 μJ.
8. 0·01 J, 7.
10. 500 μC; 250 V, 166·7 V, 83·3 V; 0·0208 J.
11. 6·06 μF.   12. 3·75 μF, 1500 μC.   13. 1·416 mm.
14. 260·9 V, 87 V, 52·1 V.   15. 0·415 μF.
16. 8·8 ×10^{-12}; 100 kV/m, 0·88 μC/m².
17. 2·81; 30 kV/m, 0·7425 μC/m²; 0·4455 μJ.
18. 1327 $\mu\mu$F; 0·531 μC, 200 kV/m, 8·85 μC/m².
19. (a) 300 ϵ_r; (b) 600 ϵ_r, where ϵ_r =dielectric constant of
    insulating material.
20. 2.
21. 0·3 μF, 0·0667 μF; 20 μC, 30 μC; 166·7 V, 33·3 V.
22. 0·006 C, 1·8 J.   23. 1·2 μF, 120 μC, 60 V.
24. 8·85 $\mu\mu$F, 56·5 V; 35·4 $\mu\mu$F, 14·1 V.
25. 100 μA, 36·8 μA, 1000 V/sec, 0·0005 J.

26. 357 V; 1·25 J, 0·893 J.   27. 0·5 μC, 3·12 ×10^{12} electrons.
28. 3·744 ×10^{21} electrons/sec.   29. 11·2 mA.
30. 115·2 J, 7·2 ×10^{20} electron-volts.
31. 18·72 ×10^{15} electrons/sec; 6·74 ×10^{20} electron-volts, 108 J.

Examples X.   Page 188

1. 900 r.p.m.   2. 16 poles.   3. 60 c/s.
4. 10 c/s, 0·1 sec; 0·1332 V, 0·1884 V.
5. 2400 r.p.m., 0·0478 Wb/m^2, 32·4 V, 50·9 V.
6. 12·74 A, 14·14 A.   8. 20 millisec, 11·44 A, 1·395 millisec.
9. 1·414 A.   10. 25 c/s, 141·4 V, 347 W.
11. 27·3 A, 66·7 c/s.
12. 3·05 A, 3·27 A, assuming points joined by straight lines.
13. 7·64 A, 1167 W.   14. 2·93 A, 50 c/s.
15. 6·45 A, 5·75 A.   16. 2·61 kV, 3 kV.
17. 5 A, 5·77 A, 1·154, 1·73. 18. 7·77 mA, 11 mA.

Examples XI.   Page 210

1. 14·8 A.   3. 132·3 V, 93·5 V.
4. 31 A, 18·8°.   5. 86·6 V, 50 V.   6. 29·1 A.
7. 22·14 sin (314t+0·11), 15·65 A, 50 c/s.
8. 147·5 V, 23·75° lead.   9. 0·0552 H.
10. 3·215 A, 0·707.   11. 63·6 Ω, 62·8 Ω, 1·57 A, 81°.
12. 12·85 A, 6·43 A.   13. 2·65 A, 0·159 A.
14. 0·1718 H, 69·6°.   15. 4 A, 5·3 A, 6·64 A, 52·95°.
16. 100 c/s, 9·51 A.

Examples XII.   Page 222

1. v=339·4 sin 314t volts, i=14·14 sin (314t−π/6) amperes,
    12·25 A, 7·07 A, −12·25 A.
2. 500 W, 10 watt-seconds.   3. 1,440,000 J.
4. 20 Ω, 34·64 Ω.   5. 10·75 A, 57·5°, 1156 W.
6. 199 V, 0·243 H, 0·5 lag.   7. 50 Ω, 0·5 W, 100 Ω, 0·6, 60 Ω.
8. 0·857 lag, 0·8 lag, 0·804 lag.
9. 0·0729 H, 200 W.   10. 16·67 Ω.
11. 0·085 H, 0·599 lag; 4·13 A, 5·52 A; 1270 VAr.
12. 4 A, 3·54 A, 5·34 A, 41·5°, 1·6 kW, 0·749 lag.
13. 93·3 W.   14. 25·21 kW, 27·9 kVA, 0·903 lag.
15. 7·09 A, 750 W, 0·529 lag.
16. 13·7 A, 10·96 A, 8·22 A, 3·29 kVAr. 17. 82·9 per cent.
18. 127·4 V, 141·4 V, 3·12 kW.   19. 79 yd.

Examples XIII.   Page 243

1. 106·2 Ω, 1·036 A.
2. 5·32 A, 106·4 V, 169·2 V, 57·9°, 566 W, 0·532 lead.
3. 1·54 A, 1·884 A, 2·435 A, 50·7°, 308 W, 0·633 lead.

4. 50 Ω, 79·6 μF, 691 W, 0·6 lead.
5. 19·9 μF, 0·625 lead.
6. 1·667 A, 1·884 A, 2·516 A, 0·662 lead.
7. 144 Ω, 1·0; 12·75 μF, 0·5 lead; 0·775 H, 0·535 lag; method (b).
8. 2·96 A, 29·6 V, 93 V, 188·5 V, 72·8°, 0·296 lead, 87·6 W.
9. 159·2 V; 16 Ω, 0·375 H; 0·1346, 0·24 lag.
10. 163 V, 0·875 lead.
11. 50·7 μF, 6 A, 378·6 V, 377 V, 1·0.
12. 1590 c/s, 0·05 A, 0·05 W.
13. 796 c/s, 0·03 A, 0·27 W, 3 V, 0·2155 W.
14. 10 A, 10·61 A, 4·71 A, 11·6 A, 0·862 lag, 1 kW.
15. 79·3 μF.
16. 126·6 $\mu\mu$F, 0·159 V milliamperes, 90° lag and 90° lead.
17. 159 μF.   18. 2·69 A, 1·57 A, 1·61 A, 0·9 lag.
19. 1·265 A, 503 c/s.   20. 324 μF, 33·3 A, 50 A.
21. 11·6 A, 0·905 lag.   22. 33·8 μF, 61·7 μF.

EXAMPLES XIV.   Page 264

3. 13 or 12, 52.   4. (a) 87, (b) 142.
5. 240 A, 498 V; 720 A, 166 V; 119·5 kW.
6. 120 A, 301 V, 36·12 kW; 240 A, 150·5 V, 36·12 kW.
7. 432 V.   8. 0·02 Wb.   9. 946 r.p.m.
10. 0·0416 Wb, 0·0208 Wb.

EXAMPLES XV.   Page 277

1. 467 V, 373 V, 0, 240 Ω.   2. 91 V.
3. 0·0219 Wb.   4. 282·66 V.
5. 8, 0·0321 Wb.   6. 6.

EXAMPLES XVI.   Page 299

1. 393·7 r.p.m.   2. 640 r.p.m.
3. 140 A.   4. 208 V, 41 A.
5. 0·01048 Wb, 76·7 lb-ft, 104 newton-metres.
6. 1005 r.p.m., 323 lb-ft, 438 newton-metres, 44·6 kg-m.
7. 469 r.p.m., 198 lb-ft, 27·3 kg-m.   8. 529 r.p.m.
9. 44·4 Ω, 842·5 r.p.m.   10. 997 r.p.m., 64 A.
11. 779 r.p.m.   12. 4·34 Ω.   13. 22·2 A, 1106 r.p.m.
14. 42·6 A, 53·25 A, 1125 r.p.m.   15. 97·5 V.
16. 4·35 per cent increase.   17. 1·88 Ω, 76·5 V.
18. 76·7 A, 1·15 A; 76·6 A, 0·096 A.
19. 581 r.p.m. for 60 lb-ft; 398 r.p.m. for 340 lb-ft.
20. 1114 r.p.m., 1·282.   21. 72·4 per cent.

EXAMPLES XVII.   Page 332

1. 0·006003 Ω;   19,988 Ω.   2. 0·9995 cm.
3. 25·6 mA.   4. 36·5 × 10⁻⁶ newton-metre.
5. 0·03797 Ω, 0·007519 Ω.   6. 10 Ω, 9·9 Ω.
7. 9995 Ω.   8. 0·0761 Ω, 1662 Ω.
9. 10.   10. 3·6 per cent, 65·8 per cent.
11. 33,800 Ω.   12. 2·5 Ω, 2·6 Ω.
13. 62·4 Ω, 23·2 mA in P and Q, 14·8 mA in R and X.
14. 8·58 Ω, 51·75 cm.   15. 0·7 V, B positive; 9·6 Ω.
16. 2020 Ω, 1·818 V.   17. 3·08 mA from D to B.
18. 53·8 mA from D to C.   19. 2·98 per cent low.
20. 1·24 per cent high.   21. 1·443 V.
22. 15 A.   23. 2·17 Ω.   24. 0·9.

EXAMPLES XVIII.   Page 345

1. 0·182 A.   2. 33·6 cm³.   3. 110, 125.
4. 32·5 A, 23·75 A.   5. 26·4 Ω.   6. 3·42 Ω, 1·86 Ω.
7. 1·35 Ω, 1·54 A.   8. 85, 12 Ω.
9. 80 per cent, 66·7 per cent.   10. 28·15 h.p.
11. 83·3 per cent, 72·7 per cent.
12. 104·4 V, 138 V, 83·3 per cent, 74·2 per cent.
13. 79·4 per cent, 64·4 per cent.   14. 21 Ah, 42 Ah.
15. 0·01625 Ω.   16. 0·0133 Ω.
17. 1·9 V, polarity of instrument being reverse of that of e.m.f. of dry battery.
18. 137·2 V.

INDEX